ROBERT MYLNE

1 ROBERT MYLNE, F.R.S., ARCHITECT, ENGINEER, SURVEYOR
AT THE AGE OF 24

From a drawing made at Rome by Brompton,
engraved at Paris by Vangeliste in 1783

ROBERT MYLNE

Architect and Engineer
1733 to 1811

By

A. E. RICHARDSON

P.R.A., F.R.I.B.A.

LONDON

B. T. BATSFORD LTD

TO

SIR JOHN STIRLING MAXWELL, BT.

First Published 1955

MADE AND PRINTED IN GREAT BRITAIN BY
WILLIAM CLOWES AND SONS LTD, LONDON AND BECCLES
FOR THE PUBLISHERS
B. T. BATSFORD LTD
4 FITZHARDINGE STREET, PORTMAN SQUARE
LONDON, W.1

CONTENTS

2 HOUSE AT BATH

From a drawing by the Author

LIST OF ILLUSTRATIONS

The numerals in parentheses in the text refer to the
Figure Numbers of the Illustrations

ACKNOWLEDGMENT

THE Author and Publishers would like to thank the following who have kindly given photographs and permission for their use in this book: *Art and Technics*, for Figs. 26 and 27; Balmain, for Fig. 29; A. C. Cooper Ltd., for Fig. 17; F. Jewell Harrison, for Figs. 15, 18, 19, 38 and 41; J. E. Hedley, for Fig. 42; London Art Service Ltd., for Fig. 8.

3 LONDON: DESIGN FOR AN OFFICE BUILDING

From a drawing by the Author

4 LONDON: NO. 1 STRATTON STREET, BUILT FOR MR. COUTTS,
THE BANKER

From a drawing by the Author

INTRODUCTION

FROM the early sixteenth century to the reign of Queen Anne the name of Mylne stood for the Master Masons to the Crown of Scotland. The palaces of Stirling, Linlithgow and Holyrood were enriched by successive members of a family of craftsmen who added to the lithic story of the renaissance in Scotland. The account begins with John Mylne, Master Mason to James III; it continues with Thomas Mylne who held office in the time of Queen Mary; John Mylne, who was Master Mason to James VI, and John Mylne, who built certain Works for Charles I. There is a record of another John Mylne who died in 1667: he also served Charles I, and survived through the Commonwealth to resume work for Charles II. Another Mylne, Alexander by name, made his appearance as a mason and sculptor; he died in 1693. The first Robert Mylne began as Master Mason to Charles II; he lived on to the reign of Queen Anne, dying in 1710. It is interesting to know that from this date members of the Mylne family made their bow as architects. First there was William, who died in 1728, and then Thomas, who died in 1763. The Mylne, however, who attained much distinction as architect and engineer in England was Robert; his career practically coincides with the long reign of George III.

Robert, the subject of this book, was the eldest son of Thomas Mylne of Powderhall, sometime surveyor to the City of Edinburgh. During the trouble of the '45 he was completing the Old Edinburgh Infirmary in the heavy classical manner favoured by William Adam and others. It is said that he was very careful regarding the education and training of his two sons; it is certain that both profited by this experience; unfortunately there is little information as to the nature of their early studies. Be this as it may, there can be no doubt of the influence of the earlier traditions of Scottish architecture and building on the minds of both young men.

At the age of twenty-one Robert, the elder of the two, set forth to give a hostage to fortune. He left Leith by sea for

13

France in April 1754; when he arrived he voyaged by river to Rouen and Paris. From the French capital he journeyed by road to Marseilles, sailed to Civitavecchia and then proceeded on foot from that seaport to Rome. From what can be gathered from the sketches he made and from the books he studied during his stay in Italy, he was a characteristic figure among his contemporaries.

Bridges and aqueducts immediately occupied his attention, for some secret intuition led him to study the method of water supply to the great city of Rome. Like the majority of young architects and artists then in Italy, he became attracted to the Academy of St. Luke, attending lectures and classes. From this impress of classicality obtained in Rome itself he never swerved in after life. It is possible, therefore, to trace in certain aspects of his work the elements of Roman and Renaissance designs which then took his fancy. While in Italy he visited Sicily, made sketches and details of Girgenti and Taormina, besides noting contemporary methods of design and construction. It was, however, the study of masonry that mainly received his attention.

Andrew Lumisden, author of the *Antiquities of Rome*, writing to Lord George Murray in September 1758, mentions that Robert Mylne had received the first prize for architecture, in the presence of a number of Cardinals. The fact that a Scotsman had been successful against competitors of all nationalities, including Italians, evidently impressed the famous antiquary.

In 1759 Robert Mylne left Italy for ever. The war between France and England was then at its height; a French invasion of England was projected. This forced travellers from Italy to England to pass through Switzerland and travel from Basle to Holland. This was, in fact, the route chosen by Mylne on his return. He crossed from the Netherlands to Harwich by packet ship and reached London in time to enter for the open competition for building Blackfriars Bridge. There were sixty-nine competitors, among whom were leading architects, including William Chambers. From the caricatures of the day, some of which are broad, can be gleaned some ideas of the jealousy caused by the architect's success at the age of twenty-seven. The great work at Blackfriars proceeded slowly for more than ten years. Mylne's diaries, limited to short statements, give an account of the many difficulties which his

5 LONDON: DESIGN FOR AN OFFICE BUILDING
From a drawing by the Author

ingenuity overcame. Dr. Johnson, who pontificated on most
things, wrote three letters to the *Daily Gazetteer* in Decem-
ber 1754 opposing Mylne's elliptical arches. In the end Dr.
Johnson owned himself beaten. The result was a lasting
friendship between the architect and the scholar. Mylne in the
meantime had not forgotten his former friend, Piranesi, to
whom he now wrote, asking the artist to prepare an etching
of the new bridge for publication in London (6).

The year 1760 brought wider public recognition: from now
on Mylne's fortune was assured. He was accepted by the City of
London in the dual capacity of engineer and architect. Not
only was his advancement associated with the building of the
new bridge at Blackfriars, but he was introduced to a new and
wider circle of patrons, eager to avail themselves of his abilities
as an architect.

The second half of the eighteenth century was still domin-
ated by the leaders of the aristocracy politically and socially.
The middling people, of whom many were City merchants

and bankers, were rising to power; the equilibrium of aristocratic privilege was being disturbed by the increase of wealth of those engaged in trade. A newer section of the public were now participating in patronage of the arts and, to some extent, of literature. But notwithstanding this dubious intervention the acclaimed leaders of society still contrived to dictate fashions. The marked increase in wealth and comfort on a descending scale called forth many criticisms and satires. Thus the second half of the eighteenth century, viewed in retrospect, appears as the last phase of that older, more substantial agricultural England before intensive industry and the expansion of towns had scarred the face of the country. Those who were active then did not view events with the eyes of historians. They scarcely noted such changes as the improvement of roads and inland waterways; they viewed with slight concern the growing streets in the environs of London, but they could not remain entirely blind to the spirit of modernity and general enlightenment associated with the newer prosperity of England as a whole. Viewed from the vantage point of today the period appears as part of the preparation for the events of the nineteenth century. The England with which Robert Mylne was to be associated for more than fifty years became very different between 1770 and 1800. There was a great change in newspaper and periodical literature; the magazine and the critical review had come into favour. The novel was now read by a wider range of the public, for circulating libraries had become established. Artisans and journeymen-craftsmen could purchase books of instruction in their own particular trades, written in terms they could readily understand. Some of these works were published cheaply in parts.

As for the professional classes, these now included artists, architects, authors and actors. The Royal Academy was founded in 1768 and protected by the monarch. The growing regard for taste was expressed in the catalogues of Birmingham manufacturers. The ultimate change from aristocratic leadership led naturally to a new order of social life, particularly in cities and large towns. In rural centres the newer order of affairs was not so evident. The age in which Robert Mylne lived and to which he contributed so much exactly suited his temperament, as can be gathered from his diaries. That he should have maintained his position as architect to St. Paul's Cathedral and as engineer to the New River Company for so

16

6 BLACKFRIARS BRIDGE

From an Engraving by Piranesi

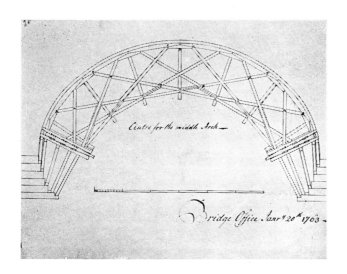

Centre for the middle Arch

Bridge Office Janr 20th 1763

7 BLACKFRIARS
BRIDGE :
MIDDLE ARCH

8 A VIEW OF BLACKFRIARS BRIDGE AND ST. PAUL'S CATHEDRAL

many years is a tribute to his native tenacity no less than to his remarkable physique.

There is an anecdote concerning John Smeaton which to some extent explains Robert Mylne's work at Inveraray. Smeaton was asked by the Duke of Argyll to visit the West Highland coast for a professional purpose. He refused, appalled, it appears, by the rough travelling. "You can recommend some other fit person?" asked the Duke. "No," said Smeaton, "I am sorry, I can't." "What!" cried the Duke, "a profession with only one man in it! Pray, who taught you?" "Why," said Smeaton, "I believe I may say I was self-taught."

Eventually, Robert Mylne was commissioned to carry out the very extensive works which still exist at Inveraray (24–27). Yet in a measure his own case was analogous to that of Smeaton's, for he had instructed himself during his prolonged stay in Italy and had modelled his personal ideas to accord with the masterpieces of the Italian renaissance.

To the young Scotsman travel was as the breath of life. The public usefulness of his career appealed to his judgement; the continual call on his ingenuity in itself was a stimulation. Curiously enough, there was a strain of romance of which at this time he was but dimly conscious, but which in due course would manifest itself in certain of his designs. This romantic strain can be traced to his ancestral lineage, particularly the castellated designs which his forebears had devised for the Stuart kings. At a time when most men would have shirked a journey by road for a greater distance than a hundred miles, Mylne set forth cheerfully time and again to travel by chaise to Edinburgh, which he usually accomplished in four days from London. His zest for these journeys must have been strong; the notes in the diary are merely laconic statements of the daily distances he covered by chaise, namely, Grantham, Wetherby, Newcastle, Edinburgh. The evidence provided by the diaries shows that, while he was engaged in constructing Blackfriars Bridge in London, he made several journeys to Edinburgh between the years 1762–5 to build St. Cecilia's Hall, an elliptical Assembly Room suggested by the example of the Opera House at Parma. (This Hall still exists and has been recently scheduled by the Scottish Ministry of Works) (9, 29, 30.)

The Hall was reached originally by an easy staircase supported on stone columns. Although altered, it still retains

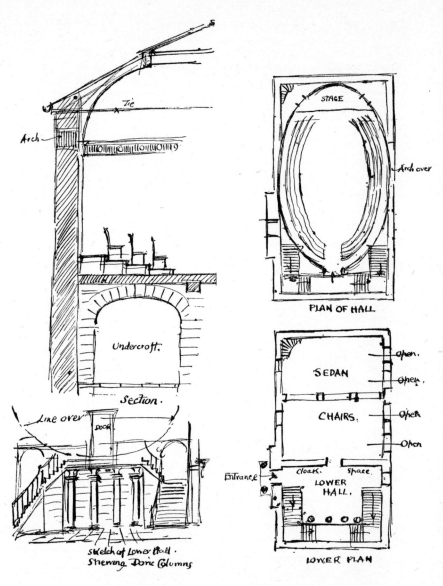

Tie

Arch

Undercroft.

Section.

Line over

Door

Sketch of Lower Hall.
Shewing Doric Columns

STAGE

Arch over

PLAN OF HALL

SEDAN

CHAIRS.

Cloak.   Space

LOWER
HALL.

Entrance

open.

Open.

Open.

Open

LOWER PLAN

9 EDINBURGH: ST. CECILIA'S HALL
From a drawing by the Author

many of the features designed by Mylne. The hall below was
used as a waiting space for the sedan chairmen. A description
of this Hall by Kincaid reads:

"The room is excellently adapted for music, being oval, having a concave ceiling of the same form; the seats are ranged round the room in such a manner as to have a large area in the middle. It only remains to add that the sole light of the Hall is from a comparatively small, oval light in the centre of the oval ceiling, like the single eye of a Cyclops. The amount of light introduced by this one vertical light, like the Pantheon in Rome, is remarkable."

Robert Mylne's first connection with the New River Company began in the year 1762; five years later he was appointed Joint Engineer, as assistant to Henry Mill, who had been associated with the Company since the year 1692. At the time of Mylne's appointment in 1767, Henry Mill was a very aged man; he died in 1770. Mylne was then appointed Chief Engineer to the Company, a post he held till his death in 1811. The foundations of the new offices in Clerkenwell were begun on June 28th, 1770; the older portions dating from the seventeenth century were refaced in 1782. Robert Mylne's facing to the Court Room has been rebuilt in recent years to form part of the latest building (33, 34).

For the next forty years the Architect-Engineer directed all the works required for the maintenance and improvement of the New River between Clerkenwell and Ware. Among other features he designed the bridges which carried roads and lanes over the waterway; he introduced such features as piers and vases in rural spots to enhance the picturesque character of the locality; at a later date he designed and erected the urn and pedestal on an island in the stream not far from the natural source of the New River (36). The greater number of features mentioned have been swept away during the past half-century. Joseph Farrington, R.A., recording Robert Mylne's death, states that he often passed the severest winter in the Court Room at Clerkenwell without a fire in the grate.

It has been found possible, by referring to the fine series of original drawings, to confirm many of the works carried out or attributed to Robert Mylne. These drawings prove him to have possessed the architectural skill of a master, particularly in his consummate knowledge of detail. A brief résumé of the names of the leading architects then in practice is not inappropriate at this juncture, for it will show the esteem in which Robert Mylne was regarded in many influential quarters.

When he entered the architectural lists in London in 1759, many of the architects of the older school were still in practice. Among these were Flitcroft (died 1769), Isaac Ware (died

1766), John Vardy (died 1765), John Wood junior (died 1782), George Dance the elder (died 1768). The practice of architecture was for a few brief years most comfortably divided between James Paine and Sir Robert Taylor.

In the north John Carr of York reigned supreme, building mansions and bridges as he thought fit, a notable example of the latter being Ferry Bridge, Yorkshire. Sir Robert Taylor (died 1788) had attained renown for his central arch to Old London Bridge, as well as for his work at the Bank of England and Stone buildings, Lincoln's Inn Fields. In 1762 James Stuart with Nicholas Revett had published the book describing the antiquities of Athens. Sir William Chambers (died 1796) had yet to become famous as the designer of Somerset House, while his pupil, Gandon, did not attain similar fame in Ireland until the early years of the nineteenth century. On the other hand, Robert Mylne's most serious competitor was the younger Dance (died 1825). Dance had won the Gold Medal of the Academy of Parma in 1763 for a design for a picture gallery. In 1764 he was elected a member of the Academy of St. Luke. Returning to London in 1765, he succeeded his father as City Surveyor in 1768. Dance brought with him all the contemporary ideas from Rome and a deep regard for the imaginative compositions of Piranesi.

Robert Mylne's Scottish competitors included that redoubtable trio of architects and decorators, the brothers Adam, who possessed great skill as designers of architecture and furniture. In fact, the Adam manner not only satisfied the aristocracy who contemplated building town and country houses, but captivated the whole range of the middle classes. The Adam style retained its hold on popular taste for more than thirty years. Henry Holland (died 1806) first came into prominence at a time when Mylne was firmly established. It is, therefore, noteworthy that Holland carried on the tradition of club design initiated by Mylne, who built Almack's as the precursor of Brooks's Club (10.)

A minute account of the professional activities of Robert Mylne could be compiled from his pocket diaries, but this would convey little of his taste or gift of organisation. The present objective is to represent the character of the man and the nature of his work. It would be evading the issue to lead students to think of him other than as a civil engineer with a natural gift for architecture. He was above everything else

22

a creator of projects and a born modifier of Nature. The design of bridges, the forming of roads, the making of causeways, the cutting of canals and the improvement of navigable rivers formed his chief interests. But he was also an artist who, benefiting by his travels, kept his eyes open. He communed most secretly within himself to prove his intuition for proportion, selection and assembling of classical motifs. Yet, despite his leaning to classical forms contact with Robert Morris's strange Gothic style at Inveraray Castle confirmed his own preference for things romantic of Scottish origin. Later it will be shown how this particular preference came into operation. He was, in fact, continually furnishing his mind, not with copious sketches, but by visual observation and memory. For classical form and composition he relied on the etchings of Piranesi; for ornament he drew upon George Richardson's decorative illustrations, published in 1776 and 1787. He had the sense of detail to a degree and he followed his taste in this regard without hesitation.

Robert Mylne was fully alive to all the implications of contemporary architecture, its observance of Palladian rules, its avoidance of curvilinear digressions and its acceptance of stereotyped and formalistic ornamentation, particularly arabesques. As an architect Mylne was a precisian. His duty as he saw it was to design the work in the most practical way and to see that it was carried out properly. For this reason his works were always soundly planned and constructed. He was thorough to the extreme; no other architect at that time went to the trouble of having plans, elevations and sections backlined to emphasise the design. As an architect he could not hope to attain to the skill of Sir William Chambers, whose sense for civil architecture equalled that of the famous French architect, Gabriel. Neither could Mylne rival the skill of the younger Dance, who in his design for Newgate achieved dramatic intensity in the simplest and most direct way. Yet both had recourse to the innumerable fantasies produced by Piranesi.

It would likewise be impertinent to compare Mylne's undoubted prowess as an architectural designer with the polished although somewhat metallic manner of James Wyatt. But Mylne had no need to imitate or even emulate any of the great architects of his day, because he possessed his own consistent idealism, so that the smallest thing he attempted of an architectural character bears the inimitable stamp of his personal genius.

He was among the first to originate the smaller type of country house: neither too large nor too small for its purpose. He contrived to impart distinction to all he created and this is seen in his working drawings.

But it was as a builder of bridges that he was most renowned; it is therefore not surprising to find from his diary that he visited Welbeck in 1764 to design a bridge for the Duke of Portland. This bridge of three arches formed the centre feature of a painting by Barrett. It has long since been taken down. There are, however, several features on the estate which suggest Mylne's hand. In this year he was commissioned to design Almack's Club House in King Street, St. James's, afterwards known as Willis's Rooms. Almack, or Mackall, was a Scotsman by birth and naturally turned to a brother Scot for assistance in carrying out the design. Almack at a later date formed Brooks's Club, an early design by Henry Holland. The large ballroom at Almack's measured

10 LONDON: ALMACK'S BALLROOM
From a drawing by the Author

100 feet in length by 40 feet in width. The internal treatment consisted of coupled Corinthian pilasters between each of the five windows, with corresponding treatment on the opposite wall, which was panelled. At each end of the room were four insulated Corinthian columns with entablature broken over each. The introduction of classic medallions, festoons and mirrors added to the rich treatment. The charm of the interior was enhanced by the segmental ceiling. There can be no doubt that Mylne's design for the ballroom derived from a design by Neufforge. It is also significant that the design of Almack's ceiling in turn influenced Henry Holland when he planned the Great Subscription Room at Brooks's Club.

While still engaged on the building of Blackfriars Bridge Mylne was appointed by the Archbishop of Canterbury to be Surveyor to St. Paul's Cathedral, to the Palace at Croydon and to the Abbey Church of St. Albans. In 1767 the Dean and Chapter of Canterbury Cathedral appointed him Surveyor. His professional association with the Church of England led also to commissions from the Bishops of Lichfield and Bangor and the Bishop of Derry. At St. Paul's Cathedral Robert Mylne was responsible for repairs to the fabric, including the main piers supporting the dome. He designed the tablet inscribed with the epitaph to Sir Christopher Wren and superintended the arrangements for all public ceremonies that took place during his tenure of the surveyorship, including the funeral of Lord Nelson. He also added the perron to the Deanery of St. Paul's and rearranged the interior rooms. At Lichfield there is evidence of Mylne's activity in the design of the reservoir and probably some of the adjoining domestic buildings.

His first architectural house of importance, the City of London Lying-in Hospital, was started in the year 1770 (11). This particular design was in the nature of an innovation and was the outcome of close consultation with the leading gynæcologists of the day. In this year he made a survey of Fulham Palace for the Bishop of London, together with No. 32, St. James's Square, which in spite of alterations in the main shows the original treatment. His other duties for the Church of England included surveys of property at Croydon and Rochester. At Tusmore in Oxfordshire (39, 40) he built a new mansion in which he introduced his favourite motif of an external

11 LONDON: CITY OF LONDON LYING-IN HOSPITAL
From a drawing by the Author

perron. This has most unfortunately been removed and the whole spirited design has been completely changed in recent years. At Wormleybury, near Broxbourne in Hertfordshire, he remodelled the earlier house, adding the fine Ionic portico and the picturesque stable buildings. The internal decorations, formerly attributed to Robert Adam, should be accepted as the work of Robert Mylne, whose taste in this regard cannot be denied. By this time, 1770, the work on Blackfriars Bridge was nearing completion. Mylne's reputation as a civil engineer was at its very zenith. For this reason it is not surprising to find him appointed by the Bishop of Durham to superintend the rebuilding of the southern portion of the bridge over the Tyne at Newcastle, the northern portion being left to another engineer, John Wooler, by the Mayor and Corporation. The two engineers accordingly worked together. This fine bridge, 300 feet in length, was taken down in 1873.

Robert Mylne's reputation as a bridge builder was now such that he was asked to arbitrate on many such structures, a notable case being the extension of the old bridge over the

Clyde at Glasgow and the bridge at Yarrow. Also at this period he made a complete survey of Inveraray Castle for the Duke of Argyll and began the series of works and improvements in the town and on the estate which stand to this day. In 1774 he became Treasurer of Heriot's Hospital, Edinburgh. This was a compliment to his Scottish connections and to the respect in which the family name was held in the city.

The next work of importance, Addington Lodge, Croydon, he built for Alderman Trevothick (35, 51, 52). In 1807 it was altered and became a country residence of the Archbishops of Canterbury. Today it is scarcely recognisable as a country house of its period, such have been the changes in the last fifty years. One or two small buildings on the estate, including lodges, remain. In the year 1775 Mylne found scope for his genius as a designer of villas of moderate size. This time the site was on the terrace at the top of Richmond Hill, overlooking the Thames and the country beyond to Windsor. Sir Joshua Reynolds was already living in the adjoining villa, which Chambers had designed for him. This still exists, although much altered. The Wick, which Mylne designed for Lady St. Aubyn, has escaped serious alteration, although the original roof has been changed and many of the fireplaces have disappeared (43–46). Mylne's design centred on an elliptical apartment which was repeated on three floors. From the windows of the saloon one of the finest landscape views in England can still be seen. Sir Joshua Reynolds had already availed himself of his own view-point next door, and had produced one of his finest landscape pictures. In this year Mylne was appointed Clerk of the Works to Greenwich Hospital, where he was engaged on several improvements. Then followed various routine commissions, such as reports on the harbour and bridge at Great Yarmouth, the bridge at Kelso, afterwards reconstructed by John Rennie, and a general report on the fabric of Durham Cathedral.

From a study of the original working drawings it has been possible to trace the buildings he designed and built in New Bridge Street, Blackfriars, including his own house, which afterwards became the York Hotel (12, 22). Most of these buildings were taken down when the railway was constructed and the bridge carried across Ludgate Hill. Judging from notes in the diaries, he was continually engaged making surveys and reports on houses and villas in the neighbourhood of London; visiting such districts as Twickenham, Old Windsor, Hanwell and Highgate.

For Woodfall, the printer of the *Letters of Junius*, he built a villa in Highgate Road, Kentish Town, the drawings of which exist.

Another important commission was the work at Inveraray, which necessitated a long journey to the west coast of Scotland.

In this connection a good many letters passed between the Duke and his architect between the years 1773 and 1776. In the same year, under the date August 29th, the diary reads:

Aug. 29 Eight days on a journey from Edinburgh, stay at Inverary, and returning as far as Glasgow. Various consultations during three days' stay, on the site of a new Kirk, a new approach from the town to the Castle, new covered way from Castle to the offices and several other matters about the Castle offices, farm, roads and grounds.	16 16 0	
Money disbursed in expenses of travelling on the said journey:	7 15 0	
Gave a design of four drawings for altering the pidgeon-house into a round temple.	12 12 0	
1777		
Jan. 15 Waited on His Grace in town, gave a long drawing, wherein Garron Bridge, the two lodges and fence wall are all introduced.	4 4 0	
April 3 Gave His Grace a design for altering, fitting up and finishing all the windows of the principal floor of Inverary Castle, consisting of a plan, section and elevation.	10 10 0	
	£122 13 11	

The detail drawings of these works, now preserved at Inveraray Castle, are among the most beautiful of their type. No architect of the day, not excepting Sir William Chambers or the Adam brothers, could command such draughtsmanship as Mylne exacted from his assistants. His designs for improvements at Inveraray from 1780 onwards included those which applied to the four principal rooms.

The drawings are described as "neat, highly finished in different colours and fit for execution". Other drawings sent at various times were for buildings on the estate, farm offices, and sheds for cattle. Most of the plasterwork was carried out by Papworth, the stuccoer in London, and sent to Inveraray for the ceilings, walls and other features. Metal sashes were

Design for an office building near Bridge Street.

12 LONDON: DESIGN FOR AN OFFICE BUILDING NEAR
NEW BRIDGE STREET

From a drawing by the Author

made by Underwood, carved trusses by Bower, artificial orna-
ments by Jacques and carving by Lawrence. From these notes it
is possible to deduce the fact that Robert Mylne designed and su-
pervised the carrying out of the decorative parts of his buildings.

In September 1783 Mylne again visited Inveraray, giving
advice and surveying the state of Roseneath. Eventually he
sent the Duke "a new and compleat design for adding to and

13 LONDON: STATIONERS' HALL. The Entrance

From a drawing by the Author

compleating Roseneath Castle into a large mansion house by
two new wings added, and altering the middle part and
offices entirely, consisting of three plans and four elevations,
all large, high finished, neat and mounted."

A most elegant single arch bridge was designed and built
by Mylne over the river in the private grounds of Warwick
Castle (41). But by far the most important engineering work
after the bridge at Blackfriars was the bridge of nine arches at
Hexham, completed in 1793 (42). Mylne's professional work
after 1799 differed greatly. He executed works at Southampton
Dock, advised on the reservoir on the Pentland Hills, works
at Selkirk, Carlisle and Belfast. For the last-named city he
designed a hospital (20, 21).

He was also called upon for advice at Bognor, Arundel and
Chichester. In the year 1796 he designed a splendid house in
Stratton Street, Piccadilly, for Coutts, the banker. This house
with its bow front, for many years prior to its demolition,
was considered to be one of the most striking landmarks in
Piccadilly (4).

Practically his last architectural work of importance was the remodelling of Stationers' Hall and the design of the east front of that building, which still exists. This work he carried out in his capacity of Surveyor to the Worshipful Company of Stationers (13, 14).

Robert Mylne was elected a Fellow of the Royal Society in 1767 and was one of the founder members of the Architects' Club in 1791.

On every showing Robert Mylne treated architecture in the practical English manner, paying respect to the trades, particularly masonry; this is to be seen in the tooling and drafting of prominent plinths and base courses. He determined upon an elevational manner which was individual and he proceeded to evolve mouldings, consoles and cornices of delicate profile. Even the balustrades and flutings which are introduced as refining elements to the façades to his country houses do not accord with accepted rules. Yet his knowledge of the classical orders was certain and this enabled him to introduce huge modillions into the cornice of the Ionic Order which embellished Blackfriars Bridge. Like many of his contemporaries he turned to Italy for inspiration in all matters

14 LONDON: STATIONERS' HALL. General view
From a drawing by the Author

of lithic design. Mylne's main objective, however, apart from a desire to attain elegance in buildings, was to achieve success in that branch of civil engineering in which competitors were few. The main need of the time was improved inland transport to meet the growing needs of industry. Mylne's study of rivers and waterways fitted him for the fresh demands made on his skill in connection with canals. His native talent assisted him in each fresh enterprise. He was a well-read man, one gifted with exact perception of cause and effect. He made himself master of facts, he elicited the clearest principles and he initiated improvements with vigour and authority. He appears always to have kept the ultimate result in mind and from this he never swerved. What is curious is that he carried his learning lightly although he had amassed an infinity of ideas and details of every kind, from architecture to pumps, besides many other mechanical devices. But he leaves no full record of his investigations, and where we feel we should chance upon a mass of data, in Mylne's case we have only the synoptical notes in the diaries. Yet there is one exception and that is the admirable record of the building of Blackfriars Bridge. On every showing Robert Mylne was very capable, as his records of Blackfriars Bridge affirm. Stage by stage he built up his own methods of constructing this great work, learning to overcome difficulties by hard experience: by sheer improvisation developing a new building technique.* And so, by continual application he convinced himself, as he convinced others, on matters which hitherto had been obscure.

*Joseph Farrington, recording a visit to George Dance in March 1810, mentions seeing "a manuscript life of Robert Milne, the architect, who had himself written it and sent it to Dance".

There is also a reference to a letter sent by Mylne to Dance, which states "that the New River is forty miles long; has two hundred bridges over it, and far exceeds in effect the works of ancient Rome".

On May 6th, 1811, Farrington wrote: "The death of Milne, the architect, was this day announced in the newspapers. He designed Blackfriars Bridge and was Surveyor of St. Paul's Cathedral, a place of honour but the salary only £70 a year. It is in the gift of the Archbishop of Canterbury, the Bishop of London, and the Lord Mayor."

This was followed by a more lengthy entry on May 8th: "I had company to dinner—Robert Smirke attended the funeral of Milne, the architect at St. Paul's, on Monday last at 8 in the morning. He died on Monday, the 6th last, aged 79. He had from about Christmas last lived entirely at his house of the New River, which place he had held more than forty years. During this period he had no positive illness but felt a disinclination to going abroad. Thus he went on until a short time before his death, having

1791. Feb.ᵉ 2. at 2 o'clock.

There was the highest tide, in the Thames above London Bridge, ever known. — It rose to the height, of 3 feet 3 Inches, above the top of the semicircular Pedestals of Blackfriars Bridge, where the Bases of the Columns stand. — It was Candlemas Day — and the moon was to change the next day, at 6 o'clock in the morning. — The tide was, calculated to be at 40 Min'. past one o'clock. . — It blew a Storm at N. West the night before. After a whole winter of stormy weather & heavy Gales from the S. West.

15 NOTE BY ROBERT MYLNE OF WATER LEVEL
AT BLACKFRIARS BRIDGE

risen in the morning as usual. He soon after said he would go to bed again which he did. He was sensible to the last. He had been a man of great application to business and it was remarkable that throughout the winter as well as summer seasons He had sat while employed in a room situated over water, very damp and witht a fire. He disregarded also the state of his cloaths and linen and wd put on a shirt saturated with dampness. He was a man much disposed to conversation and drank wine at and after his meals freely. He was extremely exact in all his affairs and noted and checked all his concerns with great care. He left one son who succeeds Him in the Office of Surveyor of the New River, a place of abt £1,000 a year, and to Him he bequeathed property to the amount of 8 or £900 a year. He also left 4 daugrs. for whom He also provided."

16 DESIGN FOR A COUNTRY HOUSE
From a drawing by the Author

Everything had to be personally organised and to a large
extent conducted. Letters and reports had to be written in
longhand; plans had first to be sketched in pencil, then drawn
to scale, after which they were laboriously and accurately
inked in. The very careful drawings prepared in Robert
Mylne's office convey the idea that the architect instructed
his draughtsmen on every detail. Sometimes, when the plans
were complete, Mylne would sketch certain modifications in
pencil, and then the process of drawing the design over again
would fall to the lot of the clerk. Then, as is the case today,
many projects were initiated and abandoned. Robert Mylne
was no exception to the general rule, for his specialised professional work touched on branches of practice which were
out of the ordinary. Add to this the number of journeys under-
taken by road, with the fatigue consequent on such events,
and the magnitude of his labours can be understood.

A Description of Mylne's Style

English architecture during the reign of George III stood
for something more than a mere statement of contemporary
building construction, although this was its surest basis. The

period was productive of many striking personalities, some of whom, with the works they created, have become historical. An age which gave rise both to Sir William Chambers and the brothers Adam, which encouraged research in the classical fields of Greece, and at the same time admitted the skill of journeymen builders, was bound to accept stars of all magnitudes. In Robert Mylne there appeared a character quite different to his contemporaries. The distinctive trait was the confidence he inspired both as a constructor and as an artist. He was, so to speak, the first of the new lineage of civil engineers; men competent to blend the ideals of two distinct professions. Smeaton, Brindley, Rennie and Telford would in turn pursue similar trends later on. But Robert Mylne, thanks to his inherited taste, possessed the creative quality essential to the practice of architecture. He planned with clarity and constructed with foresight. He possessed neither the skill for composition and planning exercised by Sir William Chambers nor the versatility for decoration enjoyed by Robert Adam. On the contrary, he worked upon the whole standard of every-day practice, perfecting the ordinary and demonstrating that a precisian in construction had a purpose to fulfil. For it was the exactness of his designs in full and part, combined with elegance and restraint, that constituted his style. Robert Mylne demonstrated his power when he designed Blackfriars Bridge; in consequence he became the acknowledged leader in this branch of professional achievement. The fact that nearly all the most responsible appointments connected with the maintenance of historic buildings were given to him shows the regard in which his skill was held.

Conversant with the attitude of travellers to the arts of Rome, familiar with Scottish ideas of masonry, he gave distinction to the buildings he was commissioned to design. Consistently simple as all Mylne's works are, they nevertheless carry the mark of individual taste. At this period the eighteenth century evolved a secular system of society which made the best use of the crafts. Mylne understood this and he sought to combine ordinary construction with classical details and at the same time avoid theatrical display. At a slightly later period Henry Holland adopted almost similar procedure, while Soane, the last of this particular school, aimed at novelty of detail. It was, therefore, in the simple domestic architecture of the towns no less than in the reasonable size of small villas

35

that the realities of middle-class social life were represented. During this period, as already mentioned, classes other than the nobility were beginning to participate in the arts and to appreciate the more subtle qualities of design and ornament. In this regard Mylne derived inspiration from Piranesi's etchings and from contemporary works on ceilings and ornament. He was in a position to select marble fireplaces direct from those London firms who employed Italian carvers. He conferred with Papworth, the stuccoer on plasterwork, and he had recourse to Scottish iron-founders who supplied grates and stoves. Thus his ornamental furnishings conform with many of the designs of Robert Adam and James Wyatt. Mylne was doubtless very sensitive regarding the embellishments he introduced for interiors. For external ornament he frequently adapted designs obtained from Messrs Coade's factory at Lambeth and in this he followed the example of other leading architects. It is curious that while many of his buildings passed almost unnoticed at the time of erection, their true significance is now acclaimed.

Architecture is a progressive art and does not favour an exact repetition of historical forms. On the other hand, it does admit a return to first principles. This has been the case since Gothic blended into the Renaissance, in itself a return to the motivating influence of classicism. Thus in architecture, the first of the arts, the desire to create afresh is foremost. The sketches and drawings of those masters who lived and worked in former times, therefore, seem to possess a quality which permeates the whole conception. This should lead to investigation of the period which encouraged the particular works and the character of the individuals who interpreted the symbols of their day. In this way it is possible to grasp the spirit of a past age and the impress of a period. But it is equally essential to take into account the character of the individual artist who acted as medium and interpreter. The work of eminent men, whatever their calling or specific genius, will invariably express the period which gave rise to special designs. The art of architecture flourishes best when it is nation deep, when whole peoples are agreed on the furtherance of principles which are judged to be sound. In the case of Robert Mylne it is perhaps unique that a whole collection of working drawings for public buildings, hospitals, offices, villas, small houses, gateways and stables should

17 BLACKFRIARS BRIDGE UNDER CONSTRUCTION

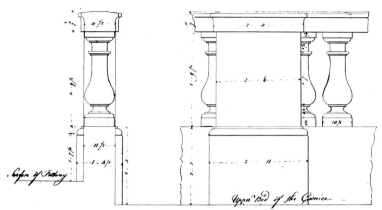

18 BLACKFRIARS BRIDGE: Detail of balustrading on
river side of parapet

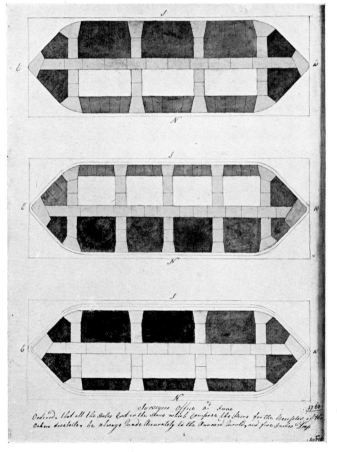

19 BLACKFRIARS
BRIDGE: Illust-
ration from sur-
veyor's private
book showing
method of build-
ing the several
piers from
which sprang
the arches

be available. The drawings of Blackfriars Bridge were collated by Mylne himself; these form an accurate day-to-day record of the works as carried out between 1762 and 1770. The architectural drawings, also in a folio volume, throw a new light on professional practice during the reign of George III. The series begins with six sheets of drawings of a small villa, each sheet is entitled Mr. Berner's Hanwell; these form part of the original contract made with the builder, T. Hardwick. The sheets measure 1 foot 3 inches wide by 1 foot 7 inches long. There is a smaller drawing showing the ground-floor plan; this was evidently the first proposal. There was no tracing paper in those days and rarely were more than two copies made of each plan. This house has two main floors; there are rooms in the attic storey, with kitchens and offices in the basement. The accommodation includes a drawing-room, 26 feet by 17 feet, a study, 17 feet by 12 feet, as well as an entrance hall, 7 feet 10 inches wide; there is a separate staircase hall. The first floor is arranged with four principal bedrooms, two with powdering closets, one without a powdering closet and one opening into a dressing-room. The height of the ground-floor rooms in the clear is 13 feet; the height of the first-floor rooms in the clear is 8 feet 6 inches. The "garrett" floor, which contained four large rooms and one small one, is shown as 7 feet clear in height. This attractive country villa was built about 1765. The principal elevation is perfect in composition and detail (31).

Another factor which contributed to the excellence of Mylne's work was the care bestowed in the making of working drawings. The skilled draughtsman and the clerks employed were evidently instructed to back the lines of plans, elevations and sections; this was done to throw into relief the more delicate thin lines. The draughtsmanship of the late eighteenth century required the finesse of skilled engravers. All Mylne's drawings are carefully dimensioned. There are preliminary studies for Mr. Trevothick's house at Addington in Surrey, and plans for office premises in New Bridge Street which became the main approach to South London leading across Blackfriars Bridge. There is a sketch design for a small country house called Bickley Place, Kent, a villa 53 feet square. There is a project for additions to Cadland House in Hampshire; in this case Mylne was called in to alter the existing arrangements. In 1775 the first plans were made for The Wick on Richmond

Hill, one of the most famous of his smaller houses. The earliest plan is ordinary and bears little relation to the superb design with the elliptical rooms (43–46).

The drawings of "Major Hamilton's near Glasgow" show a noble villa, seven windows wide, with a central pediment and a basement storey. The latter appears to have been planned partly above ground. There is a garret with four rooms under the sloping roof. The plans and elevations of a house in Fifeshire for General Sir Robert Skene are of unusual interest (47, 48). In this case the character is that of the spacious country mansion. There are four principal living-rooms with two staircases; the servants' quarters are in the basement storey. This is the first of Mylne's designs to show a semi-circular-ended drawing-room. There is another drawing marked "Idea for a Country House"; this evidently applies to the main elevations and the stables. Several unfinished drawings appear to be proposals in connection with Almack's Assembly Rooms. In 1766 Robert Mylne made a design for a house in Highgate Road, Kentish Town, for Mr. Woodfall, the printer, who at a later date published the *Letters of Junius*. The actual contract drawings for this house are dated March 4th, 1766. Reference to various entries in Mylne's diaries relate to other commissions for Mr. Woodfall. Woodfall was evidently difficult to please, for Mylne had to produce several alternative plans, but in the end he was satisfied and thought highly of his architect. It is significant also that Mylne's reputation as a man of promptitude gained him many clients. There are plans and elevations for a new printing establishment marked "King's Printing House near Fleet Street". In this design the treatment of the windows to the composing-rooms is singularly novel for the period.

Mylne apparently enjoyed a varied practice in different parts of the kingdom. Several sheets of plans show a design for the house in Fifeshire; and are marked "Study for General Robert Skene", already referred to. It is evident from the alternative ideas that eighteenth-century clients could not make up their minds quickly when they embarked on the serious task of building. While Robert Mylne was still busy with the main structural work at Blackfriars, he was commissioned by the City Authorities to design the City of London Lying-In Hospital, subsequently built on a site in the City Road. The plan dates from 1766; the composition is in three parts with administrative offices in a separate block. The accommodation allowed space for fifty beds with special pass rooms, matrons' rooms and a large chapel. Four beautiful drawings comprise the design; the elevations and the section have the signature of the architect (11).

Mylne's continued success in the City of London now gave him several new clients who desired villas. Curiously enough there was also a demand for similar buildings in Scotland. In this regard, three plans and one elevation in colour illustrate a villa at Powderhall, near Edinburgh. The overall dimensions of the villa are 48 feet 6 inches by 39 feet. This allowed for two large reception rooms, respectively 18 feet by 27 feet and 18 feet by 25 feet, and one smaller room, 18 feet by 18 feet, besides an entrance hall, staircase hall and a small room, 10 feet 6 inches by 8 feet 6 inches. The elevation is distinguished by the grouping of the chimneys into one central stack. This interesting small house does not appear to have been built. The plans for Sir Francis Gosling's house at Fulham show a variety of ingenious arrangements. This house afterwards became the residence of Sir R. Stephens, Bt. Sir Francis Gosling, Alderman of the City of London, was knighted in 1769. He was an eminent banker with an establishment at the sign of the "Three Squirrels" in Fleet Street.

In the development of Robert Mylne's plans it is interesting to observe the evolution of a novel pattern. For example, the plan for Sir Francis Gosling's house shows the germ of the idea for The Wick at Richmond Hill. In the first series of plans for the latter house Mylne aimed at a building which would have a large room facing south, commanding the magnificent view over the River Thames and beyond to Windsor Park. Another drawing entitled "Lady St. Aubyn's, Richmond Hill, Surrey" shows a further development towards the final solution. Eventually, after much study, the architect solved all the difficulties and on June 12th, 1775, the contract drawings were signed by the contractor, Daniel Pinder (43–46). These drawings, which include three elevations, two sections and four plans, show the meticulous care given to the production of working drawings by Mylne's assistants. Such is the minute detail that it is possible to interpret the exact proportions of fireplaces, doors, stair balustrading, cornices, dadoes and skirtings. From personal knowledge it can be stated that the fireplaces were carried out exactly as shown

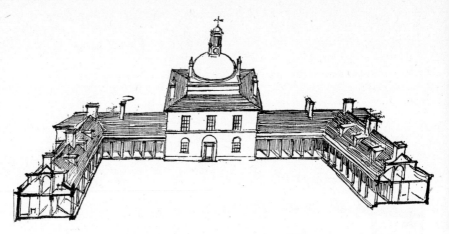

20 BELFAST: DESIGN FOR HOSPITAL. The courtyard
From a drawing by the Author

on the contract drawings. It is also interesting to know that
Mylne's assistants were remunerated at salaries of £50 per
annum with bed and breakfast. There are nine sheets of drawings marked "Durham Park" (55–58) evidently not carried
out. The plans show a large rectangular mansion with projecting
wings on the entrance front. In this example the alternative
ideas for the treatment of the entrance portico include a
design with four attenuated Ionic columns almost of colonial
proportion and elegance. About this time Mylne's plans begin
to include water-closets and other domestic conveniences.

Judging from a sketch design for a cottage it is evident that
Robert Mylne had strong inclinations towards picturesque
and romantic compositions. Thatch is indicated as a possible
covering for the pitched roofs and from this the theory can be
deduced that this design was intended for Hampshire. Mylne
was equally skilful with classical compositions which demanded
symmetrical repetition. For example, the design for a large
country mansion has a detached kitchen wing on one side
balanced by a stable block on the other. This scheme conforms
to methods usually followed. By contrast, the design for a double
cottage having two floors and a basement is most ingenious.
Externally, the elevation appears like a small lodge with a
central stack. The whole accommodation is contained within a
rectangle of 33 feet 4 inches (32). This was designed for Colonel
Duncan of Falkirk. The design for a temple in the park at

21 BELFAST: DESIGN FOR HOSPITAL. Entrance front
From a drawing by the Author

Gatton in Surrey is shown by what Mylne describes as "washed drawings". The tetrastyle portico forms the frontispiece to a cella wall with niches and giant urns. There are also plans and elevations for a house in Wales (53, 54); brick is the material in this case with local slate for the roofs. By far the most important of the large country houses designed by Robert Mylne is Tusmore in Oxfordshire. The original designs include one or two alternative elevations for the main fronts, and detailed sections. This exceptionally fine house still exists but many of the original features have been destroyed (39, 40).

Mylne's design for the Hospital at Belfast shows an attractive layout grouped about a central court. The two main wards are on the entrance front with sanitary convenience at the end of each ward. The elevational treatment includes a domical roof and lantern for the central pavilion. This design, however, was not carried out. There are also interesting plans for houses for Lord Stamford in London and a mansion near Welbeck for the Duke of Portland, neither of which appear to have materialised. The designs for houses in New Bridge Street include the double house with the circular portico which Mylne built for his own use (22). The elevations of these City houses were beautifully proportioned, the porticoes being unique in design. A preliminary design for General Skene's house, Pitlour in Fifeshire, is planned on T-shaped lines. The

43

original plans for Alderman Patteson's house at Norwich show wing walls similar to the treatment of the appendages at The Wick at Richmond Hill (23). The plan Mylne prepared for Dr. Hunter's house in Windmill Street includes a lecture theatre.

22 LONDON: DESIGNS FOR HOUSES IN NEW BRIDGE STREET

From a drawing by the Author

There is also a plan showing the alterations proposed to be carried out at Wormleybury in Hertfordshire. The circular stable building at Taymouth, a castellated tower for Blaise Castle, Kings Weston, Bristol, and several geometrical plans are among types inspired by Morris's work at Inveraray Castle.

The scope of the buildings carried out for the Duke of Argyll at Inveraray can also be judged from a circular plan with the bailiff's house and stabling at the centre. This plan was prepared by Mylne on the site during one of his visits to Scotland. The chief characteristic of Robert Mylne's plans is the regard given to their structural integrity. They are faultless in matters of organic unity and circulation while they have all the qualities and sequence which classical disposition calls for.

Although Mylne had studied antique buildings in Rome and had travelled extensively in Italy, he was wise enough to select only those forms which would suit his conceptions. Gaining from experience after designing Almack's, he avoided panelling walls with pilasters and arabesques and in his designs for ceilings he showed great reticence. It was not his purpose to imitate antique features but to give emphasis to his own power of construction. Although conversant with the strictly Roman forms such as coffered vaults, domes, modillion cornices and enriched bands; although beset with opportunities to adopt surface decorations, Wedgwood medallions and stuccoed foliage, Mylne held himself aloof from all such temptations. His preference for rich simplicity is apparent in the restraint of his finished buildings. He was one of the first architects in England to be inspired by the Greek researches of Stuart and Revett and he envied the grace which came so naturally to the works of his French contemporaries. First and foremost he esteemed draughtsmanship; secondly, ingenuity of planning, and thirdly, the impress of style which, in Mylne's case, was personal. Ingenuity combined with refinement and severity is undoubtedly the secret of his ability. His skill as an organiser of works on the great scale is recorded by the copy-books which he kept during the period of all his activities.

There is yet another aspect of the eighteenth-century attitude towards the art of architecture which has been seldom explained and more rarely understood. This concerns the seriousness of the designer. There are many of Mylne's elevations which are virtually self-portraits of the architect. He impressed his talented assistants with his own ideas; this can be seen from the beauty of the working drawings, the accurate ruling, the back lining, and the delicate washes which were introduced for especial buildings. Mylne's personal adjustments and corrections appear in pencil on many of these drawings, proving that he was seldom content with an early sketch. But it is also true that spontaneity of idea, which is apparent in his preliminary designs, was maintained. Although inclined to reticence in all matters of architectural embellishment, he could nevertheless select and incorporate the correct motifs and symbols most suited to his individual taste. As already mentioned, he held Richardson's designs for ceilings in esteem. The lessons of Greek refinement in mouldings and enrichments, which the publication of James Stuart's work had defined, were then being slowly comprehended. Sir William Chambers, a staunch Palladian and a follower of the contemporary French school, refused to be converted to Athenian grace. Robert Adam, on the other hand, borrowed freely all that suited his fancy in the way of Greek ornament. It was left for James Wyatt and Henry Holland to explore the possibilities of an amalgam of Greek

23 HOUSE AT NORWICH

From a drawing by the Author

46

and Roman detail. Robert Mylne, meanwhile, developed a style for domestic work which was in advance of its time. In architecture he cultivated a style of three dimensions in which the buildings are well proportioned, comfortable and unostentatious.

The Intimate Scene
1760–1811

Robert Mylne's professional life ran parallel to the long reign of King George III. He was twenty-seven at the time of the royal accession in 1760; in the year of the Jubilee, 1810, he was seventy-seven. He lived and worked amidst a circle which his peculiar genius had attracted. His comments on the age in which he lived are unknown, for although he noted daily events for years in his pocket diaries these are mainly concerned with appointments and expenses. His genius was a family legacy, due to deep-seated traditions of building for the royal line of Scottish kings. His style of building was, moreover, the result of visual education and contacts with the masterpieces of Italian art in Rome and elsewhere. There is something dynamic about the second half of the period in which he lived. After 1760 events moved with greater rapidity; many converging causes, acting with simultaneous force, encouraged a new social order. The Seven Years' War had brought conquest after conquest in Canada and India, opening out fresh fields for adventure and new markets for English manufacturers. It was realised that sovereignty of the seas encouraged world trade. Almost immediately London began to expand; the spirit of enterprise manifest in the days of the elder Pitt was destined to accompany the British people through the whole course of the succeeding nineteenth century.

This sketch of a period is concerned mainly with artistic achievements and daily routine, with details of building rather than the gossip of society, with the City and not with the Court circle; yet it touches upon both. The fame of the young Scottish architect who had been chosen to build the new bridge across the Thames was such that, almost simultaneously, he was invited to design Almack's Assembly Rooms in King Street, St. James's. Horace Walpole noted both events in his correspondence. Robert Mylne's view of the world in which he lived and worked in consequence became wider and richer than that of many other citizens. He knew the face of London as well as he knew the narrow wynds and tall lands of his native Edinburgh. The roads between the two capital cities were as familiar to him as were the cathedrals and the mansions he was called upon to survey. He came under the spell of London's countryside, particularly the valley of the Lea in its meandering course to Ware.

The year 1760, therefore, provides a definite starting-point for a review of events connected with the City of London. At the time in question there were schemes before the City Council for a new bridge across the Thames which would provide direct access between North and South London, and relieve the heavy traffic proceeding to Southwark across London Bridge. The new bridge was begun on June 7th, 1760; ten days later the City Lands were empowered to undertake further improvements including the demolition of nearly all the ancient City gates. It was ten years before the bridge was completed and the City provided with a main thoroughfare which gave the merchants a new business centre. Among the artists who visited the scene was the enraptured Richard Wilson who painted the majestic composition of St. Paul's Cathedral with the noble bridge at its base. In this manner the first civic improvement since the rebuilding of the City of London after the Great Fire was inaugurated.

Robert Mylne was to become a prominent figure in London. He was consulted by the City Authorities, by lawyers and bankers. Dr. Johnson dined with him at his house in New Bridge Street. He was, in fact, in demand and was looked upon as an authority on tasteful building. It was recognised that the much-travelled Scots engineer was the equal of many architects of established fame.

London, during the reign of George III, was still a residential city; its parish affairs having a deep significance. In some ways the system of living was not altogether dissimilar from that of today, for a modern note had come into being as can be gathered from the contemporary newspapers, but the ancient traditions of the City which had survived from mediaeval times were in process of modification. The spirit of the age favoured ordered development, as can be gathered from the street views of the time. There, however, little disparagement of innovations which promised to be of public benefit.

The great source of energy was London's giant river which brought overseas trade to the City wharves. The most striking spectacle to foreign eyes was the view of the dome of St. Paul's with the spires and steeples of the City churches. Here was a panorama which, by comparison, reduced Venice to a toy-like scale. London was already a great seaport. The aggregation of tall-masted ships, large and small, varied from a score anchored off Gravesend to a hundred in the Pool. All travellers then familiar with the ports of Hamburg, Amsterdam, Bordeaux or Lisbon acknowledged the superiority of the Port of London. From Gravesend to London Bridge was a journey familiar to voyagers. And not only foreigners knew this waterway but Londoners made frequent journeys by water to the Kent and Essex shores. The approach to the capital by water was one of the sights in the days of George III; the scenery was reminiscent of Holland and of Scandinavia. There was something indefinably European, yet it was a land entirely different to anything the Continent of Europe could show. At Greenwich the Royal Naval Hospital rose from the water like a fantastic ocean palace; from thence to the Tower of London the river became a continuous anchorage. The traveller gazed upon creeks and wharves alive with vessels. There was the Royal Dockyard at Deptford and the warehouses and shops of barge owners and boat builders. Wherries, hoys and lighters worked their passage between the larger vessels, and at last a long low bridge with irregular openings opposed its grey surface to the tidal waters. Thus far and no further could the merchandise of the civilised world be brought for sale to the richest market in Europe. From this vantage point London could be seen in all her majestic splendour; City merchants and their clerks were grateful to see the gilded vanes on Wren's steeples giving the directions of a favourable wind, for the overseas post came in when the tide was full at London Bridge.

The country near London during the later years of the eighteenth century showed little change since the seventeenth century. To the north, the east and the west a circle of rural villages stood on the trunk roads within a mile or so of the City boundaries. To the south was the Borough of Southwark, with its mediaeval church appearing like a detached fragment

49

of London. Beyond this the rural character was even more pronounced. On stated days, hundreds of carriers' carts and stage wagons brought country produce to the markets at Whitechapel, Smithfield, Covent Garden, and to the inn-yards in the vicinity of St. Paul's. As the traveller by coach, post-chaise, on horseback or on foot advanced into the country, he noted with pleasure the comfortable mansions of the London merchants, the dairy farms which supplied Londoners with provisions, the cottages of the labouring people and the pleasant wayside inns. A few miles further out there were parks with neat lodges and substantial brick walls. There were avenues of oaks and elms leading to stately mansions. In the villages were ancient churches with square towers; there were the windmills and the meandering waterways threading the meadows of the Home Counties.

At this period there was little to offend the eye; even the brick and tile works which occurred now and then were modest and inoffensive. Robert Mylne was acquainted with all these common-place affairs. No man of his period was more familiar with the road from London to Ware than he, not excepting the poet Cowper. It was, moreover, Robert Mylne's work in connection with the maintenance of the New River that gave occasion to journeys which are recorded in his diaries. There were two hundred and fifty bridges and up-wards of forty sluices to be inspected throughout the thirty-eight miles of the waterway. In addition there were con-siderable currents of land waters, as well as a number of brooks and rivulets, to be controlled. The winding course of the New River, from Islington into the parish of Stoke Newing-ton, and from thence across the Green Lanes at the back of Highbury Grove to the Thatched House Tavern, and so to the New River Head, demanded the closest supervision.

Mylne lived in the Water House at the New River Head, Islington, built in 1613 (which he refronted in 1782) and it was from here that he directed the various works in his charge. The New River, as it was first constructed in the seventeenth century, entered the parish of Islington by means of an enor-mous wooden trough, 462 feet in length and 17 feet high; this was lined with lead and supported by strong timbers standing on brick piers. There was a similar aqueduct at Bush Hill, near Enfield. This curious method of conveying an arti-ficial river caused so much trouble that the Company decided

24 INVERARAY GREAT FARM : General view

25 INVERARAY GREAT FARM : View of house

26 INVERARAY: SCREEN AND GATES

27 INVERARAY: A LODGE

to abolish the wooden conduit and embank the stream. Mylne, in 1776, actually raised the river-bed by forming a great embankment of clay. There are frequent notes of visits to Bush Hill in the diaries which doubtless relate to this especial work.

In those days the villages of Hampstead and Highgate were regarded by the average Londoner as being supremely rural. Even Islington was looked upon as situated in the country. The duties of the Chief Engineer to the New River Company meant journeys from Clerkenwell through the Green Lanes to Enfield, Cheshunt, St. Margaret's and Amwell. There were occasions when Robert Mylne inspected the whole course of the New River in order to report to the Board of Directors. It is permissible to accompany Robert Mylne still further afield. Not only did Robert Mylne's profession take him to distant parts of England several times a year, but frequently he visited Scotland twice in the same year. Here is a typical entry in his diary for August, 1769:

Thursday, 20th.	Set out for Edinburgh;
	at Ware;
	at Royston;
Friday, 21st.	at Tuxford;
Saturday, 22nd.	at Northallerton;
Sunday, 23rd.	at Alnwick.

The usual practice was for the architect to travel to Scotland in the autumn and stay for a month to deal with works in his native land. From the windows of the post-chaise in which he travelled he looked upon a beautiful countryside. All life was an adventure, and judging from his personal sketches, he was interested equally in Gothic architecture, field gates and machinery.

Robert Mylne thus became conspicuous as a man of culture among the multitudes of politicians, merchants, City dignitaries, writers and brother professionals, both in London and Edinburgh. He was punctilious in his attendance at committees and more than respected for the evidence he gave on several occasions before the House of Lords. His places of residence in London varied between the house he built for himself in New Bridge Street, his official residence at the New River Offices, Islington, or the house assigned to him as Clerk of the Works to Greenwich Hospital. It was not until late in his life that he decided to build the small house at Amwell as a country retreat.

Amidst all these and other activities, we read of his travels at all seasons from one end of the kingdom to another, during which he explored everything of interest, viewing bridges and buildings of importance.

The phenomenal creation of wealth in England during the happier years of George III's reign enabled the nation to weather the storm during the Napoleonic wars; the possession of such wealth brought an expansion of trade that was not in itself phenomenal. It was, in fact, the incidence of the Napoleonic wars that gave the real impetus to trade.

In 1805 the first of the great London docks was constructed by John Rennie; then the continuance of the war attracted myriads of workers to London, Birmingham, Chatham, Portsmouth and Devonport for the production of munitions. London began to expand once again, and this time the expansion was to continue unabated. As early as 1780, new residential suburbs were in course of formation at Canonbury, Highbury, Camden Town, parts of Marylebone and Kensington. Terraced houses were rising between Southwark and Greenwich. Gaps in the fields on either side of the main roads leading out of town in all directions were in the hands of speculative builders. This was especially the case from Whitechapel to Bow and from Shoreditch Church to Stoke Newington. It was in this manner that Greater London came into being. On the other hand, the nineteenth century inherited all the problems, social, political and cultural, which had obsessed varying minds during the previous epoch.

London in 1800 was still a residential city; the different parishes represented definite sections of communal life; they were not mere symbolic names applied to ancient boundaries. The population of the metropolis had grown to a million; fresh means of transport were being investigated between the suburbs and the City. Charles Lamb records his daily journeys between London and Clapton by omnibus. New problems of street lighting and increased water supply had to be met; there were projects for additional bridges across the Thames, besides increased building activity despite the prolonged war. The expansion of the inner suburbs of London, for example, Bloomsbury, Camden Town, Pentonville, Marylebone and Paddington on the north bank of the Thames, and Lambeth, Kennington,

Camberwell and Brixton on the south bank, are eloquent of the ceaseless growth which the future would implement.

When the Prince of Wales became Regent, the old manner of living as it affected all grades of society underwent considerable modification. The fashions which had swayed public opinion twenty years before were now regarded as obsolescent. There were many other signs of the changing times: political power, for example, was passing from the privileged landowners to the newer middle classes. Science was advancing, inventions and theories on almost every subject were slowly but effectually upsetting popular fallacies. Although the English compromise between mediaeval and renaissance thought had taken place at the beginning of the seventeenth century, there was still a strong bias favouring the mediaeval past and this was fostered by the Romantic school of writers. Parts of London were still mediaeval; the 'Watch' still attempted to police the City at night; there were problems to be solved concerning the lighting of the streets by gas, the disposal of sewage, and questions of more rapid means of transport within the City itself.

As yet, the excitement of long-distance travel by mail coach had not been superseded. The inns were attractive, the food wholesome, and the attendants polite. The speed of the mail coaches had been increased to ten and eleven miles an hour. The coaches that left London daily for Liverpool, Manchester, York and Edinburgh were counted among the sights of Islington when they stopped to take up passengers at "The Peacock". The black and red Edinburgh Mail, the pea-green Tally-ho and the yellow Stamford Regent were the pride of the Great North Road. Robert Mylne's journeys to Scotland, forty years before, must have seemed to the mind of the ageing architect very arduous undertakings, as indeed they had proved. The quiet restricted lives of men and women in country places when George III was young were now almost legendary. Science and democracy, fresh inventions, diverse new industries, were now part of everyday conversation. The steam engine began to take on the crude reality of horizontal movement. Already the rhythmic beat of the beam engine accompanied the toilers in the mills and factories of the north. And then there was the phenomenal increase of overseas trade which, during the time the Continental ports were closed, brought untold wealth to London.

The profession of architect and engineer now became that of civil engineer. Telford and John Rennie were commissioned to construct docks, harbours and bridges of iron. The contrast between Robert Mylne's magnificent stone bridge of 1760–70 at Blackfriars and Rennie's iron bridge at Southwark, built in 1809, was most striking.

While the City and its suburbs played a definite part in the levelling up of democratic life, during the fourth quarter of the eighteenth century, it was the long war with France, beginning with the French Revolution, that implemented the greatest industrial changes. Robert Mylne was cognizant of all the changes which have been described. In his personality, and especially in his work, he was the embodiment of the modern spirit which changed the kingdom from rural tranquillity to fevered industry. It was indeed fortunate that a talented Scotsman came to London in 1760 to build a monumental bridge across the Thames.

28 DESIGN FOR A SMALL COUNTRY HOUSE ESTIMATED TO COST £2,000

From a drawing by the Author

1762 to 1764

The first of Mylne's diaries 1762–4 records the preliminary work on the caissons and piers of Blackfriars Bridge. The notes are brief but they are interesting on account of the many journeys made by road during these two years, and the rapidity shown in getting from one place to another by post-chaise. The chief item of interest apart from Blackfriars Bridge is the entry which mentions Mylne's visit to Highgate with Woodfall, the printer of the Letters of Junius, to advise on a new house. Another interesting note dated May 30th, 1764, records a meeting between Mylne and Mr. Almack, the founder and proprietor of the Almack Club in King Street, St. James's. This fine club was eventually designed and built by Robert Mylne. The design of the great Assembly Room with its circular ceiling suggested the form of the ceiling of the great Subscription Room of Brooks's.

1762

Jan. 18   Plained Plates of Cast Iron by George Willdon next door to the Golden Fleece, Litchfield Street, Soho.

Apr. 30   Took one solution to make the sides of the Cn. serve the two piers next the shore and build the abutements without any bottoms.

May 1   Weighed a foot cube of rubbish from the yard and proved to be 81½ pounds.

May 3   Observed that the south middle pier wanted 10 inches of being down to the surface of the gravell, and the heads of the piles are 3 inches below that.

May 7   To write to Rome for an 'Ecce Homo' in tapestry for P. Garlo, to be made as the fabric el Arazi in J. Michele; to be done by To Felice Cettomai and to come from Scotland.

May 10   Fixed the 1/3 breadth of the bridge to be 21' 10"

over all   43' 9"
Executed   43' 6".

May 20   Launched the Caisson for the second pier. Drew 6–7 water and 1 inch for suction on the stage.

May 27   Delivered in a Bill of Expenses to Comr. of £69 5s. 2d.

June 5   Ground where the South 18 ft. Pier is to stand 2' 6" higher than at the middle pier.

June 6   The caisson sunk with the 1st course. 6–7.
2 ft. 6 in. high of North middle pier. 9–10.

June 7 Determined on the height of courses of south 18 ft. pier
to be:—   1st.   2' 6"
                 2   2' 6"
                 3   2' 8"
             4 & last 2' 8" (10' 4").

June 8 Stopped proceedings in the caisson for want of 32 of the 2nd
course, of N. M. Pier.

June 10	Coat and breeches for laced waistcoat:	£5	0	6
& 11	Laced suit cost:	£12	0	0
	Laced waistcoat:	£5	14	0
	Servant's livery:	£2	15	6
	A fustian suit:	£3	4	0
	Summer Cloth suit:	£5	7	9½

June 12 Gave Lord Morton drawings and estimate for Book Room of
£349 10s. 11d.

June 21 Began work again having got from Fn. the last part of the
2nd course of North Md. Pier. Caisson touched ground and
5½" out of levell crossways very well long ways.

June 29 At Elmham, oak timber delivered aboard a ship at Yarmouth
at 18 foot cube.

July 1 A Northfolk brick, 9¼ long, 4⅜ broad, and 2¼ thick, weighed
6 lbs. 10 ounces, then for a cube foot of such bricks weighs
125 pounds, 11 ounces and   7299

                                11655

July 14 Measured from the side of the South Middle Pier and found
it to be:— 69 – 7 from Pier to Piles.
                  258 – 7 water.
                  100 – 0 South shore.
                  427 – 2 to the wood wharf.

July 17 Fixed the caisson of North Middle Pier, proved to be exact
cast and wrot ½ Inch out of a levell at some places, 3 inches
at the west end and 5¼ at the East End too wide from the
other piers.

July 19 Fixed the width of the Middle Arch by the placing of the last
course of the North Middle, to be 100 – 1 at west end and
100 – 1¼ at the east end, these being taken from the stone
pier and over sides of caisson.

July 20 Launched the Bottom for the south 19½ ft. pier; the plates
and screw heads taking hold of the frupells it stuck half off
and half on.

July 21 Threw part of stone overboard and shered it. Laid it on the
stage next tide; got stones up again. Floated it to lower stage.
Put a great quantity of stones upon it.

July 22 Night's tide it unexpectedly floated again, but kept on stage
although not right. In the afternoon laid it right. Put more
stones on, and it floated no more – seemingly little damage done.

July 24 By a great tide the caisson floated again and she was again
placed so as to make the width of the arch exact by 100 feet.

58

The difference of the levell of water outside and inside was 15 feet, equall 1198 tons. The whole of the Portland part of the 5th course was aboard.

July 27	Measured the breadth of the river at Church Lane, Chelsea, and found it to be 790 feet.
July 30	Fixed the steps of stairs of Bridge to be 12 broad and $6\frac{1}{2}$ high.
Aug. 9	Finished the first springing course of the North Middle Pier.
Aug. 11	Carried the sides of the caisson off the North Middle Pier; lied them to the westward, but the water was dragging; they settled on the point west of the pier again.
Aug. 12	Morning – carried sides of caisson as high on shore as possible. Afternoon – carried them still higher on shore, and then waited higher tides.
Aug. 18	Bt. 500 Scrip at 89 – cost £305 12s. 6d.; proposed to hold 500 Scrip to 16″ Sup. Gave therefore 375. James lending me £71 1s. 6d.
Aug. 19	Afternoon – put the caisson on bottom for 3rd pier.
Aug. 22	3 tons will stand upon each foot super – a foot of the piers. The whole superficials being 3186 feet, and the whole on each pier being 9558 tons. Superfinis for a large pier at W. is about one half inch.
Aug. 24	66-1/3rd cu. ft. stands on each sup. foot of the foundation of west bridge – about 45 ft. stands on (ditto) of Blackfriars Bridge.
Sept. 11	Launched the caisson which drew above 6–7 water, but the ironwork at bottom drew about 4 inches more.
Sept. 27	City Road cost £6,000 – is 6 furlongs. in length. Road from Islington to Paddington cost £12,000 – is 3 miles in length.
Oct. 6	Finished 2nd course of South $19\frac{1}{2}$ ft. Pier. Resolved that this course should be made of Purbeck and Port. block – for this one prepared for it, was too high.
Oct. 7	Ordered the 3rd course to be made use of for the 2nd next pier.
Oct. 8	Observed when the caisson was aground that the lowest part wanted 9 inches of being down to the head of the piles. Pumps shifted; 4 men work these by night and day.
Oct. 11– 12	Began the digging out the mud for Surrey Butement; found hard gravell at 3 ft. below low water mark. Resolved to build on that, among the 48 piles which had been drove into it. Ground proved to be on that shore; first made soile, then hard black earth, with sand and gravel, then clay for 5 ft. then the hard gravell. Bored the gravell $4\frac{1}{2}$ ft. and proved the same. Began the stonework of (ditto) and put in a $\frac{1}{4}$ of the foundation for that purpose.
Oct. 16	Finished the stonework of $\frac{1}{4}$ of the foundation of Butement, and put the piles on a levell with stonework at low water mark.
Oct. 19	Observed that the face of 2nd course of Sth. Butement is $392\frac{1}{2}$ feet from the side of the South Middle Pier at the west end.

59

Oct. 21	Observed that the space between the faces of the 5th courses of both Middle Piers to be 99 −6$\frac{1}{4}$ at the west end and 99·7 at the east end, measured at the shoulders.
Oct. 22	Finished a 2nd $\frac{1}{4}$ of the Surrey Butement. 8 square pumps, on a chain pump, and 40 men at work – throwing out the water, removing the mud, and often helping the masons. 4 scoops could keep the hole always clear of water after it was once pumped out.
Oct. 30	Finished the 3rd Springing course of 19$\frac{1}{2}$ ft. Pier.
Nov. 3	Sold 400 Cons'd. at 84$\frac{3}{8}$, producing £337 10s. 0d. Launched the Bottom for the South 18 ft. Pier. Took a resolution to finish the 1st course of it before the sides of the caisson should be put on it.
Nov. 10	Finished the 4th course of the South 19$\frac{1}{2}$ feet Pier; Finished the Butement on Surrey shore up to low water mark.
Nov. 20	Finished the 5th and last course of the South 19$\frac{1}{2}$ foot Pier.
Nov. 23	Caisson with South 19$\frac{1}{2}$ ft. Pier floated; there was some water and some part of the springing course set.
Nov. 30	Observed that the South 19$\frac{1}{2}$ feet Pier is 97 – 11 at the east end, and 97 – 10$\frac{3}{4}$ at west end distant from the South Middle Pier – between the face of the Rustics.
Dec. 3	Observed by bills that Mr. P. Dixon and Spencer each owes me £3 14s. 10d. for dinner and Ryscings on the launching the caisson.
Dec. 7	Began to take down the guard works round the caisson, in order to take it from the South 19$\frac{1}{2}$ feet Pier.
Dec. 9	Finished the 1st springing course of the South 19$\frac{1}{2}$ feet Pier.
Dec. 13	1,500 Shares in the Ln. Bridge Water Works, at 75 pounds – the present current price is 112,500.
Dec. 24	Took the sides of the caisson from the 3rd Pier – drew eastward and laid this opposite to the Great Arch. Next tide let them drag through the Great Arch and rode until high water, by the North Pier, then carried them ashore at Dorset stairs. This was during the Ninp. tides and the first springing course was laid on the Pier.
Dec. 30	Proposed to have put the sides of caisson on the bottom for 4th Pier, but there came a grave frost which filled the river so with layers of ice, that all works were suspended.

1763

Jan. 10	Cartfull of ballast in Butement weighs 17$\frac{1}{4}$ Ct.
Jan. 18	Observed that the last years expenses, without (?) money, was £248 0s. 0d.
Feb. 9	Observed that ground was had away from below caisson sides: Pockett – 1

3

1–6

1–

4–6

———

Feb. 11	Lifted caisson and placed her on bottom for South 18 ft. Pier.
Feb. 28	Mr. Baldwin came home as clerk at £50 per annum.
Mar. 2	Set out for Edinr.
Mar. 5	Father died at 11 at night.
Mar. 6	Arrived at Edin.
Mar. 14	Made a Burgess of Edin. by the Corporation.
Mar. 18	Arrived at London.
Mar. 21	Attempted to launch the caisson, yet although it floated it did not clear the works of the stage on account of the tide being low.
Mar. 29	Beginning of Springtides; launched the caisson and carried her to the situation of 4th Pier. Made no water. 1st course completed.
Apr. 11	Portland stone cost the merchant in London 22 sh. per ton, and he sells it to the trade at 2 sh. 2/2, 2/3, per foot cube rough scantling.
Apr. 15	Finished the 3rd course of South 18 ft. Pier, oblidged to melt some inches of the surface of it to bring it down on a levell with the others.
May 16	Fixed the caisson with South 18 ft. Pier for good and all. The Pier was completed with part of the 1st springing course in it. Began to lay the foundation of the South West Stair.
June 17	Saw Rainham and Houghton Hall.
July 4	Launched a new bottom for the North 19½ ft. Pier; kept it down the first tide by putting to craft of Port and one of Purbeck upon it.
July 16	Gave a plan and estimate of stables to the Earl of Morton; value £708 13s. 0½d.
July 19	Finished the 2nd springing course of the South 18 ft. Pier.
July 21	Gave a 2nd estimate to Lord Morton, of stables, coach houses, hay lofts and Porters Lodge, for £747 10s. 10½d.
July 28	Send a sketch to Kingsweston of a Gateway without side doors.
July 30	Found that the exact breadth of the River to be 1106½ feet from wharf to wharf upon an average. Gave an estimate to Lord Morton of £790 7s. 5d.
Aug. 1	Began to hoist and set the 4th or Pedestal courses on the Middle Pier.
Aug. 2	Finished the fixing of the Middle Cintre.
Aug. 4	Began a new bottom for North 18 ft. Pier.
Aug. 5	Sent a sketch of a window, and another of a section of stables, to Mr. Southwell. Drew a pile from under the Middle of Cintre by it, and with 2 of screws, weight estimated to be equall to 40 tons.
Aug. 6	Finished taking away the stage from under Middle Cintre. Finished the 1st course of North 19½ ft. Pier on a bottom on the lower stage.
Aug. 15	Took the sides of caisson from South 18 ft. Pier and laid them ashore.

Aug. 16	Left the care of caisson to clerk and carpenters to carry further inshore. They broke one of the triangles by a false bearing and were obliged to shuttle the barges.
Aug. 19	Lifted the caisson further inshore.
Aug. 20	Placed sides of caisson on a new bottom.
Aug. 31	Finished the fourth springing courses of Middle and two side arches.
Sept. 2	Begun setting the Pedestals on the ends of Piers, Middle Arch.
Sept. 8	Finished the 2nd Springing course on South 19½ ft. Pier.
Sept. 18	Gave Lord Morton advise on Greenhouse – 10s. 6d.
	Ditto. on the spouts of house – 10s. 6d.
	Charges. – 3s. 0d.
Sept. 22	This day six months the Peace was proclaimed.
Oct. 28	Went to Winston Bridge and Raby Castle.
Nov. 29	Gave drawings for all the moldings of Murray's house; directions in writing for the finishings.
Nov. 30	Returned drawings altered for Norwich to Mr. Davis; 3 new drawings made, waiting on Mr. Wiseman – 5 –.
Dec. 7	Paid bills of brickwork for Lord Morton in town: £22 11s. 9½d., at Chyswick: £123 7s. 11½d., £13 2s. 0½d. All the digging of the area round the house was done by the gardners, and the filling in – estimated at £30.
Dec. 16	Paid bills for Lord Eglintorme for £3195 7s. 1d. of which paid £2438 14s. 0d.
Dec. 21	Sent to Mr. Southwell a description of making stucco floors.
Dec. 22	Paid bills of repairs to Lord Eglintorme's old house for £61 13s. 9¼d.

1764

Jan. 3	Sent a drawing and description of stalls, racks and mangers for stables to Mr. Southwell – value – £3 3s. 0d.
Jan. 12	Attended Mr. Murray – value – £1 0s. 0d. on chimney pieces.
Jan. 15	Observed that if Lord Edgefield was to pay the ½ of expenses for Charter of Poutherthall according to his letter, it would come to £14 2s. 7½d.
Jan. 20	Attended Mr. Murray on chimneypieces – value – 10s. 6d.
Jan. 24	Brother left £60 to be sent to Scotland. and for a silk gown to his sister £8 2s. 0d. Total: £68 2s. 0d.
Jan. 25	Called on Mr. Southwell – some discourse on buildings – value – 10s. 6d.
Jan. 29	Making out fair a new set of drawings which had been fixed at Norwich for Mr. Patteson. Waiting on Mr. Wiseman and add some new drawings – £5 5s. 0d.
Feb. 8	Attended Mr. Murray to look at some houses by appointment – value – 10s. 6d.
Feb. 9	Gave 3 plans and estimates of alterations in Argyle House to Marquis of Lorn.
Feb. 12	Gave Mr. Murray drawings for 3 doors and directions for shutters – value £1 11s. 6d.
Feb. 14	For Croft's letter – 1s.

Feb. 23	Gave Mr. Mytton a plan of alterations for his offices – value – £2 2s. 0d.
Feb. 26	Consultation to Mr. Southwell – value – 10s. 6d.
Feb. 28	Began work at Marquis of Lorn's.
Mar. 3	Sent a modell to Mr. Southwell: of rack and manger. Value £3 3s. 0d.
Mar. 17	Gave plan of alterations of a plan of a house with directions to Major Hamilton of the Army – value – £3 3s. 0d.
Mar. 24	Gave 2 outlines for tapestry to Marquis of Lorn of a house in Scotland. value 10s. 6d.
Mar. 30	Gave a drawing of a Door Case and Portico to Mr. Briscoe – £2 2s. 0d. Do. drawing of a cornice to Mr. Southwell – ½ guinea.
Apr. 4	Went out to Chyswick, met Mr. Paine on party wall of Duke of Dres. expenses – 3 sh.
Apr. 6	Gave Mr. Woodfall a drawing and particulars of alterations – value 1 guinea.
Apr. 10	Gave Mr. Edward Deering a drawing and estimate of a Bridge for Cowley – 3. Sent a drawing for alterations at Galloway house to Br. Order of Lord Garties: 3. Gave a copy of Do. to Garties – ½ . . . .
Apr. 27	Altered a plan and estimate of Regi. Office for Lord Morton. 5 . . . .
May 5	Went to Mr. Briscoe's at Twick. Ordered work of Portico and hall. 1 . . . . . .
May 16	Gave Major Claud Hamilton a design for a house in Scotland. 25 . . . . . .
May 30	Attended Mr. James and Crewe for Club in Kings Street. Attended Mr. Almack on bargain between him and Club in Kings Street . . . . 1 . . . .
June 1	Attended Mr. Almack and his New Club.
June 6	Gave Sir Wm. Wiseman 2 designs for a house (in lines). . . . 4 . . .
June 11	Took Mr. Casley as a clerk at £40 per annum with breakfast and lodgings.
June 12	A drawing for the front of a house with a venetian door to Sir Wm. Wiseman. . . . 1 . . . .
June 13	Attended Mr. Almack on his house in Pall Mall – 1 –.
June 23	Attended Mr. Almack on a bow window to his house in Pall Mall . . . . . ½ . . . .
June 26	Arrived at Kingsweston.
June 27	Brought from London a drawing of alterations for Kingsweston House. – 5 –.
July 2	Went into Wales.
July 4	Returned to Kingsweston.
July 31	Arrived in London.
Aug. 9	Set out for Nottinghamshire. Left at home – £50. took altogether £24 16 0. along with me: £74 16 –

Aug. 13	Sent Mr. Southwell to his house in Berkeley Square a drawing at large of cornice for dining room; ditto for base and surbase. For sides and for room finished. – 3 –.
Aug. 15	Saw Duke of Norfolk at Worksop. Left Welbeck. Arrived at Lincoln.
Aug. 20	Expenses payable by the Duke of Portland if I had come directly from Welbeck to London. 9. . . .
Aug. 21	Expenses chargeable to Mr. Patteson on account of going round to Norwich more than if gone from Lyn – £2 10s. 0d. Arrived in London.
Aug. 29	Sent drawings of a new roof to Mr. Murray and a letter thereon to Cally. 5. . . .
Sept. 3	Sent a (? bill) of some former work and some work done by others to Lord Morton. . . . . $\frac{1}{2}$. . . .
Sept. 6	Dined with Sir Wm. Duncan and gave directions about ground and house. . . . $\frac{1}{2}$. . . .
Sept. 11	Attended Mr. Southwell in town whole day on Dining Room, offices and stables. . .2. . . Gave him a drawing for outside stairs of garden front.
Sept. 14	Sent Sir Wm. Duncan plans for his houses. . . . .2. . . .
Sept. 17	Looked over Painters & Marble cutters' bill for Mr. Briscoe . . . $\frac{1}{2}$. . . .
Sept. 22	Attended Mr. Briscoe at Twickenham to see that everything was right.
Sept. 27	Sent Sir Wm. Duncan plans for two more houses. Wrote two letters to Lord Foley.
Sept. 30	Gave a plan of Assembly Rooms in King Street for Duke of York to Mr. Almack. (They were built.)
Oct. 1	Opened the Booms of Great Arch and let the Lord Mayor, the Sherrifs, Harris and Crosby, be the first that ever went through.
Oct. 5	Gave a drawing of a chimney piece for Mr. Southwell and large do. for the work to Mr. Devall.
Oct. 13	Fixed the last Key stone of South 19 ft. Arch.
Oct. 16	Attended the Court of Alderman for Lord Mayor's Day.
Oct. 22	Gave Mr. Winter a consultation on the value of a house in Pall Mall. Began to dig the remainder of foundations for East End of East Stairs, N. Butement.
Oct. 25	Launched the caisson for N. 19$\frac{1}{2}$ ft. Pier. Made as much water as kept two men at pumps.
Oct. 29	Went to Barking; gave Mr. Heard advice on breach; attended the Comms. of Sewers of Westbury; gave them advice on said breach – post chaise. 18 shs.
Nov. 1	Went to Barking; gave advice to Commsrs. of Sewers – Expenses – 18 shs.
Nov. 8	Sent 4 plans of a house in large to Sir Wm. Duncan.
Nov. 10	Finished 2nd course of N. 19$\frac{1}{2}$ ft. Pier in caisson. Went to Chyswick.

Nov. 12	Gave tenant on Surrey shore notice to quit. Altered the pumping in caisson. 2 men at said pumps.
Nov. 13	All the foundations, drains and pans, were dug by the gardners and estimated at £20. For Lord Morton and by Pratt & Co.
Nov. 14	Wrote an advert. for Mr. Almack. Examined Bricklayers bill for work at Chyswick. Remembered to have waited ½ dozen times on Mr. Garnier for granting a lease to Mr. Almack.
Nov. 17	Added another pumper to caisson. Went to Chyswick.
Nov. 19	Waited on Lady Susan Stewart and received orders for the work of her bow. ....½....
Nov. 28	Finished laying the foundations of N. Bridge of East Stairs thereof.
Dec. 6	Ordered a fourth pumper to caisson.
Dec. 8	Launched bottom for N. 18 ft. pier; some trusles under her – obliged to keep it afloat. Carried 3 horses aboard of caisson.
Dec. 9	Got the trusles from under the bottom. Kept it afloat.
Dec. 10	Caulked the joints of bottoms started by the strain of lying on trusles.
Dec. 11	Began to take up the stage on which all the bottoms were built.
Dec. 12	Loaded the bottom with 2 craft of Portland. one of Purbeck. Next tide did not move. Made a design for Fitchell to Mr. Almack ...½....
Dec. 28	Attended Dr. Grant, and gave Commrs. of Assembly in City a plan for rooms 3.
Dec. 30	Great quantity of ice on the river.
Dec. 31	Ordered all the booms from the arches and laid them under Temple wall. Took the horses from on board the caisson. Some of stone for pier still in Portland. Turned the lock so as to be open; part of 4th course set.

Memorandum for end of year–

Received about 3 months ago a modell of the Welch Bridge from Mr. Southwell. £2 2s. 0d. paid to the maker and the expenses of carriage.

1765 to 1769

The diaries for the years 1765 to 1769 record the following important events in the architect's life. In 1765 he designed a bridge at *Welbeck* for the Duke of Portland, and in the same year began the bridge in the park at *Warwick Castle*. This year he sent the sum of £54 through Messrs. Drummond, the bankers, to Piranesi in Italy. This was to pay for the drawing of Blackfriars Bridge. Among other buildings started in this year were Tusmore in Oxfordshire and alterations in Wormleybury in Hertfordshire. In 1766 Robert Mylne was appointed by the Archbishop of Canterbury to the Surveyorship of St. Paul's Cathedral. This year saw the opening of the temporary bridge at Blackfriars. In May 1767 Mylne was elected a Fellow of the Royal Society. In October the Dean of Canterbury appointed him Surveyor to Canterbury Cathedral. In November of the same year he was appointed Joint Surveyor to the New River Company.

1765

Jan. 1 Sent Cooley to attend Marquis of Lorn on ground for stables. A thaw – but resolved to continue the caisson despite the situation as there was a probability of the proper stone arriving.

Jan. 4 Surveyed Lady Susan Stewart's repairs which were finished. Finished the 3rd Arch being the South 93ft. Arch.

Jan. 5 Payed bills of mason work by Hardwicke for Lord Morton. Measured – £65 0s. 0d. Day D' – £6 7s. 0d.

Jan. 8 Attended the Treasurer of St. Bartholomew's ground – gave advice.

Jan. 11 Attended the Treasurer of St. Bartholomew's Hospital. Advised on the extension of the plans of their estate. – 1 –. Gave a medall to Almack. Attended on Marquis of Lorn on stables.

Jan. 14 Gave orders about Mr. Almack's tickets – ½ –. Made an agreement for ground of stables for Marquis of Lorn.

Jan. 21 Gave a plan of a building for the meeting of an Assembly to Mr. Farquhar. – 4 –.

Jan. 22 Gave Mr. Southwell a drawing at large of architraves for doors and windows of dining room, and another small ceiling of same, with written directions and advice on other things. – 4 –.

Jan. 26 Tried to strike one of wedges of 98 ft. Cintre. Broke one of the ears of hoops by one stroke of hammer after it was strained as hard as possible with screws on each side.

Feb. 1	Sent 2 drawings of corner panels of dining room ceiling at large to Kingsweston. – 2 –. Struck one of the wedges of 92 ft. Cintre with 2 pr. of screws and wedges. Resolved to follow that method in them all.
Feb. 5	Sent 6 plans to the Society of Arts & C, with a long letter thereon.
Feb. 9	Ordered chimney pots for Mr. Patteson – $\frac{1}{4}$ –. Gave an opinion to Mr. Lucas for the repairs of three houses belonging to Generall Rich. 1.
Feb. 16	Mrs. Grainger came as housekeeper at 20 guineas. Surveyed ground for City Assembly.
Feb. 17	Commenced housekeeping. Mr. Cooley at 30 guineas per a.; bed board & washing.
Feb. 19	Gave a plan of ground to the trustees of Assembly, and proposals from Mr. Clark. 1.
Feb. 21	Went to Chyswick. Made a drawing of sashes for dining room; ordered the work to be done. Sent them to Bristol. Paid the bill 3.
Feb. 22	Waited on Mr. Southwell. Discourse on various articles of building – a sketch of park gates – $\frac{1}{2}$ –.
Feb. 25	Carried plans of Assembly Rooms for approbation to the trustees for discussion only.
Mar. 8	Gave a section of Assembly apartments to Mr. Farquhar. – 4 –.
Mar. 9	Gave a drawing of door cornice and frieze, section of framing of doors and panels of shutters at large, to Mr. Southwell. Wrote a letter to Mr. Nicholls – $1\frac{1}{2}$ –.
Mar. 15	Examined a bill, £22 2s. $1\frac{1}{2}d$. of engraving for Mr. Almack.
Mar. 25	Sent ironwork of doors and windows of dining room to Mr. Southwell; ordering and inspecting same.
Mar. 28	Gave Mr. Murray 2 drawings in lines of the front of house; one of pediment cornice at large and a long letter on the execution thereof. – 3 –.
Apr. 1	Ordered ironwork for doors and windows for Mr. Murray and inspecting of the same. – $\frac{1}{2}$ –.
Apr. 5	Arrived at Welbeck.
Apr. 6	Sketched out a bridge for Duke of Portland.
Apr. 8	Mr. Upsdell set out from London to go to Welbeck as Clerk of the Works to the bridge of the Duke of Portland. To be allowed £50 per annum. Travelling charges and salary to commence from this day. Began digging the foundations of said bridge.
Apr. 13	Set out from Welbeck; laid first stone of Welbeck Bridge.
Apr. 14	Arrived in London.
Apr. 15	Began to strike cintre of South 98 ft. Arch.
Apr. 19	Finished the striking of one end of the south 98 ft. Arch; the wedges moving 3″ only. Settlements as per Messrs....... Attempted to raise the caisson; found too much leakage for three horses at the chain pump.
Apr. 22	Put a plaister on joint of south west end of caisson.

Apr. 23	Attempted to raise the caisson; found too much leakage for the chain pump, two hand pumps and one square pump. Desisted.
Apr. 26	Attended Mr. Murray on Chimney piece of marble and deal.
Apr. 27	Put another plaister on south west end of caisson; attempted to raise her; found the leak, stopt it; could not gain on the water; reduced the surface of stones. Tide rose to the hole where water is discharged. She would not move. Gave it up.
Apr. 28	Gave Sir Henry Manwaring drawings of 2 ceilings, 2; 4 of cornices at large, 2; one section of ceiling, $\frac{1}{2}$; one sheet of directions for finishing house.
Apr. 30	Wrote Mr. Nicholls on Mr. Southwell's business, $\frac{1}{4}$; attended Mr. Murray on chimney piece of deal & marble.
May 1	Put a plaister on end joint, and another on end joint of (?) bibb. Tried to float caisson – 4 horses, 60 men, 3 common pumps, 6 square ones. Could not do. Gave it up.
May 4	Attended Mr. Murray on a chimney piece of deal and marble. Made a drawing of it finished.
May 5	Attended Mr. Southwell on his mother's house in town.
May 10	Tried to float caisson; 6 square pumps, 3 Common Do., 1 square chain pump; the horse chain pump; 2 square pumps at east end; 4 horses, 80 men. Got down to surface of stone; stopt leaks; washed stone; chain pump broke; water increased in flood, floated caisson; moved westward – gave it up.
May 12	Went for a day to Totteridge to Mr. Chambers's; surveyed old house, situation, and gave an idea for a new one.
May 13	Expenses to Totteridge. Tried to empty caisson; 6 horses, 6 square pumps, 3 common pumps, one chain pump, one large square pump, 2 small square pumps at north end.
May 14	Waited on Clerk of St. Barth's. Hospital. Waited on Mr. Briscoe – surveyed his house, and proposed alterations of yard and lease. Attended Trial at Guildhall on Nov'n. of fleet Ditch.
May 15	Attended trustees of City Assembly of Scots. Corporation.
May 17	Attended Building Committee of Barth's. Hospital.
May 21	Ordered the work of Lady Susan Stewart's house; surveyed it; examined the bill, and paid the money – 1.
May 23	Finished the striking all the wedges of 98 feet Cintre. Proceeded to the taking it to pieces.
May 25	Finished the 4th course of North 90 ft. pier; 6 horses, 42 pumpers for 2 hours; horses all the time worked tide work; large square pump, 2 small do. 3 hand pumps, and the horse chain pump.
May 26	Waited on Sir William Duncan. Finished Treaty about ground and Hyde Park Corner.
May 27	Surveyed the Arch South 98 ft., the $\frac{1}{2}$ of bridge as being out; all the joints very fair; mortar squeezed 8th springing course of N. end; hard pinched – 2 stones of it being thicker than the others, flushed off their whole breadth; 2 joints next the keystone, a 1/16th each, 2 stones at west end of n. course dropped

29 EDINBURGH: ST. CECILIA'S HALL. Exterior today

30 EDINBURGH: ST. CECILIA'S HALL: Interior as altered
From a drawing by the Author

31 HANWELL: HOUSE FOR MR. BERNERS

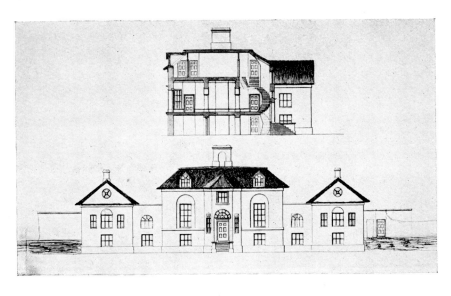

32 DESIGN FOR A COTTAGE, 1780

$\frac{3}{8}''$, two stones towards e. end of south course dropped also. Uneasy about it because it was difficult to ascertain whether it was owing to the settlement of the joints or the expansion of the arch. Observed the keystone had sunk $2\frac{1}{4}''$. Blocked up the two side courses of keystone on the Cintre; forced up those that dropped nearly to their old situation; took the mortar out of one of the joints by driving in wedges to force the side courses to the key stone. Mortar very hard; took it out for a foot upwards; put in new mortar mixed with hair, let it dry, then drove in oyster shells into it.

June 7	Lifted the sides of caisson, off the N. $19\frac{1}{2}$ ft. Pier. Laid them to the eastwards of the Bridge, because we went off eastward and because the caisson; being deeper in this than any former pier we were obliged to have new posts for triangles which allowed her to be so far in the water, that if she had been carried ashore directly, she would have grounded halfway.
June 8 & 9	Took her up again with $3\frac{1}{2}$ feet of blockings; brought her opposite to opening with difficulty because 2 large anchors and 1 small one, the only ones we could make use of, dragged. Went through the N. 98 feet arch very ill, some of the props getting foul of the pier and caisson. Lay all the flood behind the N. middle Pier. Carried her ashore at high water and turned her end for end. Grounded before we could get far enough in.
June 10	Floated the caisson further in shore in order to lift her further out of the water.
June 15	Attempted to put sides of caisson on bottom; floated her from ground further in shore by lowering the triangles on side posts of 2 chain bars in the middle. The open end had none to lower so that as the triangles were considerably below the solid part, they pulled out the sides considerably and strained the next chain bar. All of a sudden some chain bar gave way, others followed, the triangles broke and she went again down on the ground.
June 17	Attended Mr. Murray to the ironmongers – $\frac{1}{4}$. Found sides of caisson much bent outwards at bottom. Put 3 pr. of screws on – heaved then together by taking the ground away on inside. Mended triangles; left the 3 screws in – 2 at east end gone in the middle.
June 20	Put on plaister on the joints in haunches of 100 and 93 feet arches to see whether the 98 feet arch had any effect on the extreme ends of these arches. Took the resolution of loading the haunches of 98 feet arch and $\frac{1}{2}$ of pier with ballast so as to counter poise the settlement of key stone as it still kept opening on lower part of the joints.
June 22	Attempted to float the sides of the caisson; lifted fair with barges; one pr. of screws at east end broke, then a chain bar; sunk the barges to keep the triangles from being broke and sides bent out.

71

June 24	Put 4 of iron straps across the end of caisson in the same manner as at the 1st pier, and 3 more chain bars lifted fair; floated it; put them on the new bottom. Could not wait to see them settled right. Set out for Welbeck.
June 25	Arrived at Welbeck.
June 26	Laid the foundation of S. Pier at Welbeck Bridge.
June 27	Gave Mr. Chambers a design for a new house – 10.
July 5	Left Welbeck to go to Earl of Warwick's. In pocket – £18 15s. 6d.
July 6	Arrived at Warwick.
July 7	Surveyed the situation of Lord Warwick's bridge.
July 9	Gave advice to Lord Warwick on outward Court, entrance into garden and various particulars.
July 12	Arrived in London.
July 19	Threw down the 1st rib of 98 feet cintre.
July 23	Threw down the last rib of S. 98 feet cintre.
July 29 & 30	Found that the laying of the ballast on the haunches of S. 98 feet arch had the desired effect as to counter poising the settlement of key stone, for the joints thereabouts and in the soffit continued as they were. But the joints of façade side of pilasters next arch opened a little and were pointed up 3 stands well but N.E. corner opened more this day. Quere – whether from sinking of e. end of S. 19½ feet pier. Two joints in each haunch of the extreme ends of 3 arches opened a little by plaister, observations – seems to be the effect of cintres, for it is too high up.
Aug. 3	Set out for Tuzmore.
Aug. 5	Surveyed Mr. Fermor's house and situation; received instructions; gave a sketch for a house. Betty Watkinson came as maid servant at £8 per annum. Tea and sugar – found her.
Aug. 6	Arrived in London. Began to shoot rubbish in fleet ditch. gratis, 30 load came last week at 3d. each.
Aug. 18	Surveyed arches; found the tails of joints of N. haunch opened considerably, as also east end of a joint in the soffit. Investigated the cause; found the ballast men when ordered to clean the sides of pier from cintre had dug down to the good ground 10″ below the foundation of N. side of N. middle pier.
Aug. 19	Tried to float caisson. Tide did not flow high enough. Tides falling off; very low by the dry season. Threw 50 ton of stone out of her, part of the 1st course. Floated her; placed her in foundation of N. 18 feet pier. Made water. Put 3 horses aboard and 2 hand pumps at work.
Aug. 24	Went to Mr. Briscoe at Twickenham. Gave advice for Wharfing bank. Finished 2nd course of N. 18 feet pier. 4 horses – 8 pumpers.
Aug. 28	Finished 3rd course of N. 18 ft. Pier; 4 horses – 8 pumpers.
Aug. 31	Finished the fourth course of N. 18 ft. Pier.
Sept. 2	Observed an opening in the west end of the soffit of 2nd course on n. side of keystone of s. 18 ft. arch. Took it for granted that it was owing to the want of ballast on that

adjoining haunch, for it was less than the others. Resolved to add rubbish because the ballast is too wet.

Sept. 4 & 5 Finished the 5th course of N. 18 ft. Pier. Tried to put her in place. Could not do it by the inattention of workmen. This morning fixed the caisson in its place – 3 inches too far west – $7\frac{1}{2}$ too high at west end and right at east end. Cut off the difference.

Sept. 6 Filled up the side of foundation of North side of N. Pier with several freights of ballast for several days past, and the great piles being drove, observed by plaister that the opening of joints in N. haunch of Middle arch were ceased.

Sept. 7 Finished 6th course of N. 18 ft. Pier. Tide work for fear of floating her during this last course – 8 pumpers, 6 horses.

Sept. 8 All the scaffolding, 9 Inch Piles, and part of the inches of posts for N. 98 feet Cintres up and fixed.

Sept. 9 Tried the opening for N. 98 feet arch. Proved to be 97 at east end and 96·$7\frac{1}{2}$ at west end between face of Rusticks.

Sept. 14 Tried the situation of N. 18 ft. Pier. Proved $5\frac{1}{2}$ inches too far west and $9\frac{1}{2}$ too broad. (Piranesi) To Messrs. Drummond & Co. for Piranesi's Bill – £54 0s. 0d.

Oct. 1 Took one of the sides of the caisson away. Sent Mr. Nicholls, Mr. Stocking's bills received, with directions on work of bow window – $\frac{1}{2}$.

Oct. 9 Sent 3 drawings in lines of a Lodge to Mr. Farr at Bristol.

Oct. 10 Sent Mr. Southwell 2 drawings in lines of a monumental Urn to Dublin, and a letter thereon. $2\frac{1}{4}$.

Oct. 19 Finished the taking down of Bridewell Bridge. Shooting of rubbish past it. Finished the brickwork of the sewer to Tudor Street. Finished the 2nd Sp. Course on N. 18 feet Pier. Finished the first 2 courses of N. 98 ft. Arch, above P. finished the digging foundations for S. 16 ft. Pier.

Oct. 28 Paid a bill due by Court of Ald'm: £5 2s. 0d.

Oct. 29 & 30 Observed a settlement of all the n. side of N. Middle Pier, but most at east end. It showed itself at the tails of the North haunch of Middle Arch, and seems to be a continuation of that one caused by the ballast. Men digging under the kirb of that side and by the prepare of so much of the N. 98 feet arch as is set. If so, what will it do when the whole weight of that arch comes upon it. Resolved to pile along the side of the Pier as close as possible. Drove wedges into the open joints.

Nov. 1 Gave Major Hamilton a drawing for outward stair. Do. for a balustrade and for bow window, and a sheet of directions about staircase – $2\frac{1}{4}$.

Nov. 2 Finished the 3 first springing courses of N. 98 ft. Arch at each end and above the pedestals.

Nov. 8 Observed no further settlement in the N. haunch of Middle Arch; few piles drove on the N. side of N. Middle Pier. Resolved to go on with a double row of piles.

Nov. 9 For post coach to Tuxford – £1 14s. 6d.

Nov. 12 Arrived at Welbeck.

Nov. 14 Gave Mr. Woodfall different drawings for a house at Green Street – 10.

Nov. 26 Arrived in London.

Dec. 16 Sent drawings of Bridge to Lord Warwick.

Dec. 18 Attended Mr. Withers on Mr. Clever's ground – $\frac{1}{4}$. Threw the last side of caisson – down.

Memo.

One of the best chain pumps made in one of the King's yards and tried aboard of a king's ship against Mr. Erskines centrifugal water engine, when worked by 10 of the ablest men, threw out $11\frac{1}{2}$ tons in 10 minutes; Mr. Erskines $14\frac{3}{4}$ tons, with same men in the same time.

The 36th share of the King's moiety of the New River Company, whose net produce is £154 per annum. Sold Feb. 1766 for £4,400.

The bridge house lands appropriated by the City for the maintenance of London Bridge, exclusive of what was pulled down on the Bridge, amounts to: £2,300 per annum.

1766

Jan. 15 Went down to Wormley; surveyed house; compared plans and took one of bedroom floor.

Jan. 25 Attended Mr. Brown and Darher on Hospital business.

Feb. 6 Sent Mr. Fermor the drawings of his house; 3 plans, 3 elevations, 1 section – 40 –.

Feb. 10 Took Mary at £10 per annum and Ann Cowel at £7 per annum; each a guinea per annum more for tea and sugar.

Feb. 17 Finished the N. 98 ft. Arch, the usual joints in the haunches
& 18 of the arch opened at the tails. The middle row of piles with the shores to the bottom of Middle Pier's posts, did in the last 14 days bend to the north greatly, but the direction of the prepare was not at first in a straight line. Proceeded with the fillings next to Great Arch. Cut the mortar for 3 inches inwards in all the joints of the inside haunches of great arch to prevent flushing. The same also in 2 joints next keystone.

Feb. 24 Laid the barge on bottom of S. 16 ft. Pier which had 2 courses on it. Could not get all the rods fixed on this side.

Feb. 25 Fixed the barge to bottom. Springtide. Shores from bottom of barge did not affect the bearing pieces. All stood well. One iron broke. No damage. The bottom grew hollow longways because the barge was so longer than bottom. Plates bent. She floated when the water was coming over one Gunnel. Put up wash boarder; wanted 6 inches on other side. Carried over the river. But before she got there, tide turned and she

[*Footnote*]

Oct. 21 Observed that when the weight of engine fell on a pile (driving in the foundation of South 16 feet Pier) it shaked the ground where I stood being 50 feet distance, the same, but in a less degree. Returned by degrees to the wharf at Mr. Mann's door, still the same but almost insensible. Went on the butement to try it—found no motion—N. Be. a bed of gravel runs all under that shore.

lay across 2 piles at west end of S. 18 ft. Pier. Pressure of tide against her and piles made her heal on one side so that she went 6 inches down. Put more wash boards up and dung, while the water came over that side. Was almost going down. Cleared off the water. Carried a cable ashore to Crane, forced her forward till she swung. Then put her in her place – took the ground very well. At low water could not take all the nuts off. Scuttled her and took 13 away next tide. Made preparations to set 3 course.

Mar. 3	Begun to set up Cintre for S. 70 ft. Arch, which is all framed on platform ready. Began to build S. 16 ft. Pier up to high water.
Apr. 1 & 2	Eased all the wedges of Cintre of great Arch 3 inches. Moved very easy with 2 pr. of screws only like a knife going through new cheese. It appeared that the stone of N. haunch had come nearer to the bridge of Cintre than when I drove the piles on the other side of the pier. This may be owing to the middle part of settled much, before the haunches were loaded with rubbish, and thereby having squeezed the Cintre down, it rose up again when counter-ballanced by the rubbish on haunches.
Apr. 3	Threw down the 1st Rib of the above Cintre.
Apr. 4 & 5	All the Arch stands fair, even in the soffit. The same Crack up by the sides of Pilasters which shows that the arch keys in by the squeezing of the mortar.
Apr. 6	Set out for Wormleybury.
Apr. 9	Arrived at Welbeck.
Apr. 10	Felt the foundation for N. Pier of Welbeck Bridge – 7 ft. deep – good.
Apr. 12 & 13	Arrived in London. Examined the Great Arch; all stood as before the easing of Cintre, except the façade up the sides of pilasters where the crack continued to open. Ordered the Cintre to be totally struck and taken away.
Apr. 14	The Cintre for S. 18 ft. Arch finished. The 2nd. Sp. Course of S. 16 ft. Pier finished. Façade of spandrells between M. & N. 98 ft. Arch finished.
Apr. 15	Attended Mr. Brown on a question between St. Barth's. Hospital and the Bank.
Apr. 16	Observed that the Bridge Works are quite run out for stone, none having yet arrived this season.
Apr. 19	Altered a drawing for library chimney for Southwell. Examined the Great Arch; found 2 placed in N. haunch flushed, and on façade of W. front cracked. The openings at side of pilasters more on the South End than N. Do. Idea is that owing to the greater quantity of rubbish being there.
Apr. 23	Sent a valuation of ground in Baitte Lane to St. Bartholomey's Hospital.
Apr. 26	Threw down the last Rib of Cintre of Great Arch; no more flushing. Launched the 1st bottom for N. 16 ft. Pier; hung at east end, twisted a little but got it off.

May 13	Attended at Guildhall for St. B's Hospital.
May 22	Went 6 miles to Condover; surveyed Miss Leighton's house. Recommended a general plan of some alterations in the other parts. – 3 –.
May 27	Examined the haunches of Middle & S. 98 ft. Arches; found that of 98 hardly perceptible to the eye, and that of Middle one a little, as they were both pointed up about 10 days ago.
May 30	Waited on Lord John Murray.
May 31	Went to Mr. Moffat's and surveyed his house.
June 5	Gave Mr. Southwell designs for offices at end of Court Yard, 3 plans, 1 elevation, 2 sections. – 10 –.
June 10	Went to Mr. Edwards with Plans for Miss Leighton's house, which were 4 plans of the different floors of house and 2 drawings for windows, delivered them to Mr. Lee – – 16 –. Wrote Miss Leighton on her affairs – $\frac{1}{2}$ –.
June 26	Sent Miss Leighton a drawing for a chimney piece and another for doors – 4 –. Wrote her a letter – $\frac{1}{4}$.
July 9	Set out for Basildon with Mr. de Talis.
July 11	Left Basildon. Arrived at Tusmore.
July 13	Left Tusmore.
July 14	Saw Oxford.
July 22	Gave Mr. Southwell a drawing for sashes of Attick storey and waited on him – $1\frac{1}{2}$ –.
July 29	Wrote Mr. Southwell about glass plates and commissioned the same of Mr. Woolf – 1 –.
Aug. 2	Arrived at Welbeck.
Aug. 7	Set out from Coldstream. Arrived at Edinburgh.
Aug. 19	Went to Hatton. Received instructions for additions to house and New Offices for Earl of Lauderdale. Returned to Edinburgh.
Aug. 20	Began the work for fitting up the entrance of the Bridge from the N, on the side of fleet ditch.
Aug. 22	Set out from Edinburgh. Lay at Moffat.
Aug. 29	Arrived at Welbeck.
Aug. 31	Arrived at London.
Sept. 27	Went to Wormleybury.
Sept. 29	Returned to London.
Oct. 7	Appointed surveyor of St. Paul's Cathedral by the Archbishop of Canterbury.
Oct. 16	Arrived at Tusmore.
Oct. 18	Set out the foundations of Mr. Fermor's house and laid the 1st stone. Left Tusmore.
Oct. 19	Arrived in London.
Nov. 13	Finished the work of the temporary bridge.
Nov. 17	Gave Lord Mountreath a valuation of his house in Grosvenor Square.
Nov. 19	Opened the temporary bridge for the Publick; the South 82 ft. Arch not finished.
Nov. 22	Gave Mr. Southwell a design for steps to principal front, 2. and 2 drawings of cornices at large for Drawing Rooms – 1.

Nov. 28	Gave Mr. Southwell a drawing for an Attick chimney piece $-\frac{1}{2}$.
Dec. 4	Sent Mr. Southwell drawings at large for base surbase Arches of doors and windows, shutters & doors, for Mrs. Southwell's dressing room.
Dec. 5	Surveyed the Cupola of St. Paul's. Gave a Dinner to the Tradesmen of St. Paul's.
Dec. 16	Observed that the 1st bottom of N. 16 ft. Pier was out of a level 3 inches from end to end, and 4 inches hollow, that it was right in distance from N. But, and feet gd. too far up the river.
Dec. 26	Gave Duke of Portland 2 plans in lines of the principal floors for a house in do.

1767

Jan. 1	Arrived in town from Welbeck.
Jan. 22	Sent Mr. Wedderburn a plan and elevation for a Summer House in Scotland. – 4.
Jan. 26	Sent a report in writing to St. Botolph's Church to the Churchwardens. (?) Went on the river, sounded it, and provided entrance for surveyors on Embankment. (?)*
Jan. 27	Gave in a joint report with Nichols & Yeomans on Embankment of Thames, with entrance of boats – 5 – (?)
Jan. 30	Sent Mr. Southwell a drawing for a chimney piece of the mouldings thereof – at large – 2½. (?) Looked at Mr. Briscoe's wash-house. (?)
Feb. 6	Waited on Mr. Bishop; the bargain signed for building. (?)
Mar. 3	Attended a Com'e. of Common on behalf of Westham Waterworks part of Lee River – 2 – (?)
Mar. 5	Mr. Mylton called a long discourse on his house and alteration – 2 –. (?) Settled bills for Mr. Briscoe's building £62 0s. 0d. and extra work for £35 1s. 3½d. Surveyed the first but not the latter. (?)
Mar. 12	Sent Duke of Athol queres on width of river and 2 sketches of same. – 2 –. Sent Mr. Mytton a drawing at large of all his house and offices. (?)
Mar. 16	Carried 2nd bottom for N. 16 ft. Pier into its place; water above gunnel of barge in middle. Ends of timbers which were in a straight line bended 1 foot. After 6 hours bearing one iron gave way, but no prejudice. Sunk the barge at last.
Mar. 17	Surveyed old houses in Parish of St. Botolph's and attended the Court of Aldermen thereon. 2. (?)
Mar. 18	Sent Mr. Pringle 3 drawings of a porch – 2. (?) Gave Mr. Southwell a drawing of chimney piece of lady's dressing room. (?)
Mar. 21	Sent Mr. Southwell drawings at large for arches of doors, do. of windows, base, surbase, entablature ground room, 3½, all of drawing room. (?) Surveyed Pallace at Croydon, expenses ½. (?)

*The question marks in brackets occur in the original diary. *Ed.*

Mar. 28	Struck the Cintre of S. Butement Arch, wedges too stiff to move with sledge hammers; put on the hoops and 2 pr. of screws, and did it easily. The bridgens up; obliged to cut away the blockings at South End.
Mar. 30	Gave a report in writing of a survey of this Pallace at Croydon to the Archbishop. (?)* Attended the House of Commons on City Petition; nothing done. (?) Discourse with Mr. Bindley on his house.
Mar. 31	Gave Mr. Charteris designs for offices of house of rusticks on back, front, etc. –22–. (?) Examined S. Br. Arch; found the joints of the upper part of façade on all the haunches opened a little.
Apr. 2	Gave Mr. Bindley a plan of alterations for country house. – 3.
Apr. 4	Waited on the Comm. of Customs, on Hull harbour. 3. (?)
Apr. 8	Gave Mr. Southwell a drawing at large for frieze of drawing room – ½; attended him. To Mr. Broomwich for choice of papier mâché – ½. (?) Set out for Hull. (?)
Apr. 10	Arrived in Hull. (?)
Apr. 14	Arrived at Welbeck. (?)
Apr. 16	Arrived at Wormleybury, being 7 days out on journey to Hull and 1 to Welbeck. – 14 – (?)
Apr. 18	Waited on Mr. Prescot at Theobald's. Viewed situation for house and received instructions for design. Arrived at London.
Apr. 20	Struck the wedges of 93 feet Cintre back 3 inches.
Apr. 21	Went with Mr. Murray; surveyed 2 houses in Portman Square, one for Lord Arch Hamilton – 2 – (?) Waited on Mr. Mytton; gave advice and sketch of bins and panes for windows – ½. (?) Sent Mr. Southwell a drawing for ceiling of drawing room. – 3. (?)
Apr. 22	Delivered a joint report with Mr. Robson to Comms. of Customs and a plan of the harbour of Hull. – 10. (?)
Apr. 23	All the wedges of S. 93 ft. Cintre quite back; in general they went easy, some very hard. The haunches flushed very much and higher than usual. The joints were very neatly executed, the best in the whole bridge. Masons were not time enough in cutting in the joints. All this arch was mended.
Apr. 28	Gave the Commrs. of Customs a plan of the haven of Hull and a proposition for a wet Dock and a legal quay – altered and delivered a copy of Bill for wet dock. – 10 –. (?)
Apr. 29	Threw down the first Rib of S. 93 ft. Cintre.
Apr. 30	Mr. Southwell called; long discourse on fitting up of house – ½. (?)
May 4	Corrected plans for house and offices for Lord Arch Hamilton; wrote memorandums and descriptions of finishing do. – 5 –. (?) Do. for Mr. Murray – 5. (?) Threw down the last Rib of S. 98 ft. Cintre.
May 5	Waited with Comrs. of Customs on Lord of Treasury – 3. (?) Wrote Mr. Murray on sash weights. ¼. (?)

*The question marks in brackets occur in the original diary. *Ed.*

May 6	Dined with Mr. Paterson at Lodge; gave a design for Corinthian candlesticks. – 3 –.
May 8	Attended Mr. Murray; surveyed his houses in Portman Square – 1. (?)*
May 10	Set out for Tusmore. Spent. £8 12s. 1d.
May 14	Left Tusmore. Went to Caversham Grove; surveyed Mr. Bindley's house and offices. Set out for London.
May 16	Gave Mr. Bindley advice on his house and offices and method of laying out the kitchen garden and method of finishing cornices in the plan of additions. – 3.
May 17	Went to Wormleybury. In pocket. £1 12s. 0d.
May 18	Set out the foundations of Mr. Hume's house. (?)
May 19	Laid the first stone of Mr. Hume's house. (?)
May 21	Returned to London. Elected a Member of the Royal Society.
May 23	Sent an answer to Mr. Preston on the butement of Stockton Bridge. – 2.
June 6	Waited on Lord Garties to-day and 2 former days on house in Charles Street. (?)
June 6	Wrote Mr. Bindley on business at Caversham Grove. ¼.
June 12	Gave Mr. Fullerton a sketch for a house. Received instructions to make drawings therefrom. (?).
June 17	Went to Wormleybury. (?) Crossed over to St. Albans. (?)
June 18	Surveyed the Abbey Church. (?) Returned to London. (?)
June 19	Begun pumping for N. 16 ft. Pier; made a fence across hole; proved very leaky through the ballast; laid to make the dam.
June 21	Foundation proved very leaky; a great deal of stuff silted in from the leakage.
June 22	Tried one tide more; tried to clear a place to set one stone; but the sand shot in too fast. Resolved to give it up.
June 23	Gave a report to Common Council on water (board) works at London Bridge, which was attended with some expense and the making of many drawings. (?)
June 27	Sent Dr. Tebbetson a report on Church at St. Albans and the work to be done made out into particulars; wrote Dt. Tb'n. a letter. (?)
June 29	Wrote Mr. Mytton on business at Halston –½. (?) Wrote Mr. Murray on business at Cally – ¼. Remains the work of the rails to be changed. (?)
July 11	Finished setting up of Cintre for N. 93 ft. Arch.
July 16	Surveyed Mr. Fermor's house in town for purchase. 1.
July 21	Sent drawings of a house to Mr. Fullarton at Air. 15. Surveyed Lambeth Pallace throughout.
July 22	Passed a Bill of Mr. Southwell's monument.
July 25	Sent Mr. Southwell a design for a Lodge. 2.
Aug. 8	Jean Vasey came as Housekeeper at £9 per annum.
Aug. 10	Sunk the second part of bottom for N. 16 ft. Pier.
Aug. 20	Wrote Dr. Decheur on method of airing Chapel.
Aug. 27	Waited on Mrs. Fermor; surveyed house and ground – gave a valuation – £2,800.

*The question marks in brackets occur in the original diary. Ed.

Aug. 29	Set out for Wormley. Called on Mr. Prescot; nothing done – to stop – arrived there.
Aug. 31	Arrived in town.
Sept. 1	Attended Mr. North of C: to Croydon, and returned to town.
Sept. 17	Sent a drawing to Sir Wm. Main as from Mr. Hume, 1.
Sept. 22	Surveyed a house in Portman Square for Beckingham and gave an opinion thereon.
Sept. 25	Set out for Welbeck – in pocket £23 0s. 4d.
Sept. 27	Arrived at Welbeck.
Oct. 3	Finished the last Course but one of the N. 16 ft. Pier. Arrived at Wormleybury.
Oct. 5	Arrived in London.
Oct. 9	Set out for Hertford; attended a Comm'ee of New River Company on B: Engine, gage. Went to Mr. Hume's.
Oct. 11	Returned to London.
Oct. 15	Finished the last course of last Pier (N. 16 ft.); width of butement arch proved 12 inches wider at E: end than west. Attended the Board of N. River Company. Received directions for an estimate of embanking. For binding of drawings of St. Paul's: – £2 15s. 0d.
Oct. 26	Nanny came as Servant at £7 7s. 0d. Finished the N. 93 ft. Arch.
Oct. 29	Attended the Board of New River Company; gave an opinion on an old wharfing of timber; gave Lea estimate of embanking opposite their freehold/school of estates. Finished the 2nd course of N. 16 ft. Pier.
Oct. 31	Appointed by the Dean of Canterbury, Surveyor to the Cathedral of Canterbury.
Nov. 7	Passed a Bill for Lord Mayor's day – 1766/217. Wrote a long letter to Mr. Southwell. Sent him a drawing of the end of Saloon in lines; ditto of 2 frames of pictures at large. ditto of cornice at large. ditto of impost at large.
Nov. 9	Went to Wormley.
Nov. 12	Returned to London.
Nov. 14	Wrote to Mr. Southwell a long letter. Sent a drawing of chimney side of saloon; ditto of base of surbase at large; ditto of chimney piece for same; ditto of chimney piece for Parlour; ditto of chimney piece for a bedroom.
Nov. 20	Wrote to Mr. Southwell on his business. Sent him a drawing for a flower and urn in ceiling of saloon. Do. of the window side of saloon.
Nov. 26	Appointed joint surveyor to the New River Company; Salary of £200 to commence from Xmas next. Travelling expenses to be allowed. From New River Company for business done and and to be done till Xmas next, £25 0s. 0d.
Dec. 10	Begun the N. 82 ft. Arch.

Dec. 11   Went to Wormleybury.
Dec. 13   Returned to London.
Dec. 14   Began the embankment for the Ap's: Comp.
Dec. 23   Sent Mr. Southwell drawing for window side of saloon – improved nothing.
Dec. 24   Finished the north butement Arch.
Dec. 30   Wrote Mr. Southwell on Saloon.

1768

Jan. 13   Men began work at the Bridge. Sent Mr. Mytton a drawing at large for cornice and architraves of Parlour, 1. Do. of chimney-piece – 2. A long letter on several articles on finishing house. – $\frac{1}{4}$.
Jan. 22   Set out for Portsmouth.
Jan. 23   Arrived at Portsmouth.
Jan. 25   Arrived in London.
Jan. 26   Sent Mr. Mytton drawings of base & surbase at large for dining room and wrote a letter on finishing – $\frac{3}{4}$.
Feb. 2   Went to Bromley; surveyed Mr. Lockwood's Mills and intended Cut to Lime House.
Feb. 6   Waited on Mr. Murray; surveyed 2 houses in Grosvenor Square & opinion on the value – 1.
Feb. 13   A meeting with Mr. Lockwood at home on the new Cut of River Lea.
Feb. 18   Wrote Mr. Mytton on Sash Door and other parts of finishing of house.
Feb. 19   Sent Mr. Southwell a drawing of cornice of frieze over doors of drawing room – 1. Went to Wormleybury.
Feb. 21   Returned to London.
Feb. 27   Went to Bromley – met Mr. Homans, settled agreement about new Cutt. At 7 o'clock last stone of last arch of N. 82 ft. Arch fixed.
Feb. 29   Sent Mr. Southwell patterns of colours for saloon.
Mar. 5   Wrote Mr. Mytton on alteration of the stair, a/c. $\frac{1}{4}$.
Mar. 8   Sent Major Hamilton's new set of offices altered from the old ones.
Mar. 28   Went to Ware on business for New River Co. and returned to Wormleybury.
Mar. 29   Returned to London.
Apr. 2   Attended Trustees of Lee Nav. for Mr. Lockwood at Waltham Cross.
Apr. 5   The Agreement between Mr. Fermor & Rush being at an end, recollected – to have waited on Mr. Fermor several times; gave an opinion of the value of house in town, a drawing of stable offices for do. – 5 –. It afterwards was concluded.
Apr. 11   Went to Ware on business of New River Co. and returned to Wormleybury.
Apr. 12   Returned to London.

81

Apr. 16	Went to Hanwell with Mr. Bernard.
Apr. 18	Went to Limehouse and waited on Mr. Dingleys Cut. Expenses – 3sh. Sent Mr. T. Mill in Scotland designs for a house & offices, being 5 plans, 2 sections, 2 elevations – 20.
May 5	Set out for Canterbury. In pocket – £9 15s. 4d.
May 9	Returned to London.
May 24	Gave Lord Ilchester a design for a bridge – an elevation and plans of same – 5.
May 29	Set out for Tusmore – in pocket £20 10s. 3d. Examined work of Mr. Talbot's bridge at Uxbridge. From the Archbishop of Canterbury one year's allowance for surveying, £20 0s. 0d.
June 3	Gave Sir George Colebrook design for a Castle.
June 7	Gave Dean & Chapter of Canter'y (Mr. Benson) a plan & particulars of an advert' for leeting their estate in Southwark.
June 16	Wrote & sent Bishop of Bangor directions for setting up Arch.
June 21	Wrote Bishop of Bangor directions on oven.
June 22	Waited on Lady Charlotte Edwin at Putney; inspected her house & gave advice thereon.
June 25	Wrote Mr. Benson about Tooley Estate – $\frac{1}{4}$.
July 20	Gave Mr. Jeffries drawing for altering 4 windows.
July 22	Went to Wormleybury. Gave Colonel (?) and Mr. Brown a sketch of a method to remedy the deffects of Dunbarton Bridge and a letter thereon. This paid by apointment of brother.
July 26	Returned to London.
Aug. 27	Set out on survey of New River. Went as far as Whole Bridge & returned.
Aug. 29	Left off at Wormley. Returned to London.
Aug. 30	Went to Croydon by desire of Arch. of Canterbury. and returned to London.
Aug. 31	Went to Fulham.
Sept. 15	Sent Mr. Mytton drawings washed for a bridge & wrote thereon. £3 10s. 0d.
Oct. 1	Went to Peckham and afterwards to Fulham.
Oct. 3	Went to Hanwell; returned to London; went to Wormleybury. Jane Chapman came as Maidservant at £8. per annum.
Oct. 4	Returned to London. Report on Bridge for Londonderry made on 10th Oct. £10 10s. 0d.
Nov. 27	Went about the sale of Bishop of Litchfield's house.
Nov. 30	Attended Mr. Murray to survey a house at Hertford Street.
Dec. 17	Went to Wormley. Afterwards to Ware and carried Mr. Cole along with me.
Dec. 18	Returned to London.
Dec. 24	Attended Mr. Murray and surveyed a house in Stanhope Street. 1.

1769

Jan. 13	Went to Wormleybury; afterwards to Ware.
Jan. 14	Returned to Wormleybury. Went to Mr. Harvey's near Woodford Bridge. Returned to London.

Jan. 23	Went to Hanwell; afterwards to Uxbridge. Returned to London.
Feb. 1	Sent Mr. Mytton a design for a wooden bridge being an elevation, section & plan in lines. 5.
Feb. 6	The Carpenters had thrown down 2 Piles of the Cintre of the S. 98: Arch and had forgot to put in the blockings between the ribs and the Arch; one of the ropes broke and the 4 remaining ones fell near low water. It made a terrible noise and broke a great part of the timbers – one man's arms a little hurt.
Feb. 11	Went to Mr. Harvey's at Claybury.
Feb. 18	At the desire of the Bishop of Litchfield, went to Mr. Cambridge at Twickenham to look at a stove – $\frac{1}{2}$. Went with Mr. Berners to Ealing; looked at a house and gave an opinion of the value of it.
Mar. 6	Gave Lady Broughton an opinion on the value of a house in Cleveland Court. Gave Mr. Hill a drawing of cornice for drawing room at Fern, with directions about room. – 1.
Mar. 10	Gave Mr. Harvey a design for a collonade and entry to his house in Epex. – 5.
Mar. 11	Gave Mr. Hill design for a cornice for drawing room and directions for finishing the room. – $1\frac{1}{2}$.
Mar. 18	Wrote the Bishop of Derry on his bridge a long letter.
Mar. 20	Gave Mr. Wedderburn 2 drawings for stables.
Apr. 8	Gave Mrs. Molineux an estimate of the value of her house. – 2. Transacted several matters for the taking and selling houses for the Bishop of Litchfield.
May 1	Consultation with Mr. Hill. Ordered a chimney piece of Mr. Deval for Mr. Hill.
June 2	Set out for Oxfordshire; called at Hanwell; called at Uxbridge, looked at Mr. Berners estate.
June 5	Returned to London.
June 10	Waited on Trustees of River Lea at Limehouse Dock and surveyed their works at the Lock. 2.
June 17	Went to Hanwell.
July 3	Set out on a survey of the New River.
Aug. 8	Waited on Arch. of Canterbury at Croydon; surveyed old Parkhall Pallace – expenses 10s. 6d.
Aug. 12	Left London.
Aug. 15	Arrived in Edinburgh.
Sept. 6	Set out for the West Country; at Borrowstenep.
Sept. 7	At Stirling.
Sept. 8	At Glasgow.
Sept. 10	Rosneath Castle.
Sept. 11	At Ardincaple.
Sept. 12	At Hamilton.
Sept. 13	Arrived in Edinburgh.
Sept. 18	Sent Sir John Whitefood plans, elevations and sections of a house to be built at Edin. 25.

Sept.	27	Sent Mr. Mytton a drawing of chimney piece of saloon.
		Do. for the base of impost of do. at large.
		Do. for the cornice of do. at large.
		Do. for the cornice of hall at large.
		Do. a sketch for altering a Pidgeon house.
Nov.	18	Went to Croydon; surveyed Parkhill and did business for Arch:
Nov.	18	Went to Gatton.
Nov.	19	Surveyed the head of water; gave advice thereon.
Nov.	20	Returned to London.
Dec.	19	Went to Wormleybury; returned to London.
Dec.	29	Waited on Lord Milton about Mr. Fermor's stables.
Dec.	30	Wrote Mr. Fermor about Treaty with Lord Milton; $\frac{1}{4}$.

1770 to 1774

The diaries for 1770 to 1774 contain the following notes of interest: 1770: Robert Mylne submitted a design for the Hospital at Belfast. This was not carried out. 1772: He advised on the repairs to the bridge at Newcastle. 1773: He made designs for the Duke of Argyll at Inveraray Castle. 1774: He surveyed the site of the house on Richmond Hill which he afterwards built for Lady St. Aubyn.

1770

Jan. 5	Gave Sir G. Colebrook a design in 2 drawings washed of a temple for Gatton. Waited on Mr. Peeles about Mr. Fermor's lease.
Feb. 2	Went to Peckham. Surveyed state of chimney at desire of Mrs. Brown.
Feb. 9	Surveyed a house in St. James's Square for Bishop of London and agreed with Lord Warwick for it – 5.
Feb. 14	Made 4 plans of the B.H. Lands in St. G. Fields for the conveyance of the property.
Feb. 23	Sent Mr. Ellis 3 plans on vellum of Mrs. Syke's grounds.
Mar. 2	Gave evidence at St. Margaret's Hall on (?) Set out for Canterbury. Arrived at Canterbury.
Mar. 3	Surveyed the Cathedral.
Mar. 4	Went to Goodneston. Surveyed house. Considered many improvements, etc.
Mar. 5	Set out for London at Rochester.
Mar. 6	Returned to London.
Mar. 13	Sent Sir Brook & Bridges a paper of Observations on the improvement of his house at Goodneston.
Mar. 19	Attended the House of Commons on the Petition of Southwark for Daily Tolls.
Mar. 20	Gave a report to the Bishop of London on his house in St. James's Square.
Mar. 22	Set out for Oxfordshire; in pocket £12 15s. 6d.
Mar. 23	Arrived at Tusmore.
Mar. 24	Met Bishop of Londonderry. A long discussion on Bridge at Derry.
Mar. 26	Arrived in London.
Mar. 28	Waited on Sir Harbord Harbord. A long consultation on his house in the country.
Apr. 1	Made a bargain for a house in Hatton Garden for Mrs. Anderson – – – – – – – 5
Apr. 2	Sent Mr. Fermor a print of the Bridge. Waited on Sir Harbord Harbord.

Apr. 7	Sent Mr. Paterson a report on ground for Lying-in Hospl. Sent Sir Brook Bridges a list of description of Work to be done this summer – 2 –
Apr. 10	Gave Mr. Harris a Report on Estcourts houses in Cheapside – 5.
Apr. 27	Waited on Mr. Peele for Mr. Fermor on his lease of stables and wrote Mr. Fermor about it.
Apr. 28	For the Road Committee. Filled up 2 descriptions in leases of exchange of grounds between Mr. Bunn and Boyfield, and made plans thereof - 5
Apr. 29	Went to Croydon. Waited on Capt. Staples on the buildings of his farm for Archbishop.
May 6	Went to Croydon. Waited on Capt. Staples – made a proposal for his farm for Archbishop.
May 8	Met Capt. Staples and made a conditional bargain for the lease of his farm for Archbishop – 1
May 19	Gave Mr. Allen a design for an Hospital & Infirmary for Belfast in Ireland - 40
June 2	Went to Fulham. Waited on Bishop of London. Went to Hanwell – Surveyed staircase. £1 2s. 6d.
June 7	Made a bargain for next rent on Bishop of London's house in St. James's Square with Mr. Maris – 1
June 15	Waited on Mr. Brograve and wrote him 2 letters on Tooley Street Estate. – 1. Met Mr. Cox and Mr. Brograve and settled great part of the lease of Tooley Street Estate. – 1.
June 16	Settled the plan of Tooley Street Estate and method of carrying out the same with Mr. Fellows, finally - ½.
June 19	Made 2 plans of Tooley Street Estate on Parchment and sent the same to Canterbury.
June 20	Surveyed an estate of houses for Sir Robert Ladbroke in St. Paul's Churchyard and gave advise what should be done therewith.
July 14	Went to Gatton. Gave advice on the head for the lake.
July 16	Duty on wine expenses £14 11 6
	do. on slave boy . . . . £2 10 –

July 17	£17 1 6
	Money received £42 5 6

Balance £25 4 0 Remitted by
making brother pay it.

July 21	Went to Highbury. Surveyed Sluice.
July 23	Met Mr. Fellowes on the Borough Estate. Valued some buildings, enquired into the claims made for old materials and wrote Mr. Benson thereon.
Aug. 2	Signed a contract of submission for finishing the Bridge at Edinburgh, as Cautioner for brother under £500 penalty.
Aug. 3	Went to Croydon. Surveyed the Pallace, ordered some work. Returned to London.

33 LONDON: NEW RIVER OFFICE

34 LONDON: BOARD ROOM OF NEW RIVER OFFICE

35 CROYDON: THE LODGE AT ADDINGTON

36 NEW RIVER: URN

Aug. 8	Went to Ware. Gave directions for setting up the Ballance Engine. Returned to London.
Aug. 10	Inspected the Wharf at Chelsea Garden. Estimates, etc. for Mr. Dennison. – 1½.
Aug. 11	Gave Mr. Edmonstone a Design of Drawings coloured for a house at Edinburgh for Mr. Hay Campbell. – 15.
Aug. 13	Gave Mr. Dennison a plan of the Apothecarys' Company's Estate with the best method of laying it out. 5.
Aug. 17	Gave Mr. Baynes a plan of his new intended yard and wharf. 2.
Aug. 24	Gave the Treasurer of Bridewell a plan and proposal for the improvement of their estate in the precinct – – 20 –.
Sept. 1	Left London, went to Peckham, ordered a new well for Mr. Brown. Went to Croydon. Inspected ditch of some repairs at Pallace. Went to Gatton.
Sept. 2	Surveyed Temple and head of water. Ordered the work of a Poultry building and a Pheasantry – and gave a sketch for it.
Sept. 3	Went to Epsom; afterwards to Woodcate. Surveyed pond of water for Mr. Nelson and charged nothing.
Sept. 18	Set out for Tusmore. Saw Stowe. Arrived in London.
Sept. 22	Set out for Ware. Took Lucy as maidservant at £7 7s. 0d. a year – she finding tea etc. £2 0s. 0d. for horses.
Sept. 26	Attended the foundation of Ballance Engine for the whole week. Waited on Mr. Byde. Business on Mill, Land and River at Righ Bridge, Amwell.
Sept. 27	Had Old Mill, Mr. Cole and various people to dine in the course of the week.
Sept. 29	Returned to London.
Oct. 8	Went to Gatton. Surveyed the head for the water which had given way, and advised on remedy. Returned to London.
Oct. 29	Went to Whitton. Gave Mr. Gosling advice on the method of fitting up his house. – – – Nothing.
Nov. 27	Gave Mr. Clare a valuation for the renewal of the lease of houses in St. Martins Le Grand – after surveying the same – 3.
Nov. 28	Gave Mr. Michell an opinion on navigation of the River Thames. 2.

1771

Feb. 4	Attended B.H. Lands and made a bargain for the renewal of Mr. Estcourls lease.
Feb. 5	Made out and sent Mr. Brown 2 plans, clean, of his house – basement and parlour floors. – 4. Inspected chimneys in the old part of house, and ordering the defects thereof to be repaired by Mr. Hugler.
Feb. 6	Made a bargain with Captain Catherwood for Co. Clinton's house, for D. of Anglesey, for £105. per annum – – 2.
Feb. 7	Sent Mr. Dennison a plan of the estate belonging to Kings College, Cambridge.
Feb. 10	Went and surveyed houses for Mr. Charteris in George Street, Hanover Square.
Feb. 19	Met Mr. Walsh and endeavoured to settle an account between him and Mr. Fermor. – – 1.

Mar. 8	Arrived at Medenham. Surveyed River Thames from Hambeldon's Loch to Marlow. Arrived in London.
Mar. 11	Gave Mr. Coventry a design of 3 drawings in lines of a watergate for Temple Stairs. – – Nothing. They were returned.
Mar. 12	Gave the D. of Argyl a sketch of all his property about Argyl House. – – – $\frac{1}{2}$.
Mar. 19	Mr. Michel called on his affair. Attended House of Commons on Mr. Michel's affair. – 2.
Apr. 5	Examined a Bill of Repairs for Mr. Tinkins, coat merchant.
Apr. 12	Gave an opinion in writing of the value of Mr. Charteris's estate to – Mr. Reid.
Apr. 26	Gave Mr. Southwell designs in lines for 2 chimney pieces for town. Gave Sr. George Colebrook a design of 3 coloured drawings – for his Church – – 10.
May 8	Gave Mr. Southwell a design of 4 washed drawings for a Lodge and Tea Room. – – 10.
May 27	Went to Ware. Met Mr. Read on Gauge. In pocket: £8 8s. 10d.
May 28	Met Mr. Normans on Mill. Do. Mr. Cole on Bl Engine. Do. Mr. Osborne on Ware Bridge.
May 29	Returned to London.
July 4	Apointed Surveyor to the N. B. Company, and they granted the use of the house also.
July 6	Went to Ware. Visited Highbury Gate and Bushill. In pocket

```
              - £8  18   6
                     5  11
                     8   6
                  _____
                £9  13   0
```

July 17	Went with Mr. Fraine to Chelmsford; inspected a bridge in a defective state, new built at his estate. Recommended a method and returned late at night.
July 21	Went from Croydon to Gatton and examined the walls and state of the Church. Wrote a letter to Sir George on the necessity of pulling it down. Returned to Croydon.
Aug. 30	Set out for Ware. Money in pocket £7 7s. 0d.
Sept. 3	Left Ware. Went to Amwell. Afterwards to Highbury – Frame – Returned to London. William Paget came as servant at 8 guineas.
Sept. 22	Sent a sketch in lines of the plan of a house for a gentleman in Montgomeryshire – to Mr. Mytton.
Nov. 18	Set out for Tuzmore. In pocket: £10 10

```
                           10   6
                            8   0
                        _____
                       11   9   2
                        3   9   6
                        _____
                       £8   –   –
```

Nov. 25 Arrived in London.

Dec. 9 Sent Mr. Mytton 2 sketches in black lines for a house for Mr. Mostyn, and wrote 3 times.

First Trial of Ballance Engine

Memo.

Over the door of Miln's Square; that door at the foot of the stair which is in the North side of the Quadrangle – Is the Mylne's Arms on a shield in a pediment, very well cut, and on the top of the Pediment, is Palles's head, the crest, on each side of the shield, and in the corners of the pediment is the date of 1686.

On the west side of the Square is another such doorway, with the Arms and Cyphers, with 1680.

On the Leads of the Great Steeple, Edinburgh can be seen –

E D – G I D

1643

On Dumferline Church there is the Mark of the Mylne's and some initials of M etc.

1772

Jan. 2 By Mr. Matthew's Bill, he has been paid for all, and £3 1s. 6d. due to me towards this year's allowance, which is settled at £40.

Jan. 25 Went to Twickenham, survey Mr. Briscoe's house and roof; advised method of repair.

Jan. 26 Attended Mr. Wedderburn; discourse on drawings for Lincoln's Inn.

    2 plans of the whole extant.

    1 elevation of east side.

    3 plans of central building.

    2 elevations of same.

Jan. 29 Mr. Wedderburn called; some discourse on old Playhouse. Waited on Mr. Eyere about Old Playhouse. Waited on Mr. Wedderburn on do.

Jan. 30 Surveyed old Playhouse in Portugal Street.

Feb. 2 Went to Mr. Barrow, Twick'm. Common, – Surveyed his Mills, Branches of Water, and his house, doing discourse thereon. – Nothing.

Feb. 21 Attended the Bishop of Durham and Members, on the rebuilding of Newcastle Bridge; gave advice thereon.

Feb. 23 Gave Mr. Wedderburn a sketch in lines, plan and elevation of a General Register Office.

Feb. 25 Sent Mr. Mytton – for Mostyne, – a design for a house and offices complete, consisting of – 6 plans ⎫
                                      2 elevations. ⎬ – – 20.
                                      1 section. ⎭

Feb. 29 Sent Mr. Trecothick two sketches in lines of different ideas for the principal storey of a house.

91

Mar. 2	Set out for Newcastle. In pocket – £27 11s. 3d. Called at Ware – inspected the works there. Carriage to Ware – £1 1s. 0d.
Mar. 4	Arrived at Durham; inspected the fallen Bridge and did site of New One – also the Bishop's Pallace. Arrived at Gateshead.
Mar. 5	Inspected the River Tyne. Sounded the River. Surveyed the Old Bridge.
Mar. 16	Attended a meeting of the Mayor and Aldermen of Newcastle, treated about the removal of rubbish in Bishop's part, for the Bishop, and wrote him 3 letters.
Mar. 17	Attended Common Council, made a long speech on the Bridge – Report – Temporary Bridge. Delivered a message from Bishop. Left Newcastle. Arrived at Durham.
Mar. 18	Waited on Mr. Hogg – then on the Deane. Gave advice on the situation and form of the New Bridge. Surveyed the Castle and the Apartments, for the Bishop.
Mar. 19	Left Durham – In Pocket: £10 10 0

$$
\begin{array}{rrr}
£10 & 10 & 0 \\
 & 13 & 2 \\
\hline
11 & 3 & 2 \\
4 & 0 & 9 \\
\hline
7 & 2 & 5 \\
£3 & 11 & 2\tfrac{1}{2} \\
\end{array}
$$

Mar. 21	Arrived in London.
Apr. 2	Attended of Com'ee of the H. of Commons on the Newcastle Petition.
Apr. 6	Made a Schedule to Mr. Rowsell's lease of the house in Marlboro' Street.
Apr. 20	Went to Mr. Barrows at Twickenham. Took dimentions of house, etc. and considered proposed alterations at the Mills. Nothing.
July 30	Sent Lord Abingdon a Report on work at Rycott, and Bills altered – – 20.
Aug. 13	Set out for the North – Money in pocket:— At Ware. £31 10 0

$$
\begin{array}{lrrl}
\text{At Ware. } & £31 & 10 & 0 \\
 & & 8 & 3 \\
\hline
 & 31 & 18 & 3 \\
\text{Ded.} & 1 & 10 & \\
\hline
 & 30 & 8 & 3 \quad\text{In pocket.} \\
\text{do.} & & 7 & 6 \\
\hline
 & £30 & 0 & 9 \quad (£28\ 19s.\ 9d.)
\end{array}
$$

Aug. 14	To be paid by New River Comp'y. £1 8s. 6d.
Aug. 19	At Durham; Expenses going to and Return from Auchland to Durham – £1 1s. 0d.
Aug. 24	Arrived at Edinburgh. To wife – £2 2s. 0d.
Sept. 1	Left Edinburgh. In pocket – £17 5s. 9d.

Sept. 6	At Inverary.
Sept. 7	Surveyed the Castle and Apartments from top to bottom. The new apartments to be finished. Surveyed Military Bridge fallen.
Sept. 8	Old Bridge and the London Bridge – gave advice about the banks, and butement of bridge.
Sept. 10	Left Inverary. Surveyed the Garron Bridge, and one at the head of Loch Fyne. – – 1. At Dumbarton.
Sept. 11	Surveyed Dumbarton Bridge and recommended several things to be done – to Col: scheme. Surveyed Glasgow Bridge and recomended several things to be done – to Brother. At Hamilton.
Sept. 12	Surveyed the Pallace and situation. At Edinburgh – In pocket £1 19s. 0d.
Sept. 22	At Edinburgh. At Berwick.
Sept. 25	Left Newcastle – In pocket £17 5s. 0d. At Bishop Auchland.
Sept. 27	Made a sketch for a gateway at entrance – 2. Long consultation on Newcastle Bridge with Bishop Auchland.
Sept. 30	Arrived in London – In pocket: £2 13s. 0d.
Oct. 26	Wrote Lord Abingdon and sent directions for making a priory in N.E. Tower.

1773

Jan. 12	Went to Wormleybury. Gave advice on Engine and supply of water from spring. Do. on roof of portico and water closets. Do. of the figure of peire of water. Chaise. 12s.
Jan. 13	Returned to London.
Jan. 14	To Sr. Abrah'm. Hume – 9 bushels of earth @ 3s. 6d.
Jan. 20	Set out for Shropshire.
Jan. 21	Went out of the road to Tusmore. Gave directions about the work for 2 hours. At Coventry.
Jan. 24	Went from Woodhouse. At Halston.
Jan. 26	At Brunhyn, and went to Mr. Floyds.
Jan. 27	At Loton Park, Mr. Leighton's. In pocket – £11 8s. 1d.
Jan. 28	Expenses to Shrewsbury – 12. At Shrewsbury.
Jan. 29	Went to Tern. At Birmingham.
Jan. 31	At Rycott – surveyed the water closets.
Feb. 1	Returned to London.
Feb. 10	Sent Mr. Owen a new design for his house in Wales altered from the old one, consisting of 2 plans, one elevation, and a section. – – 5.
Feb. 16	Sent Mr. Hill a list of alterations and amendments recomended to be made to his house at Tern, in its present state – – 2.
Mar. 26	Gave Mr. Hill a plan, elevation and section of a large set of stables, etc. – 10. A design of 3 plans and an elevation of a gardener's house. – 4. A plan and elevation of a greenhouse. – 3. A method, with directions, for fitting up the saloon for books, billiards, etc. – 3.

Apr. 9	Sent Mr. Leighton a design for altering and improving Loton Hall, consisting of 3 plans, one elevation washed, and an elevation in lines, with a sketch of the plantations round it, and written directions.
Apr. 14	Sent Mr. Owen a design for a new house at Woodhouse of – 4 plans of house, 2 sections and 2 elevations, washed. And a small plan and elevation in lines of the whole, and also of the new front to old house, with written directions. – – – 25
Apr. 30	Sent by the D: of Argyll, to Col: Hume, a design for rebuilding the fallen bridge nearby over the Ayray – elevation, section, 2 plans washed, and 2 rough drawings. – – – 10.
May 1	Gave the Duke of Argyll a sketch of post-chaise to go round the castle at Inverary. – – 1.
May 2	Went to Islington; afterwards to Enfield. – to Wormleybury.
May 3	Returned to London.
May 4	Attended Court of Aldermen on Eyres Ground.
May 10	Attended a trial at Westminster Hall on Mr. Coleworth's house, with clerk, after repeated surveys and consultations – – 6.
May 15	Sent Mr. Hill a method for completing his house of 2 plans and 2 elevations – 5. and for the design of the greenhouse perfected in 3 washed drawings – 3.
May 19	Went to Streatham – inspected work – remedying defects. Went to Croydon – ordered work at steeple. Went to Addington.
May 24	Sent Col. Hume a description in writing of the best method to rebuild Inverary Bridge – – 2.
June 12	Surveyed a house and offices in Grosvenor Place for Lord Abingdon, and gave an opinion thereon for the purchase thereof. – – – 2. Went to stay at Croydon.
June 13	Left Croydon. In pocket £2 2s. 9d. Went to Tunbridge.
June 14	Surveyed the County bridge – sounded the river – examined it for half a mile above and below. Took the dimentions of the bridge. Returned to Croydon.
June 16	Sent Col. Hume a design of drawings for his house in Scotland – Nothing.
June 24	Gave Mr. Children a report on the bridge at Tunbridge. Expenses and all – 8.
June 29	Sent the Duke of Argyll a design for the ceiling of a room at Inverary. Procured and sent the papier mâché for the same – £5 5s. 0d. Paid carriage. 10s. 8d.
July 1	Set out for Staffordshire. In pocket – £15 12s. 0d.
July 2	Halted opposite Tusmore. Then at Mr. Mathews.
July 6	Set out from Envil – In pocket £8 10s. 6d. Examined Hagley at Brooms Grove.
July 7	Examined Ditchley. At Middleton Stoney.
July 8	At Tusmore. In pocket – £12.
July 12	Arrived in London.
July 22	Went to Wormley; surveyed bridge putting up. Returned to London.

July 29	Treasurer Berners reported the dividend to be 166 and it was restored to make it 160 for last half year. Looked into Mr. Bridgins wine vaults and found them completed – Nothing.
July 30	Wrote Lord Stamford – sent a sketch of a house and offices for Envil, and a plan of the principal floor. Sent Col: Hume a bill of Pozoluna – £38 16s. 6d.
Aug. 4	Went to Ware. Called at Wormley – inspected setting up of bridge. Set out the work of gauge – Met Mr. Richardson, Mr. Pindon and Osborne. Returned to London.
Aug. 26	Sent Mr. Hill a drawing for a lodge at the corner of the road, going up to his house at Torn. – – – 3.
Sept. 15	Went to Southgate; inspected Wilds Flash. Returned to London.
Sept. 18	Went to Ware. Inspected Works gauge, the long bank by Springhead, landmarks. Returned to London.
Sept. 25	Went to Ware. Inspected work at gauge. Set the first stone, a $\frac{1}{4}$-inch above the stone mark and one-inch above the iron bar part of old gauge. Called at Wormleybury – inspected bridge. Returned to London.
Oct. 14	Went to Wild's Flash, near Southgate; set out work of new arches, etc. Returned to London.
Oct. 22	Went to Ware. Visited works at Islington. Do. at Southgate. In pocket: £10 12s. 0d. and horses: 12s. 0d.
Oct. 25	Examined and found completely finished the bridge at Wormley. Called at Southgate and Islington. Returned to London.
Nov. 1	Set out for Tunbridge. At Tunbridge.
Nov. 2	Examined at Somerhill the stone for bridge. Visited Tunbridge Wells.
Nov. 3	Returned to Croydon.
Nov. 6	Went to Southgate – examined brickwork. Ordered stonework – let water into new cut.
Nov. 18	Set out for Warwick. At Maidenhead Bridge.
Nov. 22	Left Warwick – examined and surveyed Barford Bridge. Examined Mr. Lucy's Bridge, building at Charlecote. At Chapel House.
Nov. 23	Arrived in London. In pocket £6 5s. 4d.
Nov. 24	Attended Westminster Hall on Crooks Law Suit by desire of City Solicitor.
Dec. 7	Sent Mr. Children 3 washed drawings for rebuilding Tunbridge Old Bridge – – 6.
Dec. 23	Sent Mr. Owen drawings as for all the mouldings of a Great Room, small bow window room, and staircase, at Brungwyn, at large – – – 3.
Dec. 30	Wrote Mr. Mytton on roof of his house and sent him a small drawing in lines thereof. – – – 3.

Memo. at end of year 1773.
  Laid out in Books last year – £12 14s. 6d.
  In hay, straw and oats. – £16 1s. 0d.
  Carriage and harness. – £6 5s. 2d.
  Furniture bought to this time Jan. 7th. 1774. – Cash – £605 0s. 0d.
  Repairs and alterations of house to do..£713 19s. 6d.

Jan. 5   Sent Mr. Taylor of Warwick – a report on the state of Barford Bridge, with an alteration of a drawing and a letter. – – – 10.

Jan. 10   Went to Ware on Gauge, map, and Dunster's Law Suit. At Ware.

Jan. 12   Sent Mr. Greenway a report on Warwick Bridge, with additions to some drawings, letter to the Mayor, etc. – – – 15.

Jan. 14   Wrote Mr. Mytton on the roof of his house with long directions on method of new covering it, without altering the timbers. – – – 3.

Jan. 24   Mr. Mytton called a long conversation about his roof, various chimneys, saloon, etc. – – – 2.

Jan. 25   Settled the Cash Book for Disbursements for house or otherwise, by Mr. Mathews and found £15 10s. 0d. balance in my favour, ending 31st Dec. 1773.

Jan. 27   Mr. Treasurer declared dividend for last half year to be 132 which, added to 105£ a share reserved, makes 137 for this dividend.

Feb. 1   Gave Mr. Mytton some further directions in writing about the roof. Altered some drawings for his saloon, and a chimney piece for do. which is to be made in London. – – – ½.

Feb. 5   Went to Addington. Ordered works, etc. at Croydon.

Feb. 6   Surveyed steeple of Church; inspected the works done – ordered the remainder. Expenses 11–6d.

Feb. 7   Told Archbishop of meetings with Messrs. Heathfield, Parker & Buswick, and that there was little opportunity of obtaining Buswick's lease. – – – 3.

Feb. 10   Waited on Mr. Ryder twice, furnished him a printed plan of Argyll House altered, and explained the situation and value of all the premises on the subject of the mortgage for Argyll. House: – – –1.

Feb. 14   Sent Mr. Ryder new description of parcells for mortgage of house bought by D. of Argyll from Mr. Hodsell – ½.

Mar. 9   Attended on a view by desire of Mr. Prix with Mr. Harley and Dr. Ellis, about D. of C. of Rochester's ground in Fleet Ditch, and wrote Mr. Towpenny, their agent, thereon. – – – 1½.

Mar. 10   Gave Mr. Hillman alteration of a cottage, and a drawing of a gate adjoining, with some advice about River, Mill etc. – – – 1½.

Mar. 13   Sent Mr. Loydd 2 drawings on parchment for the contract of Newcastle Bridge, which together with all the meetings, letters and writings for said contract put at over and above the Surveyors work. – – – – 10.

Mar. 14   Gave D. of Argyll drawing for front of new town for Inverary. – – 3.

Mar. 15   Attended Court of Aldermen at Guildhall, on title to Pocock's houses, Fleet Ditch. – 1. Nothing done. Attended meeting of Committee on D. of C. of Rochester's Memorial (postponed). – ½.

Mar. 16	Gave Mr. Owen designs for 3 chimney pieces to be made by Pinder in town.
Mar. 20	Gave Mr. Southwell a drawing of the fronts of the Toll House, for a lodge. Made him a present of it.
Mar. 22	Attended at Guildhall on Com'ee for Surrey Cross Road. Attended H: of Commons on Glasgow B. Bill.
Mar. 29	Attended the Comm'ee on D: and Chapter of Rochester's demand. No business done. Wrote Mr. Towpenny on the business.
Apr. 2	Gave Mr. Mytton two plans of the end of his house for making accessarys thereto, with description how to make the same. – – 1.
Apr. 20	Gave Mr. Mytton a drawing of an Tee wall and stable over it. – 2. Gave Mr. Mytton a design for an ornamental ceiling for Dining Room, at Brungwyn, and mouldings thereof at large. – 5.
Apr. 30	Wrote Mr. Owen's man, Stevenson, a long letter on method of finishing staircase and some rooms at Brungwyn, with sketches of mouldings and stair rail. – 2. Sent a drawing for embellishing the Pidgeon House and making it into an ornamental building.
May 6	Sent the Duke of Argyll a drawing of a large shed erecting at Inverary, altered in the roof and upper parts of it, with some directions. – 1.
May 8	Gave Mr. Murray a section for library and drawing of bookcases – 2½. 14 B: were sent in two casks.
May 14	Gave Mr. Hill a drawing for a new bridge over the Tern, near his house in Shropshire, 10.
May 28	Went to Quarter Sessions at Ryegate with Mr. Cox – No Business done. Went to inspect a bridge on the Turnpike Road at the desire of Mr. Barnes; surveyed it and prescribed a method to keep it in repair. – 2.
May 30	Removed family to Islington.
June 10	Received from Leutt Scott on Mr. Carmichael's account, in the East Indies, 373 ounces of silver in bullion – value £97 18s. 3d.
June 16	Set out for Staffordshire & Shropshire. At Dunstable. In pocket:—£21 5s. 3d. Ded. paid coachman: 19s. 6d. Add for own horses: 10s. 6d.
June 17	At Hales Owen near the Lepower.
June 18	At Envill, set out for Shropshire, Lord Stanford being from home. At Tern, near Shrewsbury. In pocket – £12 12s. 0d.
June 19	Left Tern, after surveying grounds, and at Sundorn, near Shrewsbury.
June 20	Surveyed house, offices grounds, etc. and took directions for an alteration of the whole and two buildings on the top of the hill. Left Sundorn. At Onslow; surveyed house, offices, and took directions, for altering it.

June 21	Left Onslow – went to Condover, by Shrewsbury. Surveyed house and recomended severall alterations and improvements on house, by a list in writing. Returned from Condover –. At Shrewsbury.
June 22	Set out for Woodhouse.
June 23	Surveyed new offices, recomended alterations of house and offices; alterations of kitchen, garden, etc. Took directions for a house and poultry yard. At Woodhouse.
June 24	Set out for Brungwyn. Surveyed new house and old offices; recomended some alterations and improvements. Left Brungwyn. At Loton Hall.
June 25	Surveyed house, offices, grounds and approach; recomended many alterations and improvements by a list in writing out afterwards – 2. Left Loton Hall. Dined at Shrewsbury. At Tern.
June 26	Rode round the ground, recomend altering the aproach of roads to house, taking away mill, making entrance on east side of house; altering stairs, etc. etc. – – 5. Left Tern. At Bridgnorth.
June 27	Arrived at Envill. Surveyed situation of house.
June 28	Fixed on a new site for house, etc. and took directions for making a plan. Set out for London. At Shipton.
June 29	Arrived in London. In pocket £7 1s. 0d.
July 11	Went to Cobham and Leatherhead, Surry. Surveyed the two bridges. Met Mr. Parker. Nothing. Expenses 18s. At Wooden.
July 12	Sent two drawings to Mr. Parker, one a brick bridge for Cobham, the other a wooden superstructure for Leatherhead bridge, with a letter thereon – Nothing.
July 21	Christened 3rd daughter, Harriett.
July 28	Mr. Treasurer declared the dividend of N.R.O. to be 163 on the last Holy year, and 5£ per share being reserved out of it, it was settled at 158.
July 30	Sent Mr. Woodhouse a design for a foot bridge coloured, with a drawing in lines, for execution, particulars, etc. and letter thereon. – – 4.
Aug. 8	At Burton-on-Trent; in pocket £4 13s. 6d. Went to Walton. Surveyed Mr. Taylour's house and place; considered offices and took memorandums for new. At Pailthorp near Sherwood Forest.
Aug. 16	At Edinburgh.
Aug. 21	Settled with Messrs. Brown & Sons for all payments and receipts to this day and find £22 19s. 1d. ballance due me.
Aug. 24	Went over to Fife. At Col. Hume's at Pitlour.
Aug. 25	Surveyed the situation for a new house.
Aug. 26	Went to Perth and returned to Pitlour.
Aug. 27	Wrote Col. Hume a report on making a mound or dam below Inverary Bridge and the placing of the bridge. Waiting on Col. Hume, letters, etc. – 2. Left Pitlour.
Aug. 28	Saw Balfargie and Lesly house. Returned to Poutherhall.
Sept. 4	Went westward. At Linlithgow – examined Pallace, etc.

98

Sept. 11 Set out for Glasgow. At Glasgow. Surveyed the state of the Old Bridge, river, etc. Inspected the New Bridge.

Sept. 12 Gave a long report by word of mouth to the Magistrate of Glasgow on scheme for building and addition to the Old Bridge, etc. Returned to Edinburgh.

Sept. 17 Set out for the South.

Sept. 18 At Newcastle. In pocket £9 17s. 9d.

Sept. 19 Settled all the bridge affairs. Came to an agreement with the Corporation about the houses on Tyne Bridge. Satisfied about the water way under Bishop's part of Bridge, and ruins in river.

Sept. 20 Left Newcastle. At Bishop Auckland.

Sept. 22 Examined several things about the Castle, and gave advice on drains and plaister to New Rooms; garden walls, stairs, chimneys, etc. – 2.

Sept. 24 Arrived in London. In Pocket – 2.

Oct. 1 Attended St. Margaret's Hill on Trial with Crook about ground in new Road.

Oct. 5 Sent Mr. Corbel a design for adding to, altering and improving his house at Sundorn, consisting of two plans, 2 elevations, washed. – 20 G.

Oct. 8 Sent Mr. Morhall a design for an addition to his house at Onslow, and considerable alterations thereon, consisting of 2 plans and 2 elevations, rough with written directions. – 10.

Oct. 19 Sent Lord Stamford a design for a new house at Envill, consisting of 5 plans and an elevation, all washed, neat and large. – £35.

Oct. 20 Sent Mr. Owen at Brungwyn drawings at large in lines, on thick paper, for cornices of Dining Room, Hall, and Bed Chambers – $1\frac{1}{2}$.

Oct. 23 Sent Mr. Owen a drawing, washed, for a chimney piece to Hall at Brungwyn, with mouldings at large, and put another one for Dining Room in hand to be made by Mr. Pindar, consisting of a drawing in lines and mouldings at large. – 2.

Oct. 26 Sent to Mr. Wilson at Glasgow, drawing for improving, altering and widening the old bridge at Glasgow, and a form of a proposal for executing the same, writing Mr. Wilson and Dunlop on these subjects fully. – – – 20.

Nov. 1 Sent Mr. Corbet a design of a castle to be erected on the top of a hill, consisting of an elevation, section and plans, all washed. 10. Sent also a design for new modelling some of the offices at Sundorn House, and adding new ones in the room of those to be pulled down. – Writing a letter thereon. – – 6.

NB By this it appears that £13   5   0 and
7   3   6

£20   0   6 was paid into Mr. Brown's hands at Edinburgh.

| Nov. 18 | Sent a bill of Pozzolana and expenses to Newcastle Bridge, amounting to:— | £24 | 7 | 0 |

| Pozzolana – 126 Bush. | 22 | 1 | 0 |
| Expenses. | £2 | 6 | 0 |

Dec. 7 Sent to Ed'r. £70 by Mr. Donaldson's hands to pay part of Howison's purchase – and £8 to pay Mr. Laing the repairs of house in Leith.

Dec. 10 Went to Richmond to survey a piece of ground for Lady St. Aubyn on Richmond Hill, making enquiries, etc. – 2 expenses.

Dec. 13 Send a man on horseback with proposal for ground at Richmond. Drawing proposal, making valuation, etc. – – 3. expenses.

Dec. 23 Attended Mr. Ryder on the plan of the lease renewal by Lady Graenwich and others, for the front part of Argyll House, and the value of the terms thereof. – 1.

1775 to 1779

The diaries for 1775 to 1779 record the following items of main interest: April, 1775: Began work at Richmond on Lady St. Aubyn's House. April 29th, 1775: Consulted by Mr. Whitbread, the Brewer, at Chiswell Street. September 14th, 1775: Surveyed the outside of Durham Cathedral. February 22nd, 1777: Reported on Rochester Cathedral. April 3rd, 1777: Works at Inveraray Castle. July 11th, 1778: Examined Rochester Cathedral. May 30th, 1779: Gave designs for lodges at Addington nr. Croydon.

1775

Memo. at beginning of year:—

For 1774 – Expenses by House Book	£168	8	9	
Cow bought with a Calf	9	0	0	
Coals paid for	17	12	10	
Wine, rum, etc.	28	17	11	
Harry's Board wages with clerk	15	15	0	
Soap and candles	13	3	6	
	£252	18	0	

Taxes paid in 1774	£12	16	0
		1 17	6
		£14 14	2

Jan. 10 Went to Guidea Hall near Romford; examined Binyon's house – took directions for making a plan for altering and enlarging it. Inspected a place where fire was suspected in a bedroom.

Jan. 15 Waited on Mr. Wedderburn at Mitcham and viewed proposition for removing the road bridge and altering the road. Gave advice thereon.

Jan. 23 Attended Lady St. Aubyn and Sir W. Williamson on ground at Richmond Hill; entered into a calculation of the expense and other particulars. Concluded not to do anything in it. – – 2.

Jan. 26 Treasurer declared dividend to be about 149£ for the last half year to Xmas, and the 5£ per share reserved last Midsummer ordered to be reserved still. The Governor buys Mr. Ashfordby's share, and 1/12th of a share at the rate of £7500 a share.

Feb. 2 Sent by the Litchfield coach, to Mr. Taylor, a design of one sheet for altering and improving his office, pulling down part and building others, together with a list and description of some improvements on the principal apartments of the house. – – – 10.

101

Feb. 5	Sent back again to Glasgow the drawings and papers relating to the Old Bridge – altered and improved with a new elevation on the old drawing. Wrote Mr. Dunlop on the subject.
Feb. 12	Agreed with coachman to allow him 2 guineas per annum for buckskin breeches and boots, and that he should have at the rate of 5 guineas a year for the use of his own cloaths hitherto.
Mar. 18	Went to Richmond; took a new plan of the ground and settled in part the Draft of the Lease, and other business.
Mar. 26	Gave Lady St. Aubyn's a report on a method to secure the front of Clowance House with iron straps, etc. after waiting and consulting with Sir H. Williamson several times . . 2.
Mar. 28	Considered an agreement between Mr. Rich and his builder, Allen, about a house in Brownlow Street – looked at the house and gave an opinion on the nature of the bargain. – 2 (Nothing).
Apr. 1	Went out to Richmond – took possession of premises for Lady St. Aubyn – ordered to be pulled down in part. Paid deposit, etc.
Apr. 11	Took Mr. Games, on trial, as Clerk at 40£ a year – to live in the house – and to do no other business.
Apr. 16	Sent Mr. Cooke of Great Russell an opinion of advice on his ground in Lambeth Marsh, and the letting it on a building lease. – Nothing.
Apr. 19	Gave Mr. Owen a sketch of altering kitchen, etc. and making a porch for keeping smell out of the house. At Woodhouse. – 2.
Apr. 29	Waited on Mr. Whitbread in Chiswell Street. A long consultation on method of making cisterns for beer.
May 5	Sent Mr. Owen two drawings in lines for making a Flower Hot House at Brungwyn – 2.
May 6	Went with Bishop of Durham to Wimbledon. Surveyed and inspected Lady Banks's place for a purchase – opinions, etc. – 2. Quitted possession of stables in town.
May 16	Surveyed L. M. Duncan's house in Qn. Anne's Street. Considered Mr. Prumbold's proposal. Reported opinion to Mr. Woodcock; writing letters, waiting on Capt. Duncan, etc. etc. – 5.
May 17	Attended Lady St. Aubyn, with Mr. Rawlinson, and had a long conference on the defective front of Clowance House.
May 18	Sent Mr. Smith (Aldermanbury) a drawing after a sketch of his own, for a farmhouse in Oxfordshire. – Nothing.
May 21	Sent Sr. George Colebrook a letter on the state of and rebuilding Reigate Bridge, having visited twice. – – 0.
May 26	Set out for Yarmouth, to examine the Bridge. Passed through Ipswich – lay at Ulverstone at Mr. Berners.
May 28	Inspected Bridge – Haven and Roads – town. Received directions about design for a New Bridge at Yarmouth.
May 29	Sounded the Harbour. Measured the Bridge and Wharfs adjoining, etc. etc. Left Yarmouth. At Norwich.

May 30	Went to North – Elmham – took directions for a design for a Bridge – measured the place, etc. Returned to Norwich.
May 31	Returned to London.
June 3	Went to Richmond – set out house – approved of the plan – agreed for £900 the carcase.
June 10	Gave Mr. Cook a report on his estate of old houses in Lambeth Marsh, and best method of letting the same – in a letter. – Nothing.
June 11	Gave Lady St. Aubyn a survey of an estate in White Cross Street, with a minute plan at large coloured, and valuation thereof, of £1,438. – £14 9s. 0d.
June 13	Went to Wormleybury.
June 14	Set out the plan of a Cold Bath. Returned to London.
June 19	Went on survey, on wharfing in Mr. Tashmakers garden – a drain in Mr. Clark's ground – Bushill Frame – and Flash on Enfield Chace, with Mr. Garmaull and Cressy.
June 26	Waited on Lady St. Aubyn, on White Cross Street estate – gave advice on the method of selling it, etc. – – 1.
June 28	Wrote Mr. Rawlinson on defect on Clowance House, after having waited Ly. St. Aubyn. – 1.
June 30	Looked at Mrs. Bridge's house and Lord Ossory's in Grosvenor Square for B. of Durham – wrote him on the subject. – – 1.
July 9	Went to Wormleybury. Inspected building for a bath.
July 15	Set out for Tonbridge. Surveyed temporary bridge – and old bridge taking down, and set out the work of new.
July 29	Went to Bushill – Endfield, and Endfield Chace; surveyed Frame – leadwork – and Flash. Ordered work, etc.
July 31	Wrote Mr. Miller and sent him 3 drawings at large of a Bridge, over a small stream. – 10. This is the 3rd set – 2 having been lost by my servants.
Aug. 1	Set out for Tonbridge. Surveyed Old Bridge – ordered all the work, etc. Returned to London.
Aug. 3	Set out for the North. At Hatfield – In pocket – £15 9s. 8d. Paid for a place to B. Bridge – £2 11s. 6d.
Aug. 12	At Gateshead. Pozolana money £23 12s. 6d.
Aug. 14	Set out for the North. At Edinburgh.
Aug. 21	Left Edinburgh – set out for the North. Dined at Borowstiniss. At Carron. In pocket £9 19s. 0d. Gave driver. £1 1s. 0d.
Aug. 22	At Drumin near Loch Lomond and Duke of Monbro'.s place of Buchanan. Cross Loch L: in a boat. At Inverary.
Aug. 24	Looked at site of Dairy farm, etc. at Kilbryde. Do. of a lodge at Garron Bridge.
Aug. 26	Inspected all the works of the Military Bridge; compared it with the drawings; wrote a long letter of observations and alterations thereof to Col. Skene. To the Driver – £1 1s. 0d. paid at Inverary – 16s. 0d.
Aug. 28	Left at Inverary. At Dunbarton.

Aug. 29 Examined works of Military Bridge; left directions of several things to be done with Mr. Mache or Mill. At Glasgow.
To driver   £1   1   0

In all   3   3   –
Deduct for a ferry   3   –

                        £3   –   –

Aug. 30 Reconsidered the design of additions to the Old Bridge; long conversation with the Magistrates and Shaw on the subject – with advice – – – 3. Horses knocked up at Calder – took post-ch. In pocket 18*s.* Returned to Edinburgh.

Sept. 3 Waited on Col. Skene – long consultation on Inverary Bridge – wrote him another letter enforcing the purport of the former. – – 1.

Sept. 7 Left Edinburgh. Saw Dalkeith House. At Sr. G. Dalrymple's. Cranstown.

Sept. 8 Saw Crighton and Borthwick Castles. Saw Lauder House. At Smallholm.

Sept. 9 Examined Kelso Bridge. At Newcastle. In pocket – £12 3*s.* 0*d.* Spent – £3 9*s.* 0*d.*

Sept. 13 Set out from Gateside – In pocket £11 13*s.* 0*d.* At Durham.

Sept. 14 Took a complete survey of all the outside of Durham Cathedral, and minutes for a Report to the Dean and C. thereon. Left Durham. At Bishop Auckland.

Sept. 17 Left Bishop Auckland. In pocket £9 9*s.* 0*d.* Saw Raby Castle. Horses taken up from grass. At Mr. Vane's of Selaby.

Sept. 18 Took the Newcastle fly at B. Bridge; to do: £3 1*s.* 2*d.* At Wetherby.

Sept. 20 At London. In pocket £3 19*s.* 0*d.*

Sept. 27 Wrote the D. of Argyll, and sent a drawing of iron railing round the Castle, with directions. – – 2.

Oct. 5 Discharged coachman. Wrote the D. of Argyll on balusters of Inverary Bridge.

Oct. 6 Sent Mr. Spurgeon, for the Mayor and Corporation of Yarmouth, a report in writing on the Old and the New Bridge, with a design of an elevation, plan and 4 sections – all washed, for a New B.

Oct. 8 Went to Tonbridge.

Oct. 9 Set out the levells of the street, and ends of the Bridge. Returned to London.

Oct. 14 Went to Highbury; fitted machine to Stop gate. Went to Bushill frame – inspected new drain; ordered leadwork of frame to be raised. Went to Endfield Chace. Inspected new work of Flash; ordered alterations.

Oct. 29 Went to Hindon Place; looked at a House, paddock, etc. for Mr. Davenport. Gave opinion of the value, etc. 2.

Nov. 1 Appointed by the B: of Governors of Greenwich Hospitall, Clerk of the Works there. Attendance at the Admiralty.

Nov. 3 Saltershall.

37 NEW RIVER: MONUMENTAL PLINTH

38 WARWICK
BRIDGE: Detail of
balustrade and
end pier with
Coade stone orna-
ments. *See also
Fig. 41*

39 TUSMORE, OXFORDSHIRE: Entrance front as carried out

40 TUSMORE, OXFORDSHIRE: South front as carried out

Nov. 15   Sent Mr. Hogg, for the Dean and Chapter of Durham, a long report of 16 pages on the best method of repairing the outside of Durham Cathedral.

Dec. 6   Gave the D. of Argyll a design for a Dairy farm house with a large room over it, proposed to be erected on the side of Loch Fyne, Inverary. Elevation, section, 2 plans. – 16. Gave him also a design of 2 elevations, plan, and section, of a lodge and gate for the entrance into the park at Inverary, near the Bridge and fronting the Loch – all washed neatly – 8.

Memo: 1*st Aug.* 1775 –

Found on the examination of the workmanship of Tonbridge Bridge, now taking down, that several of the crop joints of the ribs of the arches (tho' not all) were joined with a stuff composed of hair and (to all appearances) pitch or tar and other. It burns in the candle when dryed. This mixture was gone towards the outer edges of the joints, but remainded in the middle parts entire.

1776

Jan. 3   Sent Mrs. Trecothick a drawing for a monument, washed, in one sheet, and wrote her thereon.

Jan. 31   Salters Hall.

Feb. 1   Treasurer pronounced that last year's dividend was £145, and taking £5 from money reserved made it £150.

Feb. 16   Attended Stationers Company on sale of old houses. At the Admiralty.

Feb. 19   Gave the Duke of Argyll a plan with elevations and sections, on the same sheet, of making the buildings behind the garden into a complete farmyard. – – 5.

Mar. 2   Gave the Directors of Greenwich Hosp: a survey of their estate on St. Peter's Hill. – 5. Greenwich Hosp:

Mar. 25   Executed a new lease of Mrs. John's House for 14 years, after cancelling the old one. Increase of rent £10 for last 7 years.

Mar. 29   Sent Col. Hume a long letter on the state of Inverary Bridge, and advice thereon. – – 5.

May 10   Waited on Lady St. Aubyn, with a draft of Agreement for taking down the front of Blowance House and rebuilding it – wrote Mr. Johns and settled him for Executive. Met Mr. Edis, and agreed for the sale of the estate in White Cross Street for £850, and wrote Mr. Wilson thereon.

May 18   Dr. Hunter discharged the Deed of Mortgage on houses in Arundel Street. The principal of £1500 being formerly paid up, and would not take any interest at all, which amounted to £278 more. He returned a Draft for £75 which he got for the first year's interest.

May 30   Sent Lord Stamford drawings at large for 3 cornices for 3 rooms at Envill. – – 1½. Sent Lord Clifford 2 Valuations of his estate of houses and ground rents, in Spring Gardens. – – – 10.

June 15	Gave a plan of part of Hyde Park to explain the scheme for watering Piccadilly – and writing a letter on the quantity consumed. – 6.
June 20	Sent Lord Stamford a drawing of a ceiling for a dining room, washed. – – 3.
June 29	Made a copy of the plan of estate in White Cross Street – on parchment for Mr. Wilson.
July 7	Sent Lord Clifford a design of 2 drawings, washed, of a lodge. – – 3.
Aug. 2	Left London – in pocket – £26 10s. 2d. Dined at Ware – examined and ordered work of gauge – staked out two pieces of ground. At Bedford.
Aug. 11	At Newcastle.
Aug. 17	Arrived at Edinburgh.
Aug. 23	Arrived at Dunbarton – examined the bridges, etc. At Glasgow.
Aug. 24	At Inverary.
Aug. 25	Surveyed the New Bridge – examined the fracture of it – advised some works to be done. –
Aug. 26	Went to the dairy – received instructions how to alter the building. Gave the Duke a design of 4 drawings, washed, for altering the Pidgeon House into a Round Temple. – – 12.
Aug. 27	Fixed on a situation for a New Kirk – a new approach from the new Town, and advised a new Covered Way from the Castle to the Offices. Set out the situation of the Lodge at Garron B: Left Inverary.
Sept. 1	Went over to Fife. At Sir Robert Henderson's.
Sept. 2	At Pitlour. At Sir Robert Henderson's.
Sept. 4	Returned to Edinburgh.
Sept. 9	Left Edinburgh.
Sept. 14	Left Gateshead. At Whitburn near Sunderland.
Sept. 15	Left Sir Hedworth Williamson. At Bishop Auckland.
Sept. 21	Arrived in London. In pocket. £7 1s. 8d.
Oct. 2	Left the Bishop of Durham, a drawing coloured, of new windows for Auckland Castle with the balconys. – – 3.
Oct. 11	Went to survey Cooks and Bisson's Mills.
Oct. 14	Removed family to Greenwich, from Islington.
Nov. 25	Joseph Carter came as Clerk at the rate of £40 salary.

Money advanced for Lady St. Aubyn:—

To the Well Digger on account –	£4	4	0
To the Gardner Wood	12	7	6
To Wedgwood –	4	14	6
	£21	**6**	**0**

Nov. 29	Went to Rochester. Took a general survey of the Cathedral and examination of all its parts, for the purpose of composing a report. Returned to Greenwich.
Dec. 3	Surveyed Field of the Parish of St. Dionis and Company's Land. Ordered some land marks. Visited work at Highbury. Returned to London.

Dec. 11 Wrote to Mr. John's at Clowance; finished the house and settling accounts, etc. – – 2. Waiting on Lady St. Aubyn, thereon.

1777

Jan. 15 Called at Mrs. Coade's; – Wrote Mr. Forsyth 2 letters on stone pipes, for Piccadilly. Waited on Duke of Argyll. Gave a long drawing where Garron Bridge, 2 Lodges, and fence walls, etc. are introduced. – – 4.

Feb. 4 Gave a Report to the Stationers Company on a house in Friars' Alley, of Mrs. Knight, as to the renewal of the lease, etc. surveying it, inspecting old plans, waiting on Court, etc. 3.

Feb. 22 Gave the Dean of Rochester a report in writing on the present state of the Cathedral, and the defective front, with a washed drawing, explanatory of the same, with advice, etc.

Mar. 14 Went and surveyed with Mr. Yeomans, all the streams, mills, etc. of Cooks, Bissons, and others near Bow.

Mar. 31 Sent a drawing for a Bridge in Wales, at the order of Mr. Owen, washed, and writing letter, descriptions, etc. – – 10.

Apr. 3 Gave the Duke of Argyll a design for altering, fitting up and finishing all the windows of the principal floor of Inverary Castle, of a plan, section and elevation, washed neatly. – – 10.

Apr. 11 At Canterbury; went to the new Cut at Stonar. Examined the banks, the river, the haven, etc. at Sandwich. Examined the Cut a 2nd time; the brickwork of bridge, dams, etc. Dined with the Comm'rs. of Sewers; made a report on the state of works at Stonar. Waited on Mr. Benson; nothing proposed to be done at Canterbury.

Apr. 13 Visited and dined with Sir Brook Bridges, at his Seat. At Rochester.

Apr. 14 Returned to London. In pocket £1 12s. 0d.

May 10 Removed to Greenwich.

May 15 Sent Mr. Crewe, near Chester, a set of drawings for altering and fitting up a Dining Room, of a plan and 3 sections, washed. – – 10.

May 21 Gave Mr. N. Hill a plan for laying out his ground, in building a town house in Cleveland Court; two floors only. – – 6. N.B. This was never paid, nor likely to be so, for no business was ever done.

May 31 Sent Sir A. Hume 4 plans of the proposed alterations of his house in Hillitrat, exact and washed, fit for execution.

June 18 At Greenwich. In pocket £21 14s. 5d.

June 19 Set out for Newcastle. Called at Ware – inspected works – altered landmarks to plan, etc. etc. At Royston.

July 8 Arrived in London. In pocket £7 12s. 6d.

July 9 At Saltershall.

Aug. 6 Wrote Mr. Mytton with 2 letters formerly on rough – casting his house or washing it. – 1.

Sept. 23 Set out on survey to Ware. At Highbury Bank. At Bushill, etc.

Sept. 24	At Enfield Flash. At Wormleybury. In pocket – £5 7s. 0d. Horses: £2 8s. 0d. Servants: 15s. 3d.
Sept. 25	At Ware.
Sept. 26	Returned to London.
Oct. 11	Removed from Greenwich to Islington.
Oct. 13	Surveyed a Gateway at Stationers Court and recommended a repair of it. 0.
Oct. 18	Board at Greenwich. Went to Rochester. At Rochester. – In pocket – £5 13s. 0d. Horses: £1 1s. 0d. Man: 4s. 0d.
Oct. 19	Returned to Greenwich.
Oct. 24	Went to Highbury – examined and ordered works. Examined works at Bushill. At Enfield.
Oct. 25	Took off the River at Bushill; set men to work to mend the cracks in lead and brickwork; cleaning river, etc. Returned to Islington.
Oct. 30	Sent Mr. Crave 2 drawings, of 2 plans and 1 section, of a new intended room at Bolesworth Castle, Cheshire. – – – 8.
Nov. 10	Went to Richmond along with Mr. Wilson, to attend on Lady St. Aubyn, on the question of the Bar to the Common. – – – 0.
Nov. 16	Sent to Dr. Hunter – 2 drawings on plan, an elevation and 2 sections of a Mausoleum, to be built at Clowance for the St. Aubyn family. – 10.
Dec. 24	For Bishop of Durham – surveyed the Coterie House in Arlington; reported the state of it; and some discourse on its value.

1778

Jan. 9	Waited on Mr. Cranford; long consultation, about ground in Piccadilly, and supplying his bath with water. – – – 1.
Jan. 10	Wrote Mr. Brown, on the roof of Mr. Wathen's House, after having called twice on Mr. Brown and examined Mr. Wathen's house. – – – 2.
Feb. 23	Sent Mr. Mytton a drawing of a wooden bridge on ropes – plan, elevation and section, washed one sheet, and wrote him upon it.
Feb. 25	Sent Dr. Hunter the drawings of Mausoleum for Sir John St. Aubyn, together with a draft of an Agreement. Wrote Mr. Becherly on former business.
Mar. 9	Sent Mr. Mytton a plan and elevation of a Dorick Temple for a Pidgeon House, washed, 5.
Mar. 10	Gave Mr. Trecothick a plan and elevation of a Lodge for his Park Gates, washed, – 4.
Mar. 16	Called 3rd time at Mr. Millars at the Old Baily about cutting away under warehouse of Stationers Hall; making good, etc. . . . 1½. For Stationers Company.
Mar. 24	Wrote a letter to Mr. Ford, for Mr. Valient about back, front of house in Church Court, after survey made about encroachment. – 1. Nothing for this business.
Mar. 26	Wrote Mr. John's on Mausoleum, at Clowance, with an additional clause to Agreement.

110

Apr. 2	Mother died.
July 10	Set out for Rochester. In pocket £2 17s. 0d.
July 11	Examined Cathedral; ordered some new works.
Aug. 17	Set out for the North. Called at Ware – ordered some works. At Buntingford. In pocket. £7 11s. 2d.
Aug. 23	At Hexham.
Aug. 26	At Drumlanrig.
Aug. 27	Arrived at Leadhills.
Aug. 29	Set out by (?) At Edinburgh. Brought Over – £11 2s. 11d. In pocket – 13s. 10d. Spent. £10 9s. 1d.
Sept. 16	Left Edinburgh. Went by Aberfeldy and by the Bass Isle, and visited Tantallon Castle – No Date – Arms on the arch of entrance, Douglass of one heart and 3 mulletts at one end, and something like a chevron at the other. Buss, a love, – Lava strata – (?) South & North and Dipping East. In pocket – £10 0s. 0d. Spent. £5 14s. 10d. At Dunbar.
Sept. 17	Visited Harbour and Castle with Scots Arms over a door of Great Hall, and one more on each side, lesser defaced. At Dr. Anderson's, Chirnside.
Sept. 24	Left Gateside. In pocket £13 0s. 2d. Saw Lumley Castle, and Cotman. At Durham. Saw Branepeth Castle. At Auckland Castle.
Sept. 27	Left Auckland Castle. At Darlington.
Oct. 30	In London. In pocket £8 3s. 7d.

1779

Apr. 28	Went to Twickenham for Duke of Argyll, to examine and inspect Mr. Giles's villa – waiting on him, treating, etc. – – 2.
Apr. 30	Waited on D. of Argyll – conversation on villas – Called on Christie; agreed for a villa at Old Windsor. do. and was off bargain.
May 29	Went to Newmans Flash; set out plan of brickwork, and the other parts of the work.
May 30	Went to Addington from Greenwich, about Lodges and Gates of Entrance; gave a design for a gatehouse and 2 lodges of 5 drawings, washed. – – 12.
June 13	Sent Mr. Trecothick a drawing in lines of a *Poors* house – a plan and elevation on one sheet. Do. a drawing for an entrance and 2 lodges, near the Tyle Miln – a plan and elevation, small. – – 2.
June 18	Went to Newmans flash. Met bricklayer. Set out dwarf walls and works at ends of arch, etc. etc.
June 22	Examined 3 bills of brickwork for Mr. Trecothick. Done at Addington where work had been set out, but not surveyed. Amounting to £165 labour only. – – 0.
July 29/ Aug.	Went round into many streets of West'r. looking at many houses to let – for Lady St. Aubyn – 2. Clerk has done the same for several days running. 1. Nothing.

111

Aug. 2	Went to Turnham Green; surveyed a house and offices for Mr. Russell – wrote him on the subject, and waited on his brother. – – – 3. Nothing.
Aug. 5	Went and surveyed 2 houses in Lower Grosvenor Street for Lady St. Aubyn and reported opinion to Dr. Hunter. – – Nothing.
Aug. 14	Went and surveyed a house in Lower Grosvenor Street for Lady St. Aubyn – waited on her Ladyship. Made a report on that and the house in Bond Street. – – – Nothing.
Aug. 16	Waited on Mr. Mitford, on house in Bond Street. Treated for taking it.
Aug. 28	Went to Bowes Farm – surveyed work at Newmans Flash – let the River into new Cut for the first time – passed through it in a boat. Ordered the remainder of works, etc.
Sept. 4	Sent Mr. Hawkins, at Stationers Hall, a report on Mr. Terry's house, in Ave Mary Lane, and the terms on which it should be let by the Company after having surveyed it, considered the proposals, etc. – – – 2.
Oct. 12	Removed to Islington.
Nov. 25	Sent Mr. Hooker of Brenchley, four drgs. viz: 2 plans and elevations, washed, and a door at large in lines – done after drawings of a house just built, from the country. – – – 0.
Dec. 19	Young Quibus born at 6 o'clock.

1780 to 1784

The diaries for the years 1780 *to* 1784 *contain the following items of interest*: *March* 30*th*, 1780: *Survey of Rochester Cathedral tower and spire*. *November* 2*nd and* 3*rd*, 1780: *Drawings sent to the Duke of Argyll for Inveraray*. *October* 1*st*, 1782: *Bridge at Broadlands for Lord Palmerston*. *October* 11*th*, 1783: *Surveyed bridge at Hexham*. *June* 2*nd*, 1784: *Designs for Rosneath Castle sent to the Duke of Argyll*.

1780

Mar. 29 Went to Rochester.

Mar. 30 Surveyed Great Tower and Spire of Cathedral. Inspected old repairs of South front, and parapets, etc. etc. Returned to London. Expenses by Dean and Chapter of Rochester. £4 5s. 0d.

Apr. 7 Set out for Shropshire.

Apr. 8 At Shrewsbury. In pocket £25 2s. 6d.

Apr. 9 At Berwick. In pocket £30 0s. 0d. Own horses to Barnet: 14s. 0d.

a/c For a great coat £1 10s. 0d.

Apr. 13 At Whitchurch; went to call at Meers; surveyed house, offices, grounds, etc.

Apr. 17 At home; in pocket £18 13s. 0d.

Brought over:	£35	4	0
Add:	10	10	0
	45	14	0
Deduct:	1	11	0
Hut:	44	3	0
Remaining:	£18	13	0

To be divided by 3) 1 10 0 (£8 10s. 0d. each. gentleman:—Sir Rob't. Cotton. Mr. Pourys, and Mr. Loydd.

May 15 Went on survey of the River with Mr. Rowe. At Highbury. Returned to London.

May 17 Set out for Ware. At Bushill; ordered several works at Wormley Flash – set out a New Cut – met farmer – no agreement. At Ware.

May 18 Visited Ballance Engine, gauge, etc. etc. Ordered some works – At Bushill, At Horsney – on Flash. Returned to London.

May 19	£2 12s. 5d., £1 10s. 0d. own horses. 5s. 0d. turnpikes. Expenses by New River Co: £4 7s. 6d.
June 30	Surveyed Duke of Argyll's house in Marlborough Street, to see if repairs had been done by Mr. Brilly, tenant, at Mr. Ryder's request.
July 8	Removal to Greenwich.
July 11	Sent Mr. Loydd of Aston a design for a new house and altering old house into offices – consisting of 4 plans, 2 sections, and elevations of the house itself, and one large plan of the house, offices, etc. all washed. – – 25.
July 17	Sent Mr. Powys, near Shrewsbury, a plan of additions and alterations to his house, consisting of – one plan of principal storey, and a plan altered of house and offices:—which last was extensive – see 4th Sept.
July 25	Sent Mr. Pigot a design for an addition to the Rectory house at Edgemond, consisting of 3 plans, and an elevation, washed neat. 15.
Aug. 10	Gave the Stationers Company a Report on the renewing Mr. Barnard's case, after surveying the same. – – 2.
Aug. 21	Went to Highbury, about pulling up sluice and bridges. Then to Wormley Flash; set out new works, etc. Wrote Mr. Harrison for Dean & Chapter of Rochester, a long letter on repairs in hand and method of repairing a defective truss in the roof. 2.
Aug. 22	Returned to London.
Aug. 28	Went to Wormley; surveyed flash – set out further part of Cut, bridge, etc. etc.
Aug. 29	Returned to London. £1 7s. 0d. Own horses – £1 0s. 0d. Expenses by New River Co. i.e. £2 7s. 0d.
Sept. 4	Sent Mr. Powys – 4 plans and 1 elevation of his house, shewing the proposed addition in all its parts – one floor being a duplicate of one formerly sent. – – £25.
Sept. 6	Sent Duke of Argyll – to Mr. Farier at Edinburgh, drawings for ceilings of the best rooms at Inverary Castle:—Saloon, Drawing Room, Dining Room & Small Hall; drawings neat, finished, and fit for execution: 30.
Sept. 7	Treaty with Mr. Papworth for making moulds for the same. – – 0.
Sept. 9	Set out for Rochester. At Mr. Campbell's at Halley.
Sept. 10	At Rochester – surveyed part of the Cathedral, next to Great Tower; directed how to restore the rotten timber boarding, etc.
Sept. 11	Surveyed the defective East Side of South Cross Aisle; prescribed temporary shores and struts, and took minutes for a report on the whole. – – 3. Returned to Greenwich.
Oct. 1	Set out for Norfolk. In pocket: £34 17 0
	deduct 8 6
	c/o £34 9 6

Oct. 2	Visited and surveyed Wormley Flash. Visited & surveyed river at Ware. At Cambridge.

$$
\begin{array}{rrrr}
 & £34 & 9 & 6 \\
\text{deduct} & 3 & 7 & 6 \\
\hline
 & 31 & 2 & 0 \\
\text{deduct.} & 7 & 5 & 0 \quad \text{spent at Yarmouth.} \\
\hline
 & £23 & 17 & 0 \\
\end{array}
$$

Oct. 3	At Lynn.
Oct. 4	At Houghton Hall. At Wells.
Oct. 7	Left Wells; called at Warham – to wait Sir M. Folleres and Mr. Hales. At Norwich.
Oct. 11	Left Yarmouth. At Beccles.
Oct. 13	At London. 12 days

$$
\begin{array}{r}
7 \\
\hline
19 \quad \text{Sir Y. Turner. In pocket £7 15s. 0d.}
\end{array}
$$

Nov. 2	Sent the Duke of Argyll, by the Post Coach, a parcel of drawings in a roll, for finishing parts of 4 large rooms at Inverary. See a list thereof. Carriage.
Nov. 3	Sent a drawing of a plan, elevation and section of a shed to be built at the Great Square of farm offices at Inverary, in room of one intended by great drawing formerly. – – 3. Wrote the Duke and Mr. Haswell on do.
Nov. 21	Went with L. M. Duncan to Hanwell, Acton Churches, to search for a proper place of Interment, etc. – – 2.

1781

Jan. 7	Went to Ware. Surveyed Wormley flash and works, Do. premises near road bridge, at Broxburn, at Ware.
Jan. 9	Surveyed a house in Hine Street, pop'd by Mr. Parcel, belonging to Mr. Cox, in mortgage to Mr. Duram's for £3,000. Reported to Mr. D: and Mr. Smith it was not a sufficient security. – – 2.
Jan. 26	Surveyed Mr. Watkins house in Bond Court, and the settlement of all internal partitions, etc. Gave advice – wrote to Mr. Brown.
Feb. 9	Went to Ware; visited works at Broxburn Bridge, and at Ware, etc. Returned to London.
Feb. 12	Surveyed a house in Stationers Court (for the Company) late Mr. Johnson. Made a report in writing to Mr. Wilkie thereon, with terms of lease, etc. – – 2.
Feb. 14	Took another survey of Mr. Watkin's house in Walbrook, and wrote him on shores to be put up in cellar. – – – 1.
Mar. 5	Sent to Inverary, by order of D. of Argyll, a new drawing for the sheds round the Courtyard of farm offices at Malt-land, with plan, elevation and section. (3) Wrote Mr. Haswell a

letter of explanation and surveyed along with Mr. Wyat, Mr. Watham's house in Walbrook; ordered Corporation to shore up the sunk partition.

Mar. 9   Went to Bull's Cross; set out work of wharfs, etc. at Mr. Leverton's. Visited work at Broxbourne Bridge, to get trees down, etc. Went to Ware on work of River Bridge, trees, etc. etc.

Mar. 12   Surveyed (for Stationers Company) a house in Stationers Court, late Mr. Johnson's, and made a report on the farm of a new lease. – – 2.

Mar. 22   Sent the Dean & Chapter of Rochester a report on the defects and remedy of piers and arches near the Chapter House doors, with two plans and a sketch section. 8.

Apr. 16   Went to Ware; visited works at Broxburn Bridge and Church. Then at Ware and Amwell – marked trees; stalked out addition to river. Returned to London.

Note   Window and House Tax at Greenwich   £1 17   0
Land Tax on house at do.   £1   8   0
A Church rate for same.   17   6
For a load of hay.   £3   0   0

May 9   Gave Mr. Foster a long report on Wells Harbour, referring to maps, etc. etc. – 20.

May 11   Cancelled Mr. Paterson's note of £505. on the Receiver General of the Land Tax, and took another for £300.

May 21   Went a survey of New River with Mr. Rowe; begun it at Hornsey. Stop'd. at far end of Prescott's Park, at Waltham Crop.

May 22   Ended at Ballance Engine – returned to town.

Aug. 2   Set off for Wells.

Aug. 10   At London. In pocket – £4 14s. 8d.

Aug. 31   Left London. Visited works at Bushill. Ordered mattess to frame, etc., – brick sewer at Bull Beggars Hole;
do. near Prescott's Park.
do. at Ware.
do. at Wormley Flash.
do. at Spittle Brook sewer. wharfery, banks, etc. At Ware.

Sept. 1   Set out with Mr. and Miss Selby for the North.

Sept. 5   At Edinburgh.

Sept. 29   Board at Greenwich. Left Edinburgh. At Alnwick.

Sept. 30   Examined Newcastle Bridge. At Durham.

Oct. 3   At London. In pocket £1 1s. 0d.

Oct. 12   Removed family to Greenwich.

Oct. 18   For the Stationers Company; took a survey a 2nd time of Mr. Johnson's house, Avemary Lane. Made a report by letter on that, and on the Barber's house.

Nov. 5   Sent Mr. Trecothick, drawings in lines for carvings to mouldings of Drawing Room. – – 1.

Nov. 12   Attended at King's Bench Westn. to be sworn in the cause between Wathen and Flight.

Dec. 22   Removed family to town.

116

Jan. 8	Paid bills of £324 16s. 3d. work done for Mr. Rivington which, as an old friend, I surveyed for nothing.
Jan. 18	Settled with Mr. Crunden the value of Mr. Cox's house in Hine street; sold to Mr. Durund for £1,550 – surveying it twice, taking dimentions, etc. etc. in all (10) including 2 on Ga. Tany. 1781.
Feb. 19	Attended Mr. Michel into Spitelfields to examine and consider of 7 houses whose leases are expired.
Mar. 3	Set out for Hampshire. At Farnham. In pocket: £20 15s. 9d., own horses: 12s. 0d.
Mar. 4	At Romsey. At Broadlands. In pocket. £15 15s. 0d.
Mar. 5	Went to Southampton. At Daman's.
Mar. 6	Set out for London. At house. In pocket £11 10s. 1d.
Mar. 13	Sent Mr. Durnford, Clerk of the Peace for Southampton, a report on the state of Romsey Bridge, and rebuilding thereon.
Mar. 16	Draft for £102 8s. 6d.
Mar. 17	Sent Lord Palmerston, copy of my report on Romsey Bridge.
Apr. 8	Sent Mr. Raven, the Dy. Clerk of the Peace at Winchester, a design of 2 plans, one elevation, and 2 sections, (all washed neat) for Romsey Bridge, and wrote on method of executing and contracting for building the same.
NB	To Mr. Maynard, Bill of Stockings. £1 1s. 0d.
June 1	Hay and straw for Greenwich £1 11s. 6d.
June 4	Set out for Winchester. In pocket. £12 16s. 6d. At Murrel Grove.
June 6	At Winchester. At Arlesford.
June 7	In London. In pocket £2 13s. 6d.
June 25	Went to Carshalton, from thence with Mr. Duran to a farm in Potters Lane. Surveyed house, offices, and outhouses. Recommended alterations and repairs, and method of proceedings. Pointed out the works to be done to the workmen. – – 2.
NB	To Mr. Cheese, Butchers Bill for last quarter - £9 17s. 9d.
July 14	Jon Thomas born in the morning. Who died.
Sept. 8	Went to Hornsey – at Wormley. New Walthsman – grass – spring in Ballance Engine. At Ware.
Sept. 9	Mr. Prior, Amwell, Spital Brook, Mudpassers. Returned to Islington.
Sept. 13	Went to Rochester. In pocket £3 4s. 10d. To Dartford – own horses 16s.
Sept. 14	Surveyed works at Cathedral, found all right, and columns on east side put into proper order. Returned to Greenwich.
Sept. 29	Set out for Ramsey. at Popham Lane.
Sept. 30	At Winchester – waited on Lord Banbury at Romsey. Begun throwing water out of foundation. Found it very easy, and the Coffer Dam very tight. Determined the foundations to be 6 feet below.
Oct. 1	Laid the first stone of Romsey New Bridge with Lord Palmerstone.

Oct. 2	Nothing but an endless depth of peat in foundation.
Oct. 19	At London.
Oct. 21	Left London. Visited repairs of stop gate, waste gate, etc. at Hornsey. Visited repairs of frame at Bushill. At Ware.
Oct. 22	Set out work at Mr. Prior's, Ware end, etc. Went to Stanstead, Amwell and St. Margaret's Churches, about Lady Mary Duncan's burying place. Visited Crescent Flash and mud panners. At London.
Oct. 27	Son Tommy died.
Nov. 1	Met Mr. Ryder; consultation on value of ground rent of L. Greenwich, etc. and on the house in Mar. Street, as to what was to be done to it. – – 1.
Nov. 4	Attended Mr. Ryder to house in Mar. Street and surveyed for D. of Argyll; considered of the rent and new tenants, etc. ½.
Nov. 12	Called at Westminster Fire Office (and a former time) paid for L. M. Duncan, duty on insurance. Received the same again from her. × £9 5s. 7d. ½.
Dec. 10	Settled with Mr. Couse, dilapidations of Mr. Willcock's house, in Queen Street, Westr. at £40. after surveying house, etc. 2.

1783

Jan. 7	Footman's wages for this year – 12 guin.
Jan. 16	To James Brown – 1 guinea.
Jan. 17	For Mr. D'd. Orme. £40 0 0 paid.
	do. at India House: 1 11 6

```
                          41 11  6
Rec'd. at India House     10 13  6
```

	Which I rec'd from Dr. Orme. £30 18 0
Feb. 3	Robert Tay for Coachman, came at 14 g. For buckskin and boots. – 1.
Mar. 5	Laid out in rebuilding⎫ – £143 9s. 8d. the house in West Bow. ⎭
Mar. 12	At Stationers Hall. Inspected cellar, warehouse, drains, etc. under Mr. Wilkie's. Ordered works of drains, rubbish and new floor. ½.
Mar. 14	Surveyed and inspected works at Stationers Hall as above mentioned). ½.
Mar. 30	Set out for Hampshire. In pocket £16 0s. 0d. At Basingstoke.
Apr. 1	Ale – £1 17 6
	Spades 18 0

```
            £2 15  6
```

Apr. 4	Set out for London. Called on Lord Banbury and gave him a report to be laid before the Quarter Session at Alston. (on the works of Romsey Bridge).
Apr. 17	Set out for Northumberland. At Ware – Inspected Mr. Prior's and Squire's; called on them both on ground and wharfs. At Hatfield.

Apr. 18	Travelled all night	
Apr. 20	At Newcastle. In pocket £50 6s. 8d.	
Apr. 21	Examined Newcastle Bridge. Changed a note. Set out for Hexham. At Bywell. Examined with Mr. Fenwick his dam head, etc.	
Apr. 22	Surveyed Con bridge. Examined Dilston Bridge. At Hexham.	
Apr. 25	Left Hexham. In pocket £46 18s. 0d. Passed through Alston More – to Penrith. At Shap.	
Apr. 27	At Chester to breakfast. In pocket about 36s. At Conway.	
Apr. 28	At Amlwch, near the copper mines, Anglesea.	
Apr. 29	At Beaumaris.	
Apr. 30	At Conway – changed a note. At an Inn – a single house, a stage east of Lanroost.	
May 1	At Shrewsbury.	
May 2	At Broadway.	
May 3	At Chapel House – changed a note. Arrived in London – in pocket £40 10s. 0d.	
May 7	Attended a meeting of persons interested in the copper mines in Cornwall, against Anglesea Petition. 1.	
May 11	Wrote out a long set of particulars of the Anglesea for instructions to Council. 2.	
May 12	Attended at the Bar of the H: of Commons and examined on the state of the Anglesea mines for ¾ of a hour. 2.	
May 17	Attended a consultation of Mr. Meggison's on Hexham Bridge, with Mr. Askew and Sir Franc's. Blake and Mr. Shaftoe. 1.	
May 18	Made out for Dr. Orme, after survey taken particulars for a repairing lease of West House in Paternoster Row.	
May 23	For Dr. Armstrong – from Pitcairn – 5. do. Wm. Hamilton – 5. total 10. g.	
May 25	Set out for Hampshire at 5. At Romsey. Surveyed and gave orders on Bridge works.	
May 29	At London.	
June 23	Sent Mr. Fenwick 3 drawings (large washes and neat) of Dam at Bywell, and repair thereof. with a particular description of the execution, and writing him twice thereon. – – 10.	
July 4	Sent Mr. Mytton one sheet drawing containing a plan, elevation and section, with separate parts on the margin, for a Spire to be placed on a Tower of the Church in Halston Park; with two letters of explanation. – 5.	
July 5	Sent Mr. Trecothick bills of carpenter's and carver's works, settled and reduced, after being measured by my clerk, who went to Addington, amounting to. £398 16s. 10d. – – 7.	
July 18	Gave Dr. Orme 4 drawings of plans of his house in P.N. Row and Fleet Street – and surveys with calculations. – – 5.	
July 28	Set out for Ware. Set out business at Highbury. Do. at Chesham. Inspected at Spital Brook; works at Prior's. Ordered works at Amwell. Surveyed mills and land at Ware. In pocket £3 3s. 6d.	
Aug. 7	Set out for Hampshire. At Basingstoke.	
Aug. 8	At Romsey. – Broadlands.	

119

Aug. 10	Left Romsey and went to Ringwood. Surveyed all the bridges there. Went to Symington – saw Lord Bute's villa in the way.
Aug. 11	Viewed Saltworths. Went to Bewley, Mr. Drummond's cottage, Suttrel's Tower, Cadland's house, etc. Southampton. Returned to Broadlands. in pocket £7 8s. 1d.
Aug. 14	In London. In pocket £2 2s. 0d.
Aug. 19	Set out for Norwich. In pocket £10 12s. 2d. At Newmarket.
Aug. 22	On trial.
Aug. 23	On trial.
Aug. 26	At London. In pocket £5 1s. 6d.
Aug. 28	Sent a report on the state of Guildford Bridge near Christchurch, Hants, to Magistrates of the County, on method of repair.
Sept. 3	Sent Mr. Mytton a sketch in lines of the manner of fitting up the end of seats of his church at Halston, with writing thereon. 3.
Sept. 4	Left London for the North at 4. In pocket £11 15s. 0d. Called at Ware – examined river at Mr. Prior's, and gave directions. At Barkway.
Sept. 8	At Edinburgh. In pocket. £18 11s. 0d.
Sept. 13	At Inveresk.
Sept. 16	Left Edinburgh. In pocket £21 19s. 6d. At Glasgow – called on Professors at the College. Saw Mr. Williamson on Doct's. Museum. Wrote Mr. Wilson. Mrs. Greenock at Rosneath Castle.
Sept. 18	Left Rosneath. At Sir G. Colqhun.
Sept. 19	At Inverary.
Sept. 24	Left Inverary. At Sir G. Luss.
Sept. 25	At Gargunoch. Sir Ge. Campbell's.
Sept. 26	Starling. Trinross. At Pitlour – making 11 days on expedition to Inverary 22. For business at Pitlour – 5. in altering plan of approach, etc.
Sept. 29	Left Pitlour. At Edinburgh.
Sept. 30	Wrote Mr. Fenwick's carpenter, on consultation of the Dam. Sent Mr. Davidson a second report on Hexham Bridge for the Magistrates of Northumberland.
Oct. 9	At Alnwick. Attended meetings of Justices. Long deliberations, Advised on method of proceedings. – 5.
Oct. 10	At Newcastle. At Bywell.
Oct. 11	Inspected Mr. Fenwick's dam and proceedings. Went over report and directions with Mr. Richardson – 2. At Hexham – surveyed bridge from end to end with a view to repair, etc. At Newcastle.
Oct. 14	At London. In pocket. £6 5s. 4d.
Oct. 25	Went to Highbury and Bushill – surveying bridges, wastes and drains at Stone Sluice. and making surveys for bank at Bushill.
Oct. 30	Wrote the D. of Argyll on timbers for Rosneath. Set out for Romsey. In pocket – £9 17s. 6d.
Oct. 31	At Broadlands. In pocket – £19 3s. 0d.

Nov. 3	Gave Lord Palmerstone advice on cornice and pediments of house, etc. 1.
Nov. 5	Left Romsey. Waited on Lord Banbury. At Guildford.
Nov. 6	In London – in pocket £14 5s. 0d.
Nov. 11	Left Mr. Ellis plans and descriptions of house to be pulled down in Water Lane for A: Company, Surveyor, etc. etc. – – 5.
Nov. 13	Surveyed the front of a house in Stationers Court belonging to the Company, in lease to Mr. Russell, and tumbling down. Ordering the necessary work and repairs. – 1.
Nov. 17	Surveyed a wall and windows at Gardner's Hall, near the gateway and on the inside.
Nov. 24	Went to Bushill on business of frame and Mr. Oliver's path to Chishurst, and met Mr. Auber on wharfing. From thence to Ware about Prior's wharf and great business at Amwell. At Ware.
Nov. 28	Called on Mr. Windus and on Mr. Woodcock about purchase of ground in Stanstead Church for L. M. Duncan. 1. Made out and sent a report on wall at Girdless Hall, windows, etc. 1.
Dec. 16	Went with Mr. Crofts to Ealing; surveyed a house; consulted on alterations; valued the rent, etc. Trouble – 2. This done for nothing as for a friend.

1784

Jan. 7	Sent Mr. Davidson a long report of opinion and advice on Hexham Bridge, with a long estimate of a supposed repair thereof. – – 8.
Feb. 8	Sent in a tin case to Rosneath 2 small drawings, of 2 floors, and a model of trussed girders with written description. Case 3s. –.
Feb. 24	Went to Bushill to stake out ground bought, order arrangement of new works, etc.
Feb. 27	Wrote Mr. Deacon Phillips, Edinburgh, and sent him by post coach a large set of drawings for markets and shambles at Edinburgh, consisting of a large plan, 2 elevations, and 4 sections, all neatly washed, drawn and figured. Tin case, letters, etc. ½ g.
Mar. 7	Set out for Hampshire. In pocket £12 16s. 2d.
Mar. 8	At Romsey. At Broadlands.
Mar. 13	At Romsey. At Murrel Green.
Mar. 14	In London.
Mar. 22	Attended a Committee on Vestry of Bow Church, on repairs.
Mar. 24	Went to Bushill on works of Bank.
Mar. 25	Attended a meeting of surveyors for the Committee of City Lands, on value of house in the Old Jury. – – 2.
Mar. 26	Waited on Mr. Murray and surveyed a house for him in Grosvenor Place. Valued it at 2,000 pounds, including fixtures; gave opinion. etc. etc. – – 2.

Apr. 1	Made a bargain with Mr. Kimpson for Dr. Orme for a house in Fleet Street, at 33½ £ An. clear and Neat Rent, for 21 years, after Midn. tenant to insure. Met Messrs. Peacock, Lewet & Scott on the value of houses in the Old Gewry.
Apr. 9	Went to Bushill. Afterwards to Ware. At Ware.
Apr. 10	Measured work at Amwell. Returned to London.
Apr. 13	Sent Dr. Orme a list of improvements recommended to be made at Lamb Abbey. – – 2. Nothing – being an old friend.
Apr. 24	Surveyed house on Lambeth Hill for College of Physicians. Sent to Rosneath 6 drawings of the details of building S.W. New Wing, with instructions as to the manner of building it.
May 4	Sent Mr. Campbell at Rosneath 7 drawings in small of N.E. Wing with a letter of explanation.
May 11	Gave Mr. Hingeston a report on the state of his house lease and value thereof, after examining accounts, agreements, etc. – – 2.
May 15	At Bushill. Sent Mr. Campbell at Rosneath several small drawings and instructions how to build the turrets and corners of roof part and parapets. – – 5.
June 2	Gave the D. of Argyll a design for Rosneath Castle, to add to it, of 3 plans and 4 elevations, large (washed neat), minute and particular. – – 40.
June 18	Sent Dr. Pitcairn a plan on vellum of estate on Lambeth Hill for College of Physicians, on a survey taken and writing particulars for setting same. – 3. Getting a Notice Board painted for same. Making plans for letting same and instructing Beadle thereon.
July 9	Sent the Duke of Argyll a small plan for farm buildings in Glenshire. Made a copy of it and writing a letter thereon. – – – 5.
Aug. 15	Set out for Romsey. In pocket £20 18s. 6d. At Winchester.
Aug. 19	Paid a Bill of mason work by Mr. Hookey to Romsey Bridge, to be paid by Lord Palmerstone.
Aug. 20	Left Romsey. At Mr. Sloane's, South Stonchum.
Aug. 21	At Southampton. At Cowes and Newport, Isle of Wight.
Aug. 22	At Steephill. At Shamphill. At Cowes.
Aug. 23	Left Cowes and by water went to Gosport. Gosport.
Aug. 25	At London.
Oct. 5	Sent Mr. Sloane a design for the façade of his bridge; a single sheet, washed, and writing thereon. Wrote Mr. Raven and sent him a final report to the Justices on complications at Romsey Bridge, and abstracts of accounts, bills settled, etc. etc.
Oct. 6	At Bushill – last time this season.
Dec. 20	Wrote Mr. Davidson, Newcastle, after reading Mr. Errington's bill in Chancery. 2.
Dec. 21	Attended on part of M. T. Society, the suit between them and Mr. Kennet.
Dec. 25	Wrote Mr. Campbell at Rosneath on the business at that place, with directions, etc. etc. – – 2.

41 EARL OF WARWICK'S BRIDGE OVER THE RIVER AVON. *See also Fig. 38*

42 HEXHAM BRIDGE

1785 to 1789

The entries in the diaries for the years 1785 to 1789 do not record many outstanding undertakings. In 1785 Mylne visits Inveraray and begins a series of work for the Duke of Argyll. He also prepares a new design for Ridley Hall Bridge. In 1786 he reports on a bridge for Londonderry, designs works at Tobermory, examines Rochester Cathedral and attends committees of the House of Lords and House of Commons. He reports on the Navigation Bill, also deals with electrical rods (lightning conductors) for Islington Church. In 1787 he visits Bath and Bristol and in 1788 he reports on harbours, piers and houses for fisheries in the Hebrides. In 1789 Mylne prepares drawings for Scottish fisheries at Tobermory—"A present for the Public good", and calls on Lord Salisbury at Hatfield.

1785

Feb. 6	At Bushill.
NB	From Mr. Treasurer of the Scottish Hospital for business done £1 17s. 6d.
	To Mr. Mair, said Treasurer, a bill of things bought £8 19s. 0d.
Apr. 8	Mr. Trape called from Lord Dudley and others about a Junction of the Birmingham and Dudley Canal – 2.
Apr. 10	Mr. Griffith called; a long consultation on a bridge over the Menai; this was a 2nd conversation. – 5.
Apr. 21	Wrote Mr. C. Campbell, of the brick walls inside of the East Wing at Rosneath, as proposed by the Duke. – 1.
NB	From Mr. Griffith on behalf of the Straits of Menai £10 0s. 0d.
June 25	At Bushill – horse & whisky 10s. 6d.
July 5	Gave the D. of Argyll a 2nd sketch of the farm in Glenshire – the first being returned.
July 14	Attended a sale in Chancery, on Barlows houses for Committee, and for Mr. Eddington, after giving him a valuation and survey thereof. – 3.
July 20	Called at Barings, Putney Heath, to look after his business. Surveyed Mr. Rush's villa at Wimbledon for Duke of Argyll.
July 25	Went to Ealing; surveyed the D. of Marlborough's Place and then advised Mrs. Bland's at Isleworth for Duke of Argyll.
Aug. 1	Went to Down Place; took a survey and all the particulars of house, offices, garden and land to be sold.
Aug. 2	At Windsor. Went to Twickenham; enquired about Lord Radnor's. Viewed Lord Fortiscue's and March's of Twedale's. Returned to London.

Sept. 2	Set out for Scotland. Called at Ware on piece of oak, large, for fire engine. At Royston. In pocket £13 14s. 3d.
Sept. 6	At Greenlaw. At ditto.
Sept. 7	Examined Mr. Hamilton's farms. At Edinburgh. In pocket – 5s.
Sept. 15	Set out for Inverary. In pocket £19 0s. 6d. At Mr. Orme's. At Murdieston.
Sept. 16	At Rosneath. Examined building; corrected some parts – made alterations. At Clachan. Ordered improvements.
Sept. 18	At Inverary. Visited New Bridge at Loch Dow.
Sept. 19	Set out new Road from Lodge, thro' the Deer Park, and fixed the site of a new entrance and lodge.
Sept. 20	Drew lines for banks of earth at ends of New Bridge, and borders of water – moval of Park, Wall and Road and Entrance of Deer Park. Visited Inn – New Town – Maltland and Cascade Bridge.
Sept. 21	Crossings of 4 roads in Pleasure Grounds considered – New Lodge & Gates staked out – Gateways to Loch Dow bridge; improvements on Lodge Sheds & walls at Garron Bridge. Ice house considered.
Sept. 22	At Springhead building – considering lowering ground about it; went to house for Dairy, considered alterations there.
Sept. 23	At town, considering entrance to Avenue and Gap, North Sides of Inn, and Springhead, on entrance from Town and Lodge – arches over public roads to carry private – At New Lodge, Loch Dow Bridge, and gates of 4 roads.
Sept. 24	Made a drawing for front of Dairy on the circle for Cross roads – finishing door of Saloon – on harleing – altering chimney piece.
Sept. 25	At the Springhead: lowering bank and well. At Town, on Lodge and Crossings of roads – at entrance of Circle and 4 Cross Roads. Made a drawing for do. and one of sheds, behind screen wall at Garron Bridge.
Sept. 26	Left Inverary. At Rosneath. Examined buildings – ordered many alterations on the design, on the workmanship, etc. etc.
Oct. 7	Cholerford. Rimside Moor House. In pocket £12 7s. 0d.
Oct. 8	Went cross the country by Rothbury and to Ridley Hall Bridge – inspected ruins, situation, materials, foundations, etc. for a new design. At Hexham.
Oct. 9	At Newcastle. In pocket £6 7s. 6d. Wrote Mr. Davidson on boreings at Ridley Hall Bridge. At Durham.
Oct. 12	Called at Ware – inspected piece of timber for beam to fire engine. In London. In pocket £1 16s. 3d.
Nov. 10	Sent Duke of Argyll a drawing of an Ice House, adapted to the ground under the Fosse, of the Castle at Inverary. – – 3.
Nov. 15	Went to Ealing; surveyed D. of Marlborough's house for D. of Argyll – minutely.
Dec. 11	Gave the D. of Argyll a new drawing of a front for Inverary, with gateway at corner as an entrance. – – 6.

Jan. 4 Wrote Mr. Davidson on the business of Ridley Hall Bridge etc. $- - \frac{1}{2}$.

Jan. 9 Called on Mr. Allen, Clements Inn, about land to be sold at Ealing – and twice before – for D. of Argyll. It would not answer so gave notice $- - \frac{1}{2}$.

Jan. 27 After various attendances; made, an agreement with Comm'n of City Lands – for taking part of ground on Lambeth Hill, making plans etc. B: of Physicians for £39 10s. 0d. Received for this a piece of plate.

Jan. 31 Gave the Irish Society a report on a proposition for a Bridge at Londonderry after various consultations and enquiries from Messrs. Macoold Roche, stating papers and attendance on them – 10.

Feb. 6 Gave the Duke of Argyll a large drawing of front of Inverary Town for workmen.

Feb. 8 Sent Mr. Slade a long paper of queres for a Bridge at Boston.

Feb. 10 Altered for Duke of Argyll, the back, front and plan of first floor of Rosneath Castle. 1.

Feb. 21 Gave Mr. Griffiths, amended and improved state of his case on Menai Straits. – 8. Attended him to Mr. Stracey at the House of Commons. – 1.

Mar. 10 Attended a consultation, on Menai Straits and Bridge, at Mr. Parry's, with Mr. Griffith etc. 2. Met Mr. Bishop.

Mar. 13 Gave D. of Argyll a letter of answers to queries on Screen Wall – Lodge, and alterations of Inn at Inverary. – $\frac{1}{2}$.

Apr. 4 Gave the Duke of Argyll a design for a New Lodge and Entrance going to the Deer Park – of 6 drawings, neat and clean washed. – 8.

Apr. 7 Attended the House of Commons on the Severn Navigation Bill – all day – 5.

Apr. 11 Attended again on B. Bridge Petition. Attended at Bar of H: of Commons on Severn Navigation Bill. – 5.

Apr. 18 Went to Egham; viewed Church and chancel; took measurements, particulars, etc. for L. M. Duncan's vault. Called at Ealing on D. of Argyll's business.

Apr. 26 *Not* at B: Attended the H: of Commons on the Bill for the New Parry Road Trust. – 0.

Apr. 27 Attended New Surry Road Bill. 0.

Apr. 28 Attended the B; B: Sundays Toll Bill, going into the House. 0.

Apr. 29 At Bushill.

May 1 Called and surveyed repairs of plaister at Stationers Hall, which with former attendances and opinions thereon – 3.

May 18 Attended House of Lords – on to B.S. Toll Bill.

May 19 Attended House of Lords and was sworn at the Bar.

May 20 At Bushill.

May 28 At Ealing with the Duke of Argyll – on dairy, drying ground, etc.

June 6	Called on Mr. Carbonell in Hinde Street; surveyed offices, drains etc. Treated afterwards for the sale of the house, and several meetings, but could not agree. Valued the premises at £1900 but could not agree. – 3.
June 20	Attended House of Lords on Surry Road Bill. 0.
June 21	Went to Wormley, inspected Bridge, pointed out the cause of failure to Mr. Leech, gave directions of repairs, etc. 2.
June 22	Set out for Rochester, with the City Solicitor, on B.B. business. He paid expenses.
June 23	Returned to London.
June 25	Went to Mr. Smiths, Putney Hill, surveyed Dam and form of Pond, gave directions etc. Considered of a room, new, to house etc.
June 27	Surveyed a Board etc. etc. of new fire Engine at Islington, and Bank at Bushill.
June 28	At a meeting of B. B. Committee, appointed surveyor thereto at £50 per annum from Mid'r. last.
July 4	Sent Mr. Troward a copy of 2nd Report on Hexham B: and examined copies of Interrogatorys, for do.
July 7	Called on Mr. Hardcastle, Temple, on Mr. Leigh's Chancell at Iver, for L. M. Duncan.
July 18	Trial at Guildhall.
July 19	Attended L. M. Duncan to Chapel at Ilford – viewed do. – enquired particulars, etc.
July 27	Dividend of N.R.C. for $\frac{1}{2}$ year declared to be 206 and 1080 reserved.
July 28	Set out for Margate on Mr. Paterson's business. At Margate.
Aug. 1	At London.
Aug. 4	Attended Mr. Dancer, Examiner in Court, of Chancery, on Hexham B: Cause, and gave papers and answered all questions relating thereto. – – 2.
Aug. 9	Went to Wormley – inspected Bridge again, ordered more shoreing and the necessary works of repairs. – 2.
Aug. 21	Called at Mr. Maile's and directed alterations on a chimney piece of Dressing Room at Argyll House. 1.
Aug. 25	Waited on L. M. Duncan – went to Iver Church – surveyed the Chancel, etc. for a vault. – 2.
Aug. 29	Waited on the Vestry of Islington Parish when the works to be done were finally settled and explanations given.
Sept. 5	Waited on Stationers Company. Made a report on windows requested by Mr. Lawrence, and enjoyed by Mr. Salte, and on windows of Publick House. – – 1$\frac{1}{2}$.
Sept. 11	Waited on Mr. Smith, at Putney Heath – conversation on new room, etc. 1. Called on Baring.
Sept. 16	At Bushill. Wrote out for Islington Church, particulars of electrical rods, and corrected Mr. Reynold's draft for the other works. Bank will be completed.
Oct. 6	Wrote L. M. Duncan a long letter on vault proposed to be built at Lundie.

Oct. 16	Sent Mr. Davidson, at Newcastle, a design and 4 drawings and 2 long writings, for rebuilding Ridley Hall Bridge, and laying the foundations – containing instructions, etc.
Nov. 29	At Bushill – filled the New Cutt with water for the first time, and it settled in many blotches, very much. Stopped it up again.
Dec. 2	At Bushill. Filled the New Cutt again. It stood now very well, but let all the hot water out to mend the claying of the sides.
Dec. 12	At Bushill, and turned the River into the New Cut, for the winter – the last time this season.

1787

Jan. 2	Waited on Sir A. Edmonstone for Duke of Argyll, on business of Mr. Holland's house, and sent him afterwards a calculation of the value thereof, by the year. – 2.
Jan. 4	Wrote Mr. Davidson on business of Hexham Bridge for ensuing Quarter Sessions. $\frac{1}{2}$.
Jan. 20	Sent the D. of Argyll a plan of the Saloon at Rosneath, with a new method of making the stairs, for entrance, biliard table, etc. writing 3 letters thereon. – 2.
Jan. 31	Gave L. M. Duncan a design for a burying place etc. to be built in Scotland: a plan, elevation, section etc. with a written description of the ground; a copy of it in lines – 5; and a fair copy of it sent to Scotland with directions in writing for its construction } 3.
Feb. 2	Waited, on Sir A. Edmonstone for D. of Argyll's intended purchase of Mr. Holford's house, and made calculations for Mr. Norris.
Feb. 3	Waited on Lady Mary Duncan and Mr. Woodcock on burying place etc. 1.
Mar. 9	Went to Carshalton – surveyed for Mr. Duran in the Grey-hound Inn etc. and the state of it.
Mar. 13	Attended Mr. Dunn on Dungeness.
Mar. 14	Called on Mr. D. Oyley at the Customs House, about Dungeness' lights.
Mar. 26	Set out for Ware. Called at Highbury – set out work – at Bushill. Visited Dr. Walter's premises. do. Mr. Rogers at Wormley. do. Lord Monson's fences at Broxborn. At Ware. In pocket – £6 8 6

$$\frac{2 \quad 15 \quad 10}{£3 \quad 12 \quad 9}$$

Mar. 27	Viewed works at Amwell End – Gauge – Spring – Mills, Ballance Engine, Amwell, etc. Ordered works and instructed Mr. Stephenson.
Mar. 28	Left Ware. Surveyed Sir A. Hume's Bridge at Wormleybury. Ordered works, etc. £2 15s. 10d.

Apr. 11	Set out for Dungeness. Surveyed the Bridge, found it stands perfectly well, and no settlement in the brick arches. At Tunbridge.
Apr. 12	At Lydd.
Apr. 13	Went down 4 miles to Lighthouse – surveyed do. examined distance to shore. At Lydd.
Apr. 14	Thro' Romney.
	At Hyeth.
	At Dover.
Apr. 15	At Dover.
Apr. 16	Set out for Town – In pocket £10 16s. 1½d. At Canterbury.
Apr. 17	At London. In pocket £12 0s. 0d.
Apr. 23	Wrote Mr. Brown, Mason, Lundie, on Lady Mary Duncan's vault, with instructions.
Apr. 25	Gave Mr. Dunn a long report on Lighthouse at Dungeness, and the proper position for a new one. 10. And 6 days absence from London on survey to the place – 12.
May 14	Having surveyed stables etc. in Northum. Str. and houses in Albemarle Street, of Mr. Coutts; gave Mr. Brown valuation thereof. Robin went to Mr. Compton's.
May 15	Sent Mr. Durand two plans of alterations etc. of Greyhound Inn, and long written particulars of the works thereof, repairs, etc.
May 28	Gave the D. of Argyll a design for padding to the offices of Rosneath Castle, and making severall improvements thereon. 5.
May 29	Gave Mr. Smith a design for a Gateway in Somersetshire – of 2 drawings washed very neat and minute, in figures etc. 4.
May 30	Gave Mr. Murray a design of 2 plans and written particulars for altering, improving and repairing his house in Fleet Street.
June 5	Waited on Mr. McDougal – on his ground for Leith harbour, which with former attendances and advice in the H. of Commons. 5. Waited on the Apothecary's Company at their desire about ground in Bridge Street. Nothing to be got for this.
June 9	At Bushill; put water into new cut and made the current pass through it, by taking up the Dams.
July 31	Delivered to the Irish Society, Guildhall, for the Corporation of Derry, Ireland, a design for a bridge of many drawings, reports, papers and estimate, with 15 gs. allowance for brother. – 100.
Aug. 2	Sent Mr. Durand a new plan for alterations etc. at Greyhound Inn, at Carshalton.
Aug. 29	Met Mr. Agassiz on Margate Harbour.
Sept. 8	At Bushill.
Sept. 10	Sent a plan and long letter to Mr. Macdougal on his estate at Leith, and Leith Harbour dock etc.
Sept. 11	Gave to Mr. Agassiz for Commrs. of Margate Pier, 2 drawings of the rebuilding the Pier and of various forms for that purpose, together with a long letter and several others to Mr. Sawkins for that business.

Sept. 14	At Bushill.
Sept. 15	Wrote Mr. Sawkins, and sent a set of boring rods to Margate. Set out for Portsmouth with brother. In pocket £8 14s. 7d.
Sept. 16	At Gosport.
Sept. 20	No. 1.
Sept. 21	Left Gosport. Saw Taylor's Mills at Stoneham. At Southampton. At Romsey.
Sept. 22	Examined bridge – waited on Lord Palmerstone; requested to have cracks stopping. Viewed Salisbury Cathedral – saw Wilton. At Deptford.
Sept. 23	At Bath – viewed the Circus, Crescent and Cathedral. At Bath – bathed, etc.
Sept. 24	At Bath – spent on whole journey to Bath by Portsmouth – £11 4s. 0d. & at Bath – £1. 12s. 0d.
Sept. 26	At Ilchester.
Oct. 2	Finished survey. Set out from Ilchester. In pocket £2 15s. 0d. Saw Glastonbury. At Wells.
Oct. 3	Saw Cathedral of Wells. At Bristol – saw west dock – the crane, draw bridge, etc. – the bridge.
Oct. 4	No. 3. Saw the walls – St. Vincents Rock. The Downs etc. – Blaize Castle. Kingsweston. At Bristol.
Oct. 13	Leave Bath. At London. In pocket £4 15s. 0d.
Oct. 16	At Bushill.
Oct. 24	Called on Mr. Agassiz – on Margate Harbour.
Oct. 25	Wrote Mr. Montgomery a long letter on Bridge for Londonderry, in answer to one of his. – – ½.
Dec. 18	Attended the Irish Society at their request on Derry Bridge affairs.

1788

Apr. 13	Mr. Taytell, Language Master, commenced at £21 a year; that is – 8 months of 4 weeks each – 3 lessons a week or 96 lessons in the whole year for 4 girls.
Apr. 14	Annual Meeting & Dinner of Bridge Committee.
Apr. 21	At Bushill – Mr. Cooper's horses 15s. 6d. and man 1sh. Turnpike 11sh. Expenses thereof 17s. 6d.
May 2	Attended Blackfriars Bridge Committee.
May 4	Set out for Margate. At Sittingbourne – with Mr. Agassiz. In pocket £29 0s. 9d.
May 5	Took up Mr. Taylor at Canterbury. Arrived at Margate.
May 9	In consultation with Sir T. H. Page and Mr. Nichols for 5 hours. Agreed on a result.
May 10	Attended a meeting of Trustees of Harbour and reported the joint opinion thereon. Went to N. Foreland Lighthouse, and to Ramsgate. Returned to Margate.
May 11	Left Margate. At Sittingbourne.
May 12	Arrived in London.
May 31	At Bushill, Coopers horses. Wrote and send a report on Margate Harbour Pier etc.

131

June 2	Went survey of New River with the Board. Dined at 4 Swans, Waltham Cross. At Bell at Hertford.
June 3	Dined at the Angel, Edmonton. In London. Expenses by N.R.C. – 7s. 0d. and £1 12s. 0d. Coopers horses.
June 11	Subpoened by Mr. Mayhew, being the last day of Trinity Term.
June 13	Waited on Lady A. Clavering for a house – looked at 3 different ones – advice, letters, coach-hire: 7sh.
June 16	Sent the D. of Argyll the drawing of the front of Inverary, having made a final addition to it, of 2 doorways at the end of the street, with the same for a larger scale, at top – in a roll by Lady Augusta. 2.
June 17	Dined with Mr. Kinlock – gave him drawings of his stables, lumber Room, etc. and of building, 2 new counting houses etc. in lieu thereof – consultations.
June 28	Set the water wheel to work, on being rebuilt almost entirely.
June 30	Surveyed 2 houses in Hanover Street and Argyll Street for Duke of Argyll; wrote His Grace thereon – coach-hire etc. 2¼.
July 1	Mr. Mumby came as Clerk at £35. At Bushill, when the last length of the lead of frame was taken away. Dined with Mr. Walker, Southgate.
July 2	Waited on Mr. Kinlock twice and gave him a plan for Counting houses in front of his house.
July 9	Made a long report on Harbours, Piers, Houses etc. for Fisheries in the Hebrides. Set Water Wheel to work, with new additional pumps and gear.
July 23	Set out – at 5. At Bushill – visited works, gave directions. At Ware, about Red House, Walkoman's house etc. At Kettering. Expenses by N.R.C. £1 10s. 0d.
July 28	At Carlisle.
July 29	Trial on Hexham Bridge for 10 hours. At Carlisle.
July 30	Set out. At Ridley Hall – examined works at Ridley Hall Bridge. Saw a Government bridge on road – on Rock-by.
July 31	Set off. Visited Dilston New Bridge. Viewed Corbridge – But'. arch South. At Newcastle.
Aug. 8	Made a purchase for a house in Argyll Street for D. of Argyll. – £1000. Wrote many letters and valuations about it.
Aug. 19	Drinking water – 2s. 6d. Bathing. £1 0s. 6d. Stockings. £2 14s. 0d.
Aug. 24	At London. In pocket £9 1s. 6d.
Aug. 26	At Bushill. Wrote Mr. Sawkins on business of Margate Pier with long observations on the prices and proposalls for the works.
Sept. 8	Wrote Lad. A. Clavering on her house and works, and sent a plan, neat, of Parlour floor.
Sept. 24	Went to Newington to set out new main and repair cistern; from thence to Sluice House at Highbury on alterations of 2 houses etc.
Sept. 29	Wrote Mr. Davidson and sent him for the Magis' new instructions for the pier at Ridley Hall Bridge – a long letter etc. 5.

Sept. 30	Mr. Dunmore gave up the watering the Bridge and demanded 26 per week.
Oct. 2	In pocket £21 1s. 4d. Set off for Norwich – Coopers horses. Visited works at Bushill. Ordered works at the River and both Walkoman house. At Barkway.
Oct. 3	Cambridge. At Norwich. In pocket £13 15s. 0d.
Oct. 7	Left Norwich. At Thetford.
Oct. 8	In London.
Nov. 5	At Bushill. Finished the work and paid off all the workmen.

1789

Jan. 23	Wrote Mr. Patteson of Norwich, and sent him a long report on Mills, W. Works etc. with a map on rollers, a plan of the Mills, working Shop, ground etc.; a plan of Chapel; field with reservoir, cisterns etc. and other small drawings. 50.
Jan. 28	For Stationers Company – Surveyed Mr. Wills house in Stationers Court, from top to bottom, for a repairing lease.
Jan. 30	Attended joint Committee of City Lands and Navigation. Attended on Piles and Water Way of Raban's Wharf at Pudle Dock.
Feb. 5	Made out and sent the Stationers Company thro' Mr. Field, a report and particulars of Mr. Willis's house for a repairing lease of 21 years. – Altogether 3.
Feb. 9	Wrote Mr. Patteson on the report of Water Works of Norwich, and plan of proceedings.
Feb. 27	Wrote Mr. Patteson on Mills, etc.
Mar. 16	Gave the Duke of Argyll a design of 3 drawings for Scottish fisheries, of a customs house etc. at Tobermory. A present for the publick good.
Mar. 17	Waited on the D. of Northumberland relating to the River Colne; his end.
Mar. 19	Met at Waghorn's Coffee house, Petitioners of River Colne – a conference of 3 hours, when they gave it up.
Apr. 6	College – Physicians.
May 28	Attended a consultation at Mr. Graham's on the Cromford Canal. – 2.
May 30	A long consultation at home with Mr. Ujaton on the Cromford Canal Bill – 2. Sent Lord Salisbury a plan of the Choir of St. Paul's, with seats etc. – 10.
June 1	Wrote to Norwich – a long letter on new works. – 1.
June 2	A long conference with Mr. Evans on Cromford Canal Bill. – 1.
June 8	A long consultation with Derby gentlemen and all their witnesses, on Cromford Canal. Again at Mr. Graham's Chambers with the same persons on the Bill; writing out observations, questions, etc. 4.
June 19	Attended at Bar of House of Lords, all day, on Cromford Canal Bill. – 3.

June 20	A long consultation with 6 gentlemen and Mr. Plumer on Cromford Canal Bill. 2.
June 22	Attended Bar of House of Lords on Cromford C. Bill, and examined for an hour. – 5.
June 26	Waited on D. of Argyll on business of purchases on Inverary and Rosneath. Attended at House of Lords on C. Canal Bill. 2.
June 27	Purchases 1. Gave an alteration for a Gateway to principal street of Inverary – 2, and on Rosneath.
June 29	Attended H. of Lords on C.C. Bill – Coach 7. And again at Lord Stanhope's. 3.
July 1	Attended H: of Lords on C.C. Bill – 3. coach 4. 0.
July 12	Set out for Ware. At Bushill, Chishurst flash, Spital Brook. Walksmour House – Mills – Gauge. Guests house, bridge etc. At Ware.
July 13	Set out for Ware – Baited. At Hatfield – called on Lord Salisbury and dined at St. Albans with Dr. Pollat, at Inn. Then went to Mr. Strutts at Rickmansworth – all night.
July 14	Surveyed Mr. Strutts Cotton Mills, Dams, Waters, River Colne etc. Mr. Roves's cottage garden, meadows etc. The (?) trunks and flooding the meadows. Collecting and adjusting evidence etc. and stayed at Rickmansworth – all night.
July 15	Left do. and visited Spring falling into the Colne. At Uxbridge and arrived in London. Attended a Committee of House of Commons on buildings etc. of their real state and road situation.
July 20	Went – set out for Hertford. Inspected Ballance Engine.
July 21	Attended trial of Mr. Strutts Mill. Called at Ware. Looked at Walkoman's house etc. At Bushill – inspected works and ordered some business. At London.
July 24	Gave Mr. Durrand a design of 3 plans, 2 elevations and section for a house at Woodcote. Nothing in respect of this as additions were afterwards executed to old house.
July 26	A long consultation with L. Macdonald on villages, towns, fisheries, buildings for do. Harbours, Piers etc. Got nothing.
July 28	Sent a report to Mr. Field, Master of Stationers Company on state of hall etc. 3.
Aug. 20	Set out for Edinburgh. At Ware – examined Mills, rebuilding at Royston by Hawkins – wrote him etc.
Aug. 27	Went with Magis'r. etc. of Edinburgh and examined all the heads etc. of water at Kiberton, Comiston and Swanston – all the pipes etc.
Aug. 29	Examined the works from Heriots Warf Resr. to New Town – searched for defects – sorted the difficulty. At Baberton.
Aug. 30	Returned to Edinburgh.
Aug. 31	Trial on Water Works.
Sept. 1	Left Edinbr. In pocket £17 3s. 0d. At Perth.
Sept. 2	Viewed Dunkeld etc. At Taymouth. Examined offices, position of house, situation, grounds – proposed addition to house – new stable offices etc. Position for a new bridge – farm offices – Island façade for road bridge. Took plan of offices – surveyed the building and contents of house.

Sept. 8	At Murdistown.
Sept. 9	Projected a Painting Room with new window and fireplace for Mr. Hamilton.
Sept. 10	Left Murdistown. At Edinburgh.
Sept. 11	Surveyed waters of Powburn Braid Burn – Dud: Loch and for Town's water works, the meadow, etc.
Sept. 12	Surveyed Powburn, Braid Burn, Comeston cistern, Swanston do. ; New track to Green Craig Glen Barn, Bonaly South Run etc. At Baberton.
Sept. 14	At Duns Hotel. Surveyed Poutherhall. Washing 5sh. Hair drying. 4sh.
Sept. 19	Leave Edinburgh. At Dumfries.
Sept. 20	St. Mary's Isle.
Sept. 21	Leave Lord Selkirk's.
Sept. 25	At Matlock Bath. Surveyed the Derwent, Maston Weir, Cromford Bridge, Bonsal Brook – see pocket book. At Derby.
Sept. 26	Surveyed the River, Derby – Mills, the Town Mills, Silk Mills, Water Works, Holme Mills, etc. (see books). Left Derby. At Leicester.
Sept. 28	Arrived in London. In pocket £1 5s. 7d.
Oct. 6	Attended the Court of Assistants of Stationers Company, and gave an estimate of a new slating roof for the Hall – explained it etc.
Oct. 7	Met Mr. Durand on business of Carshalton, purchase etc. etc.
Oct. 22	Mrs. Brathwaite went into Arundel Street House.
Oct. 24	Set out on a survey of the Duke of Northumberland's waters, mills etc. on Hounslow Heath. At Sion, Isleworth, Twickenham, and Common and Hounslow Heath Powder Mills, and then went to Hampton Court Green.
Oct. 25	Examined Bridge – Pallace – Green – Hounslow Heath Copper works – up the River, then to Longford.
Oct. 26	On streams adjoining to Colnbrook, to point of partition, and then returned to London.
Nov. 13	Set out for Norwich. In pocket £15 15s. 4d. by Waltham Cross, Hocheral. At Thetford.
Nov. 14	At Norwich.
Nov. 17	Left Norwich. In pocket £3 11s. 4d. At Thetford.
Nov. 18	At London – in pocket £1 13s. 0d.
Nov. 28	Set out on survey to Sion House, Hampton, Staines etc. Viewed waters in Park, and Pleasure Ground at Sion, Isleworth Mills, Bushy Park, and Kingswater. At the Tay Hampton Court Green.
Nov. 29	Went to Staines – viewed Finch's Mills and Ashby's Mills at Hyth End. Then Stanwell Mills and Bullocks Mills at Longford.
Nov. 30	Went up the meadows and took the levells across all the streams. At London – In pocket £2 13s. 10d.
Dec. 12	For Mr. Durand, examined and reduced of work, by Barnes, brick and plaister work, £192 2s. 5d. after interogation of him and his work.

1790 to 1794

Judging from the entries in the diaries for the years 1790 to 1794 Robert Mylne appears to have spent a good deal of time in consultations on canals and inland navigation. He mentions meetings with Rennie and attendances at committees both at the House of Lords and at the House of Commons. He travels to all parts of the country and to Scotland, prepares designs for a church at Inveraray, goes on horseback on the Pentland Hills, surveys Wilkes's house in London, begins repairing Blackfriars Bridge finished twenty years before. Surveys the quays at Southampton, meets James Watt at Soho and makes sketches for additions to the Lodge at Addington for his old client, Mr. Trevothick. In 1794 he was called in to consult with Soane on the condition of the great dome of the Bank of England. The report bore the signatures of Mylne and Soane. It was in this year that Mylne set out the foundations of the house at Amwell which he intended should be his country home.

1790

Jan. 9 Finished a correspondence with Mr. Northey on Mrs. Hamond's dispute. 3 visits to her, postage etc.

Jan. 10 Sent Lord Albane 5 drawings of 2 cottages in one building, for Scotland, with long letter thereon. – 10.

Feb. 3 Rennie.

Feb. 15 Sent Provost of Edinb'r. a long Report of 26 pages on Water Works, their use and establishment, with a map and section long. –

Feb. 16 Attended H. of Commons, and Petition on the Norwich Water Works. Proved allegations. – 2.

Feb. 25 Met Mr. Scot on Delapidations between Mr. Durand and Mr. Byne. Dined – settled Norris for Umpire. Expenses – 17s. 6d.

Mar. 2 Surveyed Mrs. Hamond's new house etc. gave list of things to be done with it. – 1. Attended H: of Commons at desire of Mr. Black on Woucester Canal Bill – 1. No business done, by delay.

Mar. 3 Attended a Com'ee. of the Commons against Woucester Canal Bill. Some consultations. – 3.

Mar. 8 Set out for Birmingham. Brother died at Dublin. At Oxford. Remained in pocket – £26 2s. 2d.

Mar. 9 At Soho – Birmingham.

Mar. 11 At Droitwich. At Woucester. Surveying the Severn.

Mar. 12 At Stourport. At Stewponey, near Stourton Castle.

Mar. 15 At London.

Mar. 16 Attended the Lord Chamberlain by order, on the Bills of St. Paul's, at his house, with Mr. Calvert etc.

Mar. 21   Attended a meeting at the St. Alban's Tavern on the Woucester Canal. – 2.

Mar. 22   Sent Mr. Wheeler 2 estimates of increases on the Woucester Canal, and Bill.

Apr. 1   Met Mr. Longbottom on Liverpool Canal etc.

Apr. 7   Set out for Ware. In pocket £4 0s. 0d. Went to Hornsey – inspected bridges – proposed cut thro' Mr. Mead's land and waste gate etc. Went to Bushill; surveyed lands, arch, the church, houses, etc. Went to Ware; examined Waltsman's house.

Apr. 8   Went to the Mills – survey, measured etc. the New Mills, cistern and ballance engine, gauge, Cut, and ordered works. Went to Amwell – tried experiments.

Apr. 9   Opened up 3 leaks out of the River; found the same strong and copious. Returned to London. In pocket 12s. 7d.

Apr. 11   A long consultation with Messrs. Wilson, Longbottom, and addition, on the lines of Lancashire Canal.

Apr. 12   Making out estimates, accounts, papers etc. etc. on the Leeds and Liverpool Canal. Attended H. of Commons on do. when matters were settled with proprietors.

Apr. 13   Gave Earl of Bread Albane an estimate of additions and alterations of Taymouth house and a small drawing for the side of a Road Bridge.

Apr. 15   Attended a Comm'ee of the H. of Commons on the Liverpool Canal Bill. – 4. Attended the House of Commons all day on the Woucester and Birmingham Canal Bill. – 4.

Apr. 17   Went to Carshalton with Messrs. Norris and Scott, and took a survey of the Delapidations of Mr. Byne's house.

Apr. 20   Attended Committee on the Severn Navig: Bill – the whole day – H. of Commons.

Apr. 22   Met Messrs. Norris & Scott on the Arbitration of Delapidations of Mr. Durand's house – could not agree.

Apr. 23   A meeting with Mr. Young and Mr. Burton on the works of the proposed improvements on River Severn and methods of doing them.

Apr. 29   Met Mr. Norris on Mr. Byen's Delapidations – tried to agree.

May 3   For Stationers Company, examined wall etc. in Mr. Horsefisher's bedroom, and proposition for a window therein. ½.

May 10   Attended H. of Lords and Com'ee on the Severn Bill – when it passed and was finished.

May 14   Sent Mr. Mackenzie 2 drawings for an Inn at Tober Morry – and Calculations – a present to the County.

May 16   Sent Mr. Perry, for the Stat. and Wore Comp: a long Report on improving the Severn.

May 22   Met. Mr. Norris and Richardson on the Sloan Street Estate; made an estimate of the present and probable rents, and made an award between them, of £830 a year to be paid for 99 years. – 10.

May 29	Went to Woodcot; waited on Mr. Durand on additions to house, offices etc. Made out a small plan, formerly for this place but laid aside.
June 1	Went on the New River; examined the late breach near the arch beyond Sluice – ordered further works. Proceeded to Hornsey. Set out the New Cut, and Bridge etc. and ordered up the Waste Gate.
June 5	Went with Mr. Telby and Mr. Stirling to Isleworth and viewed D. of Northumb'ds. River from Marchant Mill to Hill's Mill on the matters in dispute between them. – 3.
June 11	Begun the 2nd coat of Thames Gravel for the Bridge.
June 18	Sent Duke of Northumberland, long Report, letter and Map of a survey of his Cut, Mills there, property etc., and observations on the River Colne, etc. – 40.
June 19	Went to Woodcot; set out foundation work etc. of additions to house, offices etc.
June 24	Sent Lord Bread Albane a large design for improving, adding to, and altering the Castle at Taymouth, and making offices there; consisting of two sets of drawings to different scales, of 4 plans each and 2 elevations. – 50.
July 2	At Woucester – 4.
July 4	Viewed works at Boson, locks, etc. At Stourport.
July 6	Set off down the River. At Holt fleet.
July 10	Left Holt – sounded the Severn on all the stroles down. In pocket £43 19s. 3d. At Woucester.
July 11	Went down the Severn, to Tewksbury and sounded the Shoals to the Mouth of the Avon. At Cheltonham.
July 13	Arrived in London – 4. In pocket 30.
July 24	At Carshalton and Woodcote.
July 26	Made a drawing of the proposed Cut and new Locks at Stourport on Mr. Young's map of the land. Wrote him a long letter of instructions, and sent him the map.
Aug. 13	Went up the Thames in the Navigation Barge to Staines – Viewed works and improvements.
Aug. 21	Sent Lord Bread Albane a design of 2 sheets for a set of stables, coach houses, Brew-house, and many other offices, consisting of 2 plans, and an elevation, and a section. – 15.
Aug. 28	At Woodcote – farm etc.
Sept. 6	Went to Ware – met Mr. Hawkin and Mr. Cooper, on Ware Mills, Cistern etc.
Sept. 8	Sent a drawing and a model of an engine to scower the Severn, to Mr. Fieldhouse at Stourport, with a paper of directions – how to make and use it. Model and expenses – 4.16.
Sept. 13	Went to Hornsey; put water into new Cut – ordered the remainder of works and several new matters on different parts of the River. Went also to Bushill – examined works and ordered amendments various.
Oct. 21	Set out for Cirencester. In pocket – £22 5s. 0d.
Oct. 22	At Cirencester. Pocket £15 12s. 6d.
Oct. 27	Set out for London. At London. In pocket £15 15s. 0d.

Nov. 13 Went to Woodcote and New Farm, with advice on a Windmill proposition. 1.

Nov. 16 Went to Hornsey, Bushill and Ware. Set out new addition and works at Mr. Mayhew's ground at New Severn. Examined Bushill Banks and other works. Levelled gauge with Tambling Bay, at Ware.

Nov. 17 Attend Ballance Engine, rate of going. Made report out on leaks at Amwell – ordered various works. Returned to London.

Nov. 19 Attended at Stationers Hall on Rowley's buildings etc.

Nov. 23 Examined City leases relating to Stationers Warehouses, City Wall and Comptrollers office.

Nov. 24 Attended General Court of Stationers, rec'd. ordered to build a wall, etc. Gave in a plan of all the property relating to the City Wall, boundaries etc. Taking measures etc. thereof.

Nov. 25 Sent to Mr. Chambers for Thames & Severn Navigation – 2 drawings and long directions in writing for coffering the bad places of the Tuperton Tunnel, letters etc. 10.

Nov. 26 Sent Mr. Young, for the Severn, Navig: a plan of the New Cut at Stourport, on a new and improved survey made by Young, with writing directions, letters etc. for the execution. – 10 (see former charge).

Dec. 4 Sent to Mr. Young the drawings of David Weyre & Namstyle's Shoals of the Severn with the – to be placed thereon, and with written directions, letters etc. 10.

Dec. 10 Attended a meeting of Com'ee of the Thames and Severn Navigation, and delivered a report in writing, with 2 drawings, for best supply of water to summit level and other matters. – 30.

Dec. 28 Passed the whole day with Mr. Tilverlock, on the various papers for letting 2 leases of Norwich M: and improving the same. 2.

1791

Jan. 29 Wrote Messrs. Hay & Co., Plumbers, Edinburgh, on business at Rosneath, for Duke of Argyll, severall times. 1.

Feb. 1 Waited on the Stationers Court, made report, and attended all day on proposal made by Mr. Leach.

Feb. 4 Attended all the forenoon on Court at the Stationers Company Hall and settled differences between Mr. Rowley and the Company.

Feb. 14 Gave Mr. Berners a design for an Obelisk, washed neat, fit for execution, to be erected at Wolverstone, Suffolk. – 5.

Feb. 15 Gave Mr. Marsh, for the proprietors of English stock of Stationers Company, a report and survey of Mr. Loydd's house in Ave Mary Lane. – 3.

Feb. 19 Sent, for Stationers Company, to Messrs. Dance & R. a description of the premises left to Mr. Rowley, and 2 plans thereof drawn on the parchment deeds. – 2.

Feb. 21 Attended at Somerset House.

Mar. 1	Attended Court of Stationers Company and made a final report on all matters in dispute between them and Mr. Rowley. – 2.
Mar. 8	Attended all day on the Woucester Canal at the House of Commons, relating thereto. 3.
Mar. 9	Attended at Somerset House. Sent Mr. Rivington, for Stationers Company, a drawing and description of a window to be let to Mr. Rowley. – 2.
Mar. 11	Made out and sent a new estimate to Mr. Wheeler on the annual expence of the proposed Woucester Canal. – 2. Attended, by desire, Comm'ee of S. and W. Canal Company on Bill of Wouc'r. Canal etc. – 2.
Mar. 15	Attended the D. of Argyll to Ealing, on Sale, and met Mr. Wildman to shew him the premises, furniture, stock, grounds etc.
Mar. 16	At Somerset House – Report agreed to. Waited on Mr. Ryder relating to Argyll House.
Mar. 18	Mr. Perry and Mr. Jones came to Islington – a long consultation on Woucester Canal and matter to oppose it. Read Deed for Norwich W'r. Works; altered them a little. – 2.
Mar. 20	Went to Hornsey, Bushill, Ware, & Amwell. In pocket £3 13s. 0d. Settled several things at Mr. Mead's, Mr. Blackburn's and Mr. Hawkins. At Ware Mills.
Mar. 22	Wrote Mr. Dance on Somerset House.
Mar. 28	Wrote the D. of Argyll on Ealing and house in Argyll Street. 1.
Apr. 1	Attended meeting on Woucester Canal, and then at the Bar of the House of Commons etc. All day – 5.
Apr. 5	Sent the Duke of Norfolk the keys and surrender of his houses in Arundel Street.
Apr. 9	At Woodcote.
Apr. 12	Waited on D. of Argyll on business particularly on the sale of Ealing Grove etc. Calling on Mr. Christie, on do. Giving him instructions and particulars for sale.
Apr. 13	Gave Mr. March some advice on his house and a small drawing of a Greenhouse.
Apr. 19	Attended the House of Lords, on the Montrose Bridge, at the desire of Mr. Ross. – 2.
Apr. 25	Set out for Lechlade. At Faringdon.
Apr. 26	At St. John's Bridge, after breakfasting with Mr. Lovedon. Surveyed from Bridge up to Canal, and then down from Bridge to Buscot. At Mr. Lovedon's, Buscot Park.
Apr. 27	Set off down the Thames from Buscot – surveyed all the way and left off at New Bridge. At Kingston Inn.
Apr. 28	Began at New Bridge and surveyed all the way down to the 4 streams, Turnpike Br. At Oxford.
Apr. 29	Went to Osney Mill, Loch, and up to Godstow B. & L. Came back and down to Folly Bridge & Mill etc.
Apr. 30	Set off from Oxford Wharf. Left off at Abingdon. At Henley.
May 1	Returned to London. In pocket: £13 12s. 6d.
May 4	Attended at H: of Lords to be sworn on Montrose Bridge Bill.

43 RICHMOND HILL, SURREY: THE WICK. Elevation as carried
out. The vases and roundels are in Coade patent stone. Contract drawing signed "Daniel Pinder and Robert Mylne,
June 12th, 1775"

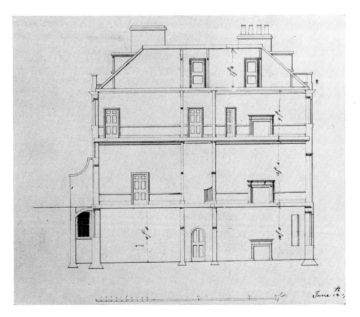

44 RICHMOND HILL, SURREY: THE WICK.
Cross-section giving details of doors and
fireplaces as actually carried out

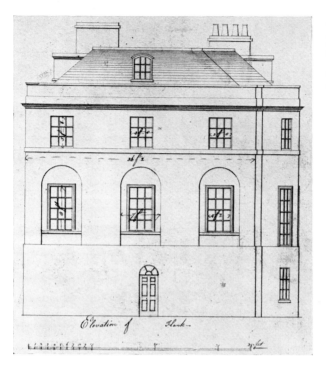

45 RICHMOND HILL, SURREY: THE WICK. Side elevation. Contract drawing

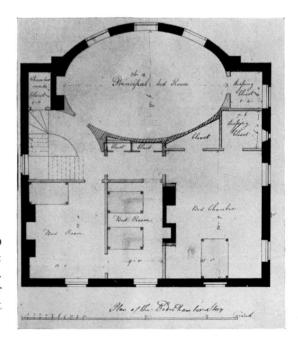

46 RICHMOND HILL, SURREY: THE WICK. First-floor plan. Contract drawing

May 11	Attended all day on the W. & Birm'm Canal in Suffolk Street, and at H. of Lords – nothing done. – 3.
May 13	Attended Comm'ee of H. of Lords on M. Bridge Bill – not called again ; gave via etc.
May 14	Went to Richmond – set out Mr. Sayers building.
May 20	Attended all day at House of Lords on B. and Woucester Canal – not called as evidence. – 3.
May 22	Went with Mr. Campbell to Wilmington and examined his additional building.
May 23	Wrote to Messrs. Hay & Co. on the lead work of the kitchen building at Rosneath with long directions, see papers, former letters, thereon.
May 26	Attended at Bar of H: of Lords on Birm: Canal Bill – examined an hour at the Bar. – 5.
May 27	Lord Bread Albane. ⎫ Lady Mary Duncan. ⎬ called on. Mr. Christie. ⎭ Gave directions to G. Burton on works of the Severn etc. 1.
May 31	Wrote to Mr. Clavering on Bills, ground rent etc. Met Mr. Norris & Dyke on Temple Mills etc.
June 2	Met Mr. Baillie on purchase of Ealing Grove etc.
June 3	Attended the House of Lords on W. and Birm; witnesses for it examined. – 2.
June 7	Sent a Report to the Lords of the Treasury on Somerset House. Attended all day House of Lords on the Birm. Canal – Sworn again. – 3.
June 8	Attended meeting of Thames Comrs. Kings Arms Palace Yard. – 2. Attended all day Commrs. of Lords on Birm. Canal. – 3.
June 11	At Ealing – Met Mrs. Baillie; gave directions. Met Christie; gave instructions for sale of furniture. At Richmond, on Building.
June 14	Sir G. Rouse called and asked several questions relating to a Bridge and Causeway in Suffolk, near to Lowestoft. 1.
June 23	Wrote Mr. Perry a long letter on the Severn and resigning my employment for the improvement of it. 2.
June 26	Went to Marlow. At Marlow – examined Marlow Loch etc.
June 27	At Temple Mills etc. Viewed and considered the state of Mills, Works, loch, houses etc. Do. at Hurley Mills – state of river etc. At Marlow.
June 28	Called on Mr. Alnutt. Left Marlow. Returned to London. In pocket £11 2s. 2d.
June 29	L. M. Duncan. Mr. Hoare.
July 1	Sale at Ealing – went to it and did business in it, for the Duke. Expenses £1 1s. 0d.
July 5	At Ealing, all day, on finishing the sale. Examined remainder of business, giving directions etc. 1.
July 6	At the York and then at Mr. Norris's; proceeded on business of Temple & Hurley Mills with Norris & Dyke etc.
July 8	At Mr. Hoare's, New: Set out the sides of River at his place.

July 11	Settled finally the affair of Temple Mills with Mr. Dyke and Norris, £28,000.
July 12	Finished the affair of Ealing, and gave possession to Mr. Baillie. Wrote the D. of Argyll a long letter on proceedings.
July 14	Set off on a survey of the Thames. At Kensington. Expenses £8 10s. 1½d.
July 15	At Abingdon. Went down the Thames with Mr. Treasher. At Wellingford.
July 16	Left off at Whitchurch and Goreing, and by land to Mapledurham etc. At Reading.
July 17	Went to Newbury and from thence to Wantage and to Mr. Lovedon's at Buscot Park.
July 18	Began the survey of the Thames – at Lechlade – with the Com'ee of the Com'rs. and proceeded down to New Bridge and from thence went to Kingston Inn.
July 19	Began at New Bridge and proceeded to Folly Bridge. At Oxford.
July 20	Report forming and then back to Medley, and came down to Botley Road Bridge. Remained at Oxford.
July 22	Proceeded down and left off at Goreing and went by land to Reading.
July 23	At Henley – to finish the report and proceeded with Mr. Lovedon – repaying the expenses. At London.
July 26	Surveyed Mr. Wilk's house, Ave Mary Lane, for the repairs lately done to it, being let on lease agreeable to report thereon. 1.
July 28	Half a year's dividend declared at £212 and 20 a share besides, reserved for New Marylebone Men.
July 30	Attended Mr. Burmester's cause at Guildhall. Called on Mr. Sleby and gave him a copy of the report on the Dispute between Messrs. Hall and Marchant. 1.
Aug. 1	Wrote Lord Bread Albane on his business. Viewed again Barge house of Stationers Company and wrote Mr. Baldwyn and Hollyer. ½.
Aug. 21	Went to Mr. Campbell's, Kent, surveyed new building etc.
Aug. 22	Went to Croydon on trial and to Woodcote with Mr. Parry. Sent L. Aug. Campbell's Dog.
Aug. 23	Went to Isleworth along with Mr. Trucaton and settled the difference between Mr. Hill and Marchant about the Head W. of one and Tail W. of the other, for Duke of North'land.
Aug. 24	Went to Croydon again on Mr. D's. trial. Waited for the event and referred with Mr. Parry in a chaise.
Aug. 26	Went to Ware on business of Ware Bridge and Amwell ponds etc. In pocket £4 9s. 7d. At Mr. Osborne's.
Aug. 31	Attended Mr. Pigot, as evidence on Mr. Durand's trial of glass lights etc. 1.
Sept. 14	Viewed Stationers Company Barge house at Lambeth – wrote advert'mt. for letting it. 1.
Sept. 15	Surveyed Mrs. Vints house, Ave Mary Lane; estimated repairs, made a report etc. to the Stationers Co. 2½.
Sept. 16	For Ipswich. At Ipswich.

Sept. 17	Proceeded to the Enquiry on the dispute between Messrs. Duson, Pinnerton & Tousters, of Stou Market navigation; heard witnesses etc. took a view, received papers. At Ipswich.
Sept. 18	Went to Wolverstone, examined with Mr. Berners situation for Obelisk, settled the business for it, with Tovel Mason. – 3.
Sept. 19	Returned to Ipswich. Proceeded on enquiry, heard evidence. Received accounts etc.
Sept. 20	At Norwich.
Sept. 21	At meeting of Com'ee of Water Works in the Town Hall. Gave advice etc. thereon and on proceedings. At Barbourgh, near Norwich. In pocket £18 14s. 11d.
Sept. 22	Set out for Lynn. At Lynn. Visited and viewed Lynn harbour, wharfs, channel etc. In pocket £16 14s. 1d.
Sept. 23	At Lynn – Surveyed the west side of Lynn Harbour to the north and south of the ferry, and in the afternoon – the water works and shoar down, on east side.
Sept. 24	Went down in a boat and examined the channel, to a buoy a mile north of C: Bentinch's house. Returned with flood, passed thro' Lynn and went up the Ouse to Islington and returned to Lynn.
Sept. 28	Left Lynn. In pocket £2 13s. 0d. At St. Germans.
Sept. 29	Surveyed all about Downham. At Downham.
Sept. 30	Left Downham.
Oct. 1	At Cambridge. In pocket £7 15s. 6d.
Oct. 3	At Ware.
Oct. 4	At London. In pocket £3 5s. 0d.
Oct. 5	Wrote Mr. Stirling and sent him 2 copies of award on Mr. Marchant and Mr. Hill's Mills, for the Duke of Northumberland.
Oct. 12	Surveyed house in Darkhouse Lane for Stat: Company. Estimated repairs. Made a report etc. 2½.
Oct. 13	Surveyed Mr. Horsfield's front of house as to defect in brickwork. Ordered remedy. ½. Surveyed Mr. Wilkinson's house, N.11, Wood Street, to renew the lease.
Oct. 17	Began paving Blackfriars Bridge.
Oct. 21	Ended the paving one half of it at ½ past 3.
Oct. 22	Went to Ware. Examined Mr. Hoare's part of the River. Viewed sluice or gate at Mr. Walker's, Southgate – ordered works to it. Called at Bushill, Stephenson being dead, and went to Amwell – viewed works. In pocket £10 17s. 3d.
Oct. 29	Sent Stationers Company, by Mr. Baldwin, a report and advice on House, N.11. Wood Street. – 1½. Also a letter on repair of front of Mr. Horsfield's house. ½.
Nov. 2	Sent Mr. Creasey a long report on the Ouse, Lynn Harbour, and Cambridge River. Wrote Mr. Golbourne. 30.
Nov. 3	Gave Mr. Trecothick drawing for the fitting up his library. 2.
Nov. 4	Meeting, on award, held at Varley's house on Stowmarket Navigation and Dispute.

Nov. 8	Wrote Mr. Burdon a long letter and a long consultation with Mr. Nauton on Sunderland Bridge. 1.
Nov. 12	Went to Richmond on Mr. Sayer's business. Called at Isleworth Mill, Water Y. above Mark: Waited on Lady Derby – surveyed settlements on her house – and remedy. 1.
Nov. 12	Made and signed an Award on the Stow Market – Navigation.
Nov. 22	A long consultation with Mr. Creasey at home on the Ouze Navigation. – 2.
Nov. 23	Sent Mr. Creasy a plan of Lynn Haven Town and river above it and below it, for the Ouze proposition, and for the use of Mr. Watt's new survey thereof.
Dec. 2	Finished the paving and opened the use of B. Friars Bridge.
Dec. 5	Examined and certified a Bill of Rubbish work, done by Parsons for Stationers Comp. of £32 14s. 0d.
Dec. 6	Wrote a long letter on a Bridge for Sunderland. 1.
Dec. 9	Consultation with Mr. Creasy on Ouze. ½.

1792

Jan. 7	Viewed Mrs. Hamond's Brew-house in the Borough.
Jan. 15	At Nottingham. In pocket £22 5s. 1d.
Jan. 16	Attended General Meeting.
Jan. 17	Went from Leen Bridge to Long Eaton. Erewash Canal Mouth – down the Trent and returned to Not.
Jan. 18	Went to Pinston Colliery. To Codnor & Langley Mill and Trowel – and Nott'm.
Jan. 20	Went to Wilford Ferry again and down the River. To Trent Bridge and Musters Place, and at Nott.
Jan. 22	Viewed castle and Church. Dined with Mr. Turner. At Nottm.
Jan. 23	Left Nott; went to Sotton, Long Eaton, Sawley. G. Trunk Canal. Down the Trent to Lawley Bridge and thence at Loughboro'. In pocket £17 3s. 6d.
Jan. 25	At Ware – visited gauge, Stopgate, Chad. Spring, Ware Bridge, Amwell etc. etc. Arrived at London. In pocket £7 7s. 6d.
Jan. 30	Surveyed Mrs. Hamond's Brewhouse and estates. Waited on Mr. Calvert.
Feb. 7	Sent Mr. Cradock a long Report with Apendix on the Nott: Canal, on the C: land, on the – do. and on Navone to Notting: 20G.
Feb. 14	A long consultation with Messrs. Cradock and Turner on the Nott: Canal and Erewash Canal etc. 2.
Feb. 28	Called on Mr. Baldwin, Pater N. Row. Called on Mr. Britten, and examined the objectionable frame on the top of his house. – 1.
Mar. 4	Attended a consultation with Mr. Plumer and Lane on the Severn River Improvement. 2.
Mar. 6	Altered Petition against the Nott: Canal Bill and altered plan, etc. and added thereto of the Erewash Can: Company's interests in said Bills. – 2.

Mar. 7   Waited on Mr. Craddock on Erewash and on Nottingham Canal Bills etc. etc. 1.

Mar. 9   Went on the Cause of the Indictment, on the Severn. Left London. By the Uxbridge roads. At Oxford.

Mar. 10   Went and surveyed the Thames and Oasely Pound Loch, etc. At Woucester.

Mar. 11   Went to Holt Shoal with Mr. Plomer, Lane, Brookholding, Fieldhouse & Young – examined plans, soundings etc. etc. and returned to Woucester.

Mar. 14   Left Woucester. In pocket £8 1s. 0d. At Henley, at 12.

Mar. 15   Trial postponed to next Assizes. Set off *11* for London.

Mar. 16   Attended the Commons against the Nott: Canal, and *for* the Rochdale. 1 & 2 N.

Mar. 18   Attended a consultation at Mr. Milles-Chambers in Lincoln's Inn, on the Nott: Canal. – 2.

Mar. 20   Sold out £1,000, 3 per cent. Consols at 96¾ a loan a £1000 to Mr. Osborne.

Mar. 28   Visited Mr. Tempest and Lambton on the Sund: Bridge Bill – long consultation. – 1. Attended Mr. Turner to Mr. White's and settled clauses of restraint on Nott. Canal Bill, having considered them over night and altered three drafts. – 3.

Mar. 29   Attended all day (H. of Commons) on Nott: Canal Bill and afterwards in the evening. – 4. Attended Sunderland Bridge Bill and gave long evidence thereon; this and former opinion – 3.

Mar. 30   Attended consultation on the Nott: Canal for 4 hours with Mr. Milles at Alice's Coffee House and settled plan of arrangement to oppose the same – the clauses etc. etc.

Mar. 31   Went to Richmond on Mr. Sayer's business – found little done, and that wrong that was done. Resolved to give it up in all respects.

Apr. 4   Attended all day on Nott. Canal Bill. Consultation with Mr. Milles, advice etc. 3. Attended on Grantham Canal Bill; put off consultation with Mr. Jackson, Mr. Brough, Mr. Dixon, and witnesses on the Bill, and matter for opposition. 3.

Apr. 7   Went to Woodcot, to inspect works and settle bills. Called at Clapham.

Apr. 10   Went to Dartford – examined Dartford Church inside and outside, tower, side aisles, etc. At Mr. Fleet's at Hawley.

Apr. 11   Met Gentlemen of the Committee. Gave a report – viva voce, on the proper repairs to be done thereto, and alterations also. – Returned. At London.

Apr. 14   Viewed Mr. Wilkes house, Ave Mary Lane, and settled the schedule thereof, on Stat's. Company. ½.

Apr. 16   Gave Duke of Argyll plans of a double cottage to be built in near to Rosneath.

Apr. 18   Met Mr. Jackson (by desire) at Part: on consultation to oppose the Grant: Canal Bill, on Mills, Waters, etc. – 2.

Apr. 20   Attended the Com'ee on the Grant'm. Canal Bill for Duke of Newcastle. 3.

Apr. 23	Attended at Guildhall on Mr. Britten's affair. Nothing done.
Apr. 24	Sent Mr. Fleet for the Parish of Dartford a long Report and Apendix for the repair and alteration of the Church, with a plan, section and outline of west front. 10.
Apr. 26	Attended Messrs. Cradock & Turner at Waghorne's, and settled all the clauses to be inserted in Nott: Canal Bill. – 5.
Apr. 30	Attended a meeting of the Grantham Canal Bill at Sir R. S. Stone on the River Devon. 2. Attended all day at Com. of the House of Lords on the Nott: Canal Bill – gave evidence thereon and consultations. Expenses 10s. 6d. 5.
May 4	Attended all day at H: of Lords on the Nott: Canal Bill. Examined much – 5. Expenses 5s. 6d.
May 7	Attended Committee of Com'rs. on the Grantham Canal Bill. *not* exam'd. Gave advice – consulted with Counsel.
May 8	Attended Mr. Britten's affair at Guildhall. Attended again at Grantham Canal Bill, not examined. Advice etc. – 3.
May 12	Attended again on Sir R. Sutton, Gissop and Jackson, in Hanover Square, and the Com'ee on the Granth: Canal Bill. 3.
May 14	Attended a meeting of Sir Rich. Sutton's on Grant: Canal Bill and gave a clause for the Devon waters. Attended at H: of Commons etc. etc. 3.
May 15	Attended again at Com'ee of Commons on said business and gave a sketch to explain the clause. – 3.
May 29	Attended meeting at C. & Anchor, of the Ouze drainage & Navigation, on proposed Bill. – 3. Gave many explanations.
May 30	Attended on the above meeting at do. and then on the Bedford level Corporation to whom also many explanations were given. – 3.
May 31	Went to Ware and to Amwell. Begun works of pumping out river. Branch found no difficulty from any spring.
June 3	Went to gauge, stop gate, tumbling bay, Mill, Ballance Engine, etc. etc.
June 5	Returned to London.
June 16	Laid out the line of the New Cut near Lynn, on the Ouze Navigation and sent the Map back again to Mr. Watte. – 5.
June 21	Wrote Mr. Watte on the Map, New Cut etc. see 16th. – 0.
June 22	Went to Amwell. Examined the branch of the old River.
June 25	Returned to town.
June 27	Surveyed an estate of Mr. Campbell's at Hundon Square – examined, measured etc. etc. made valuations. – 2.
July 2	Viewed Mrs. H's. estate, at St. Margaret's Hill. Called on Mrs. Perkins on sale etc. Viewed Mr. Allen's house etc. Wrote Mrs. Hamond thereon. 1.
July 3	Surveyed for Stationers Company Mr. Chawner's house, in respect of furnaces fire, flews, and settlements, and made a written report to the Master, Mr. Baldwyn. 1.
July 5	Left London – by Uxbridge, Amersham, Windsor. At Aylesbury.
July 6	At Oxford. At Woodstock.
July 10	Meeting on party wall. At Eynsham.

July 11	At London. In pocket £1 13s. 6d.
July 14	Waited on Mr. Chawner, by desire of Stationers Company, and shewed him the works necessary to be done for prevention against fire. ½.
July 16	Sent the D. of Argyll a design for a double church at Inverary of the following drawings: a plan, elevation, 2 cross sections, and 1 long section, all neatly washed, figured etc. etc. 25.
July 20	Went to Amwell and Ware on the repairs of tumbling bay etc. Ordered pumping works for tomorrow. Pumpt out water. Inspected foundations.
July 24	As I could not leave town, wrote various letters on the dispute on the Severn improvement, to Mr. Houring – Hall – Gesson etc. with directions – when the trial was again put off. – 3.
July 30	Waited on Mr. Baldwin, Pater Noster Row, no meeting, tho' appointed.
Aug. 1	Sent Mr. Black a report, a map and an estimate of a Canal in Oxfordshire from Thurp. 20.
Aug. 3	Set out for the North (In pocket £5 18s. 10d.) stopt at Ware and inspected works etc. at Tumbling Bay. Gave directions. Met Mr. Rooks. Went on northwards; viewed river & mills etc. at Cambridge, and went on to Ely.
Aug. 4	Went to Wisbech. Down the River to the New Cut. Returned to Wisbech.
Aug. 5	Went to Germans Bridge and surveyed New Cut etc. In pocket £2 1s. 3d. At Boston.
Aug. 11	At Leith – viewed Harbour, bridge, links, road, new streets, lands, etc.
Aug. 12	Traced small run of water thro' the gardens etc.
Aug. 13	Viewed North Leith, Peirs, shores, etc. Attended a meeting – dined – consultation to 9.0'clock at night.
Aug. 15	At work on new dock. Went to Leith – examined rivers and ways to and from the proposed new dock.
Aug. 21	Viewed the aqueduct from Loch End to Leith, by desire, considered the subject and wrote Mr. Tibbald a long letter of advice etc. thereon and its difficulties. Expenses 5.
Aug. 24	Went to Baberton.
Aug. 25	Began draft of report on the plan of harbour.
Aug. 26	Went on horse-back, on the Pentland Hills, and viewed the reservoir etc. at Green Craig Vale.
Aug. 28	Went to Leith on survey. Took soundings from elbow of North Pier thro' the Channel to the Beacon. Expenses 6sh. A meeting with the Leith Com'ee.
Sept. 2	Set off for London. In pocket £79 11s. 6d. At Selkirk.
Sept. 5	At Wyersdale, side, Mr. Cawthornes.
Sept. 6	Went and took a complete view of all the parts where the matters in dispute lay. Proceeded to examine evidence all the afternoon. 5.
Sept. 8	Set out. In pocket £8 10s. 6d. At Liverpool.
Sept. 11	At London. In pocket £53 9s. 4d.

Sept. 19 Went to Dartford, settled complaints on Mr. Martyr's workmanship, about rounding off corner, stopping door, etc.

Oct. 17 Sent my plan and report on the Harbour of Leith, docks, etc. $\frac{1}{2}$ of 42. This included the rough plans, 2, given at Edinburgh for temporary discussion.

Oct. 26 Met Mr. Calverton on Mrs. Hamond's estate. Sale. – 1. For Mr. Dunn – went to B. Museum, searched for a Pamphlet, 1723 on do. etc.

Oct. 27 Stopped watering the Bridge. The pipe stolen before the 17th.

Nov. 7 Meeting on Arbitration – of Dispute in Lancashire. Met at the York, heard Counsel and solicitor etc. Adjourned to the 24th.

Nov. 9 Waited on Mr. Jackson, by desire, on the business of the Grantham Council, and the waters of the Devon – long conversation. – 1.

Nov. 16 Met Mr. Rennie on the business of the Ouze.

Nov. 20 Went to Addington – examined library and works of bookcases etc. – stables, offices and road.

Nov. 21 Examined the Church – its walls etc. The situation intended for new stables, the kitchen offices and water closets. Returned to London.

Nov. 24 On the Arbitration of the Wyer etc. heard further evidence and closed the enquiry. – 3. Held a Conference with Mr. Creasy and Rennie on the Ouze, and his intended survey. – 3.

Nov. 30 Met Mr. Stirling, by appointment, on the Braunstone & Hampton Gay Canals. Consultation and advice thereon. – 3.

Dec. 6 In pocket £12 2s. 6d. Left London to go to Southampton.

Dec. 7 Called at Twyford. At Southampton.

Dec. 8 Surveyed the Quays, water, environs, sounded from quay, crossed the River, viewed the town, etc.

Dec. 9 Made a sketch for a Pier.

Dec. 11 Returned to London. In pocket £5 9s. 0d.

Dec. 14 Left London for Yorkshire. In pocket £48 16s. 6d. Called at Amwell and Ware. Viewed works done – ordered post and railing etc. water level.

Dec. 15 At Grantham. Surveyed the Witham Mowbeck end of Canal at Grantham.

Dec. 16 Went to Croxton and Branston with Mr. Dixon. Surveyed the Devon, reservoir & Canal. Down to Bottesford. Returned and lay at Grantham.

Dec. 17 Left Grantham. At Newark; went and surveyed Mills and mouth of the Devon etc. At Newark – Kingston Arms.

Dec. 18 Examined water and the mills. Left Newark. In pocket £34 11s. 0d. Set Mr. Dixon down at Retford. At Doncaster. At Thorne – met Mr. G. Thompson.

Dec. 19 Went up to Stainforth Cut, surveyed line of New Cut, sea banks, drains, levells etc. Passed down the Dam to Thorne Quay, and so back to Thorne.

Dec. 20 Went along Cut to Anthorpe and to Keadly. Returned back on the same line to Hissl. At Mr. Stovins at Hirst.

Dec. 21 Returned, on Horse, by Hatfield.

Dec. 22 Bad morning. Considered plans of 3 navigations. Attended meeting of Com'ee of Dove & Dearn – a conversation. Set off on survey thereon; stopt at Worsbush Bridge – viewed Mill and the Dove and Dodworth. Went on to Barnsley.

Dec. 23 Went to Bridge on the Dearn and surveyed the line round the Wors: Bridge, and then up the Meads etc. to view – returned to Barnsley.

Dec. 24 Attended a meeting of the Com'ee of Dove & Dearn. Went to Oldham's mill and surveyed the line of C: from thence down to Swinton Cut, the land, brooks, springs, etc. then rode to and remained at Rotheram.

Dec. 26 Bad day, in a chaise to Sheffield; viewed line, lands and brooks to that place. Viewed the termination and place for bason. Attended a Committee – made a Report viva voce to the meeting on this Canal.

Dec. 27 At Halifax. Met, Mr. Crosley Brigghouse.

Dec. 28 Viewed the upper end of the Caldor, and the Canal from Sowerby Bridge to Todmerdon, and took all the mills on the land, viewed the River, and the line and ground of the Canal etc. At Manchester – surveyed Canal and end of Bury Canal.

Dec. 30 At Manchester – No Mr. Rennie at the Swan. Finished the Rochdale.

1793

Jan. 4 Called at Uxbridge; Conference on the Colne with Mr. Brook, partner with Mr. Clark. At London. In pocket £40 1s. 4d.

Jan. 24 Set off for Gloucester. At Oxford. In pocket – £21

	4 14	6
	2	6
	£25 17	0
In hand at return –	10 10	0
Expended –	£15 7	0

Jan. 25 At Gloucester.

Jan. 26 At Stroud river, and Westminster. At Gloucester.

Jan. 27 At Berkeley and the Severn.

Jan. 29 At Newark and returned. Made a report to a Com'ee viva voce, long & minute. At Gloucester.

Jan. 30 Set off for London. In pocket £17 6s. 6d. Arrived in London In pocket £10 10s. 0d.

Feb. 3 Attended at North'd. House, met Mr. Starling and Mrs. Henshall on the part of the H. Gayhouse – a long discussion, explanations of propositions, waters, streams etc. – 5.

Feb. 4 Met Mr. Rennie – consultation on the Rochdale. Attended at the Commons the whole day on the 2nd Reading of the Bill and Committee. 3. (not called).

Feb. 5	Consultation with Mr. Stirling on the H. Gay: and the Branstone – went with him to Scon, viewed the Brent, Duke's gardens around, fences, etc. and mouth of the Brent. Then viewed the bridge and water at the railshead for the H. Gay, etc. 3.
Feb. 8	Attended Mr. Stirling on North. House, some Gent'n. at Uxbridge, and Mr. Simcock on the Hampton Gay. The Uxbridge persons and Mr. Stirling afterwards at Waghorne's, in consultation. by the Duke – 2.
Feb. 12	Attended the Com'ee of the Glocester Ca. in Cecil Street. Went with Mr. Flindall to Richmond, waited on Mr. Cambridge, explained the difficulty at his mill – consultation afterwards in town. 3.
Feb. 13	Attended the Rochdale Canal at a Com'ee of H. of Commons. – 3.
Feb. 14	Attended with Mr. Rennie a consultation at Mr. Graham's with Mr. Plumer on the Rochdale Ca. Gave them 2 clauses and a drawing for measuring water, and an estimate of quantity wanted. 2.
Feb. 16	Went to Richmond, ordered last of works for Mr. Sayer's house at Richmond, and inspected state of another house and ordered common repairs thereof. 1. Expenses 4s. 6d.
Feb. 18	Consultation at home with Mr. Dixon on the Grantham Can. Settled a set of clauses for the waters of the Devon. Waited on Mr. Jackson with them etc. 2. Attended the Rochdale Can: Com'ee all day. – 3. Gave an estimate of the Glocester, in a new method, altered from the former. 1.
Feb. 19	Attended a Com'ee on the Ouze Navigation, Man'r. Build's. Then general meeting on the Kings Arms. Gave explanations on the subject – ans'd questions of opponents, recomended the Cut etc. 3. Expenses 10s. 6d. Attended a Com'ee on the Petition of the Glocester Canal – gave evidence etc. 2.
Feb. 20	Sent Mr. Wells long report and estimate for the Glocester Canal, and the 3 plans to the Annexed thereto. See 29th Jan. Plans 15 ⎱ 20. 5 ⎰
Feb. 21	Consultation with Mr. Stirling on the Braunston. Wrote a paper of claims etc. for the D. of North'd. – 1.
Feb. 23	A meeting with Wat. & Gol. on the Ouze, and the section. – 2.
Feb. 26	A meeting and long conference with Mr. Jessop on the Braunston Ca: for Duke of Northumb: relating to waters and lands, fences and conditions agreed on. 5. Attended at Reading of Gloc. Canal Bill in the H: of Commons. 2.
Mar. 5	Attended the Glocester – going to Mr. Welles, Cecil Street, then to Mr. Webbs, Mortimer Street. Gave explan's. on various parts of the land. – 2. Meeting with Mr. Stirling etc. on the Branston – 1. Attended Com'ee and gave evidence on the Petition for the Ouze Nav: etc. all forenoon. – 3. Expenses 9sh.

Mar. 6	Waited on Sir P. Burrel with Mr. Stir; explained the nature of the Bran: Canal and the waters of the Colne. Attended the Com'ee on the Ouze Petition – was examined again. – 3. Meeting with Jessop and conference and above. – 2.
Mar. 7	Attended Com'ee on the Gloc. Canal, settling the Clauses etc., went thro' the Bill. – 3. A long Conference in the Lobby with Sir P. Burrel, Mr. Jessop, Mr. Praed and Mr. Stirling, on the Braun. Can: and its waters etc. 1.
Mar. 8	Left town with Mr. Golborne. At Tetsworth. In pocket £8 0s. 10d.
Mar. 10	Went to Holt Shoal, along with Mr. Golborne, Hall and Young. Met Mr. Hiddhouse, examined the shoal, plans, made surroundings etc. etc. Observations on effect of currents etc. Consultation with Mr. Lycester, Mr. Lane, & Williams, on the approaching Trial. etc.
Mar. 13	Attended trial from 9 to 6 in evening – Gave long evidence as a witness on Gettie's verdict given against the scheme.
Mar. 15	Returned to London. In pocket £10 16s. 7d.
Mar. 17	All day at work on the Ouze – 2. Consultation on the Dearne etc. with Mr. Thorn.
Mar. 21	At Braunston – no business with us. – 1. Attended Petition on the Dearne & Do. Gave evidence. 3. Conversation with Mr. Edmunds on do. 1.
Mar. 22	Conversation on the Ouze with Golborne & Max. Attended on the Braunston – Nothing, 2.
	Do. on the Lords on the Glocester Ca: Sworn – consultations. 3.
Mar. 23	At work, all morning on the Ouze papers. – 2. Made great additions to the Map of the Thorne Canal, for engraver. 1.
Mar. 25	A visit from Edmunds, on the Dearne & Dove, on reservoirs, mills, etc. 1. Attended C'e of Lords on the Glocester C: Gave evidence – Bill came thro'. 3. Attended C'e. on the Braunston – nothing. Consultations with Mr. Stirling. – 2.
Apr. 1	Called on Mr. Wheeler, on Mr. Bishop's lands and business.
Apr. 2	Dined with Lord Hard: on the G: Brink: much consultation thereon. – 1.
Apr. 6	Went by request to Dartford, surveyed the works by Martyr – considered contract and performance. Opinion on coating the outside to be considered.
Apr. 10	Waited on L. Beverly. Explained D. of N. objections. Attended Mr. Stirling to W. Guildhal. Met Mr. Millers. Got petition signed – got it presented. Consultation with Mr. Stirling. 3.
Apr. 11	Met. Mr. St: – Sworn at the H: of Lords. Employed Mr. Milles – wrote out papers for him, made calculations etc. 3.
Apr. 15	Attended the H: of Lords on the Braunston Canal for D. of North'd. Gave evidence, long, having made long calculations and papers for Counc's. Business ended. 3.
Apr. 17	Attended House of Commons on the fate of Rochdale Canal, on the 3rd reading. Thrown out.

Apr. 23	Attended Barnsley C. Com'ee on behalf of the D. & Dove. Consulted with Mr. Jessop, altered clauses for Lochs; read over and marked the Barnsley Act. 3. Met Mr. Sparrow on the Trent – a long cons. explanations etc. 2.
Apr. 25	Met Messrs. Jessop, Rennie, on the Trent and parallel Canal – Long Conference. – 3.
Apr. 26	Studied the object of the Trent, above Nott' Bridge. Met Messrs. Jessop & Rennie thereon, and the land from Nott. to Shardlour – long conference etc. for 6 hours. Came to resolutions. – 5.
May 6	Attended a Co'ee of Enquiry at the Com: on the Thames Com'e. Gave evidence thereon, and on lower Thames. 3.
May 8	Attended Com'ee on Thames Nav: Gave some more evidence etc. 3. This and 2 more articles above could not be paid for by Com'rs. of the Thames as it was to shew the impropriety etc. of their conduct.
May 13	Gave the D. of Argyll an amended design for the double Church at Inverary, the former not being perfect:—a new plan and elevation and the section altered. Nothing – as it was an amendment.
May 20	Met Mr. Trecothick. Gave him a design of 3 drawings for altering the Church – Addington. A sketch for new stables and other offices.
May 21	Went to Amwell – surveyed by the way the stone sluice, the Drains Ditch at Bushill, Mrs. Th's house etc., Mr. Mallish's waste gate and matters End: Chase. At Amwell.
May 22	Examined manifold Ditch in a minute manner.
May 25	Returned to London. In pocket £6 4s. 6d.
June 3	Waited on Mr. Tre: in Bucklersbury on his stables, church, and library. Met Mr. Tricker on Mrs. Hamond's wall.
June 9	Went up the River past the Mill to the Ballance Engine and examined it. Surveyed manifold ditch – gave directions etc. at Chadwell Spring.
June 10	Measured Amwell Springs – gave directions on works of different kinds. Returned to London. In pocket £3 13s. 2d.
June 12	Attended the House of Commons after several days investigations on the New Road proposed by the Albion Mill Company. B. Bridge business.
July 5	Waited on S. G. Yonge, by desire, on the affairs of the Western Canal – 2. and on a former occasion for receiving instructions – 2.
July 11	Sent Mr. Trecothick a new plan for stables offices etc. on a square scheme.
July 12	Left Tron, to go to Devon.
July 14	At Cullompton.
July 15	Went on Select Com'ee of Canal. Consultations, advice, receiving instructions on survey. At Exeter – surveyed River, Bridge, Sluice.
July 16	Went down Old Navigation to County Bridge – surveyed Topsham, and Harbour. At Topsham.

July 20	At Bridgwater. Finished Canal Survey. At Cross, near Axbridge, went to Bleydon near the Mouth of the Axe. At Bristol.
July 21	Surveyed the River etc. At Bath.
July 22	Left Bath.
July 23	At London.
July 30	Sent a long Report on the G. Western Canal with many calculations & estimates therein and soundings etc, Strictures on the Exeter and Taunton Navigation and the Somerset Canal, Whitworth, plans etc. 30.
Aug. 2	Went to Windsor. Attended a meeting of the Com'rs. of River Thames. Dined there – went to Marlow.
Aug. 6	Returned to London. In pocket £11 17s. 10d.
Aug. 9	Mr. Gray from Exeter called, about a Navigation to Crediton. Nothing – this was a fetch.
Aug. 23	Set out for Windsor – in pocket £21 8s. 0d. Measured the Kings Stream. At the Swan. Measured the town's Cutt and Stream.
Aug. 24	Attended a meeting at Town Hall. Gave in Report – answered many queries about the Cutt, River, Windsor Bridge etc. 2. Returned to London – in pocket £19 16s. 6d.
Aug. 26	Attended a meeting of Comm's. on the Canal Co. from Taplow to Isleworth, was appointed jointly with Mr. Whitworth, Engineer thereto. Received instructions to make a survey.
Sept. 1	Returned to London. In pocket £7 7s. 0d.
Sept. 2	Set off to survey New Canal from Boulters Lock. In pocket £7 7s. 0d. Began at Taplow Mill – came down to Dorney etc. and lay at Eton.
Sept. 3	Ended at last, Belfont. At Hounslow.
Sept. 4	Came down the line to Hanworth Park, Twickenham etc. etc. and ended at Rails-head. Returned to London. In pocket £5 18s. 4d.
Sept. 9	Meeting at Mr. Crowthers Chambers. Made a report in writing, delivered a new plan and estimate of Canal, from Isleworth etc.
Sept. 10	Went with Subcom'ee to Twickenham. Viewed Mr. Coles and other premises at Stone bridge; settled the line of Canal. Dined at Richmond and viewed the railshead.
Sept. 11	Waited Mr. Chapman about the Stat'rs. Company's business – ordered iron rails etc. to be painted and other works done. 1.
Sept. 13	Journey to Glocester.
Sept. 18	At Glocester – Attended a Committee – made report.
Sept. 19	Went to Whitminister. Finished at this place & moved to Berkely.
Sept. 20	All day, setting out Canal etc. At Berkely.
Sept. 21	Left Berkely. Measured the Cam. Returned to Glocester. Took levels and sounded river etc.
Sept. 22	Set out for Bristol with Mr. Hall. In pocket £20 11s. 6d. At Bristol.
Sept. 24	At Cirencester.
Sept. 26	At Gloster. In pocket £11 0s. 0d.

Sept. 27	Dined with Mr. Comeline.
Oct. 2	Arrived in town. In pocket £11 7*s.* 4*d.*
Oct. 4	Waited on the Stationers Stock: Compt. about wind in a house, let by them to the porter of the resid: in Amen Corner etc. $\frac{1}{2}$.
Oct. 14	Attended a meeting of Isleworth Canal at Mr. Cr's. Gave them a report on middle line etc. 3. Report. 3.
Oct. 17	Set off for Norfolk etc. At Cambridge.
Oct. 18	Attended meeting of Com'ee of Ouse Navigation the whole forenoon. Left Cambridge. At Ely.
Oct. 19	At Lynn. Surveyed above and below Lynn from jetty to the Crutch, taking levels, fixing low water and high water marks.
Oct. 20	Surveyed North side of harbour from the Old Hall to the Crutch beacon. Corrected map and noticed Hodkinson's errors.
Oct. 21	Levelled from jetty above Sandham to the Crutch and compared levels of high and low waters. Left Lynn – Met Messrs. Creasy, Watte, Golborne at Downham, Mr. Jeffery's.
Oct. 22	At Denver's, surveyed sluice and corrected drawing; took soundings. Proceeded up the Ouze with observations etc. for side rivers. At Ely.
Oct. 23	Went upwards all the way to Clayhithe, observing, surveying and writing. Took Mr. Watte my plan of the Ouze etc. for Map. At Ware.
Oct. 24	In town to breakfast. In pocket £10 19*s.* 3*d.*
Oct. 28	Wrote Mr. Creasy and sent him a paper of additional works proposed on the Ouze. Wrote Mr. Watte's twice on the maps etc.
Nov. 1	Left town. At Ware.
Nov. 2	Furnishing Mrs. Godin's house. Sent Dow: to get perfect the owners etc. and (?) of London Canal.
Nov. 4	Returned to town. In pocket £2 19*s.* 6*d.*
Nov. 5	Set out with Com'ee of Delegates to Bolters Loch, and going from thence along the line of Canal, waiting on diff'nt persons and shewing the line and various parts of it.
Nov. 6	Returned to London.
Nov. 10	Settled finally the Dartford Church affairs and certified the Bill at £1125 17*s.* 6*d.* Wrote Mr. Williams and Martry thereon. Sent Mr. Dow: to Mr. Trecothick's to measure.
Nov. 19	Surveyed Marl: Street House, and wrote many letters thereon.
Nov. 30	Went up on a survey of Fleet D. River with Lewis, Dance, Cockerel & Wyat.
Dec. 9	Went to Stratford – surveyed Messrs. Cooke's Distillery as to use of waste water etc. 2.
Dec. 11	Meeting surveyors at York, Hotchson, Fleet Ditch Sewer – long consultation.
Dec. 16	Inspected Stationers Company's estate, Friers Alley.
Dec. 18	Viewed Stat: Co. Estate, Friers Alley. Met Mr. Robinson.
Dec. 19	Attended Stat: Company and reported progress.
Dec. 23	Went to Bushill on works of arch etc. Sent Mr. Crowther 2 plans of the Gibbons and the Bm. Abbey Estates made by M. and line of Canal drawn on each of them. 10.

Jan. 3   Went to Bushill on works of Great Sewer etc.

Jan. 5   Went to Twickenham; called on Mr. Sayers – ordered work of balcony support, water pipe etc. Then – Waited on Mr. Cambridge on his Mills and Lands for Glocester Canal and various parts of his works. Long and tedious. – 3.

Jan. 7   Went to East Cheap with Mr. Burton. Met Mr. Peacock and Frisher – surveyed and examined party wall of Mrs. Hamond's houses; condemned the wall etc. 3. Reporting to Mrs. Haw.

Jan. 12   At work all day on making a Card plan for London Canal.

Jan. 14   Fleet Ditch – meeting – at the York. Long disputes, reasonings etc.

Jan. 22   Receiving a letter from and writing a long answer to Mr. Moxon, on behalf of the Hull D. Company. – 1.

Jan. 28   Attended a meeting of London C. Com'ee. Gave advice etc. delivered 150 Card plans etc. – 3.

Feb. 4   Attended a meeting of the Com'rs. of the Thames Navig: on behalf of the London Canal. Gave evidence, opinions, etc. 3.

Feb. 8   Wrote Mr. Trecothick, on stables, Church etc. 1. Wrote to Gloc'r. on Canal, estimate, bricks etc.

Feb. 13   Attended Com'ee on the Petition of the Ouze 3.

Feb. 14   Waited on Mr. Wil'm. Gibbons on the London Canal, and about his property near Stanwick – 2.

Feb. 16   Gave Mr. Crowther, another plan of the London Canal, complete. 2.

Feb. 18   Attended Com'ee on the Ouze all forenoon. 3.

Feb. 24   Waited on Sir W. Gibbons, settled with him all matters of Stanwell, except Mr. Pope's. Gave him a plan of a new line for that purpose. 2.

Mar. 2   Attended Com. of Commons on the Petition of the London Canal – gave evidence self & clerk. 4. Waited on Com'ee of Eau Brink, advice etc. 1.

Mar. 3   Attended H. of Commons on the Eau B: Cut, to be heard at the Bar. – 3.

Mar. 7   Attended the Com'ee of London Canal, at a Conference with a delegation of the Kennet & Avon Canal, on a New Line from Reading thro' Wind'r. to London. 3.

Mar. 12   Attended H. of Commons on Eaubrink Cut and examination of witnesses against it. 3.

Mar. 16   Studying the question of Hull Harbour yesterday and to-day. – 3.

Mar. 19   Gave Mr. Tricart, drawings of a Digging Engine for G. Berkely Canal – to get a model thereof. 5.

Mar. 21   Wrote G. & Berkely a long letter on F. Engine. Attended the House of Commons, on the Ouze as above. 3.

Mar. 22   Attended Com'ee on the London Canal when the same was postponed till next session. 3.

Mar. 31   Waited on Mr. Rollestone on the K. and Avon and the S. and Severn Canals. Nothing to be got.

Apr. 5	Went to Mr. Hoare's ponds etc., and on bridges in the road, wastes, and Highbury bank.
Apr. 7	Attended Com'ee on the E. Brink all day – no hearing – expenses: dinner & coach hire: 10 sh.
Apr. 10	Attended Com'ee of E.B. Bill, and gave advice on the proposition of Mr. Foster and Sir T. Page's agency, plan etc. 3. Expenses 10 sh.
Apr. 12	Attended Messrs. Burley & Dunn on D. of Bolton's Water Works, received instructions etc. 1. Went to Cook's Distillery with Mr. Rennie, to view the waste water and other particulars, and settled a plan for a water wheel and other works. 3. Coach-hire: 11 sh. Gave a drawing, first idea, of said wheel etc.
Apr. 18	Set out for Amwell. Viewed the 2 bridges, sluice, Highbury Bank, Arch-Bushill, Mellish water, Treacher's house etc. At Amwell.
Apr. 26	Met Mr. Chiffin – on Barn to be Cut, farmyard etc. Left Amwell; surveyed length of river, near Brox. Church, Gravelfield etc. Returned to London. In pocket £5 6s. 0d.
Apr. 28	Called on Johnson, at Mrs. Hamond's wall – settled chimneys, stairs etc. 2.
May 3	Set out for Hackwood, Hants. Viewed Canal at Bradford. Viewed Staines Bridge. At Basingstoke – went and viewed Park House, and ponds at Hackwood. Met Mr. Brazier at Basingstoke.
May 5	Set off for town. At London.
May 6	Attended all day on the Com'ee and in the House of Commons on the E. Brink Bill. 3. Expenses 7s. 6d.
May 7	Attended Com'ee at Guildhall. Attended Consultation at Com'ee Room, Man'n. Buildings, and then in H. of Commons till 9 on the E. Brink. Mr. Phillips ended and Mr. Graham opened. Expenses 7.
May 8	Attended Mr. Soane at the Bank; examined and surveyed state of Great Dome with him and Mr. Dance; condemned it all, rotten. Made a report thereon jointly to the Governors. 5. In pocket £16 1s. 0d.
May 19	Attended H. of Commons on the E. Brink Cut – nothing done. Gave Mr. Creasy calculations on falls on the Ouze etc. 3. Expenses 6s. 6d.
May 22	At work for an hour with Mr. Dettagne on deeds of Norwich Water Works.
May 24	Went to G. plan Cistern, on its being pulled to pieces – ordered and set out a new one – Viewed bridges in Green Lanes. Proceeded to Bushill – examined arch and works. Set out new additional work at east end. Plan of Mr. Mellish's ground etc. Returned to town.
May 25	Attended a meeting of the London Canal; subscribers to receive instructions for surveys of the Thames and different lines of Canals from Reading to London. 3.
May 31	Went G. M. Cistern – then to Bushill works, Mellish ground, sewer etc. Then to Ware and Amwell.

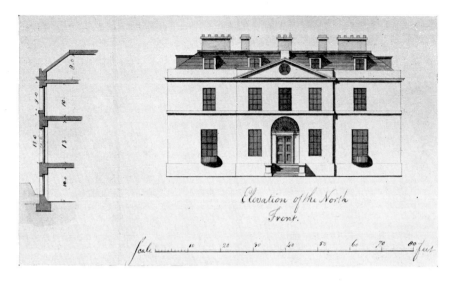

47 STRATHMYLE FIFE: General Sir Robert Skene's house.
Elevation of North front

48 STRATHMYLE, FIFE: General Sir Robert Skene's house.
Alternative elevation

49 PITLOUR: FRONT OF HOUSE

50 PITLOUR: THE HALL

June 2	Set off for town – visited Bushill works. In town. In pocket £10 15s. 2d.
June 3	Attended Mr. Chapman at Stationers Hall on the subject of the Wood Street Estates. 1.
June 4	Made out a long report on supply of water at Hackwood, and necessary improvements thereof – 9 pages – Sent it to Messrs. Burley and Dunn. – 10. In pocket £27 4s. 6d.
June 5	Left town to go to Glocester. At Henley.
June 6	Went to Abingdon. At Brimscombe Port House, of the Company.
June 7	Went down the Strand Canal to Whitminster. At Glocester – begun view.
June 9	Attended a meeting of Com'ee all the forenoon and the whole day. Dined together. Went and examined Mr. Trye's machine.
June 10	Set out the figure of the New Bason. The Island, streets etc.
June 11	Set off for Berkeley. Went to Branwood, Sharpness, Pill Mouth. At Berkeley.
June 12	Went to S. Side of Pill Mouth and down to Merrett's house etc. Examined Colateral Cut. At Berkeley.
June 13	Com'ee at breakfast. Went to Pill Mouth etc. Line of Canal & Colateral Cut. Went Whitminster with Com'ee. At Glocester.
June 23	Viewed and examined a house in Bedford Square, North Side, for Mr. Campbell, gave him a paper of observations thereon. 1.
June 27	Wrote Mr. Dehagne and sent him 2 plans of Norwich Water Works, copies of the ones lately made, for the Deeds, on parchment; one done in part by Milne. These drawings (3) and altering the Deeds, Meetings with Mr. Dehagne, letter, parcels etc. altogether. 16.
July 5	Set out for Amwell. Settled works by G. Man Cistern. Viewed and settled works at Bushill – arch, bridge, sewer etc. At Amwell.
July 8	Set off for the Thames. In pocket £16 7s. 0d.
July 9	At the Sun, Maidenhead. Went to Cookham – surveyed branch of Thames from thence to river at Sir G. Young's. Returned to Maidenhead. Set out for the Bridge down to Windsor. At Eton. Met Mr Whitworth.
July 10	Set off down the river. Dined at Staines.
July 11	At Sheperton.
July 12	Dined at Hampton Wick. Went to Horton Common. At East Bedfont.
July 13	Set off for London. In London 12 o'clock.
Aug. 1	Meeting of T's. at Henley.
Aug. 2	To Amwell – inspected and ordered works at G. M. Cistern. Do. at Bushill – arch, road bridge, and waste gate. At Amwell.
Aug. 4	Set out foundations for New House.
Aug. 5	Returned to London. Meeting of London Canal. Canal Subscribers, report by Mr. Rennie brought – nothing done. 3. Attended a Court of Stationers Company. Reported a new plan of estates, Wood Street. 5. Attendance to-day 2.

Aug. 7	Board. Set out for Glocester at one. Measured Finch's allowance. Examined Burn. Abbey lands; found water of the Thames 14 Gs. down at M. H. Bridge. At Kensington.
Aug. 8	At Glocester – conference with Mr. Grazebrook until night.
Aug. 11	Renewed Conference with Mr. G. Dined together. Attended meeting of Commissioners. Long Conference between them and Mr. G. on Bristol Canal.
Aug. 13	Set out for London at 5. – by Cirencester, Burford, Oxford and Uxbridge. Arrived in London at 9. In pocket £7 11s. 0d.
Aug. 21	Attended Stationers Hall by desire on the matter of Plinth to a Gateway, for its repair. ½. Went with Mr. Cross – surveyed wharf and warehouses, Southwark, near London Bridge.
Aug. 22	Consultation with Ross on warehouses and wharfs in Tolsey Street. Opinion on value etc. – in all 5.
Aug. 23	Went to Amwell.
Aug. 26	Returned to London – Called at Bushill, viewed Treacher's house, the bridge, and sluice, finished, and the works of arch – ordered more. In pocket £5 15s. 2d.
Sept. 2	Attended Stationers Company – bound Robin Prentice to Mr. Holland. Delivered to Court 4 papers of particulars and conditions for letting several premises in Wood Street and Friers Alley. 4. Attended letting of houses – 2 being agreed for – 4. Reference to general plan etc. Examined the kitchen – reported on alteration of various fixtures etc. 1.
Sept. 4	To Scotland. Set out at 3 o'clock. Called at Bushill – inspected – ordered more of the works. Called at Amwell. Marked out Mr. Small's grave. At Royston. In pocket £31 13s. 0d.
Sept. 9	At Edinburgh, and at Dumbroons.
Sept. 13	Went to Baberton.
Sept. 14	Went to Redhall & Cn. Inglis.
Sept. 15	Went to Haton, and Dalmatroy. Dined with Lord Morton.
Sept. 16	Returned to Edinburgh. At Mr. Brown's. Dined with Admiral Duncan's.
Sept. 21	Dined with the Provost.
Sept. 25	News of Maria's death. Dined at Leith.
Oct. 1	Arrived in London. In pocket £13 2s. 3d.
Oct. 7	Attended at Stationers Hall, when 2 houses, Nos. 11 & 13, were let and all matters finally settled. Ordered some additional works in kitchen etc. ½.
Oct. 8	Measured Mrs. Hamond's party wall – made out Bill and delivered it to Mr. Costen. Wrote twice to Mr. Selby – called at Alnwick. Inspected plans at Sessions, of the Paddington branch Canal and the New London Canal – on behalf of the D. of North'd.
Oct. 12	Surveyed River up to Springs gauge, T. Bay, and ordered some works. Inspected Bal. Engine, Timbers near ground, banks etc.; found water very low, Gate 10½ gr. open – key can't come off. River low, weeds sunk down, Mill at work the Sunday. Ordered to shut down.
Oct. 13	At Amwell.

Oct. 14	Called on Sir H. Hume to see his wants. At London.
Oct. 15	Wrote Mr. Creasy on E. B. Cut and proposition from Lynn etc. postage – 1. Took the Dilapidations by Mr. Lambert at No. 11 Wood Street – Stationers Company. Met Mr. Delight for, Messrs. Cantwell & Goodal against – on a party wall at Mr. Sayer's house.
Oct. 18	Set off for Glocester. At Henley.
Oct. 19	At Glocester – $\frac{1}{2}$ past 4.
Oct. 20	To be at Glocester. Dined at the Bell.
Oct. 22	Dined with Mr. Fendall. At Maston all night.
Oct. 23	Called on by Mr. Webb of the Lower George to survey St. Nicholas Church & steeple – Dined with Mr. Frye.
Oct. 24	Surveyed and examined minutely the several parts of St. Nicholas Church & Steeple. Dined at the Bell.
Oct. 25	Dined with Dr. Cheston. A meeting.
Oct. 27	Meeting at Glocester. Washed – Dined with G. Meeting. Surveyed remainder of business at St. N. Steeple.
Oct. 28	Attended a Com'ee of G. & B. Canal. Set off for London. At Buscott Park. In pocket £4 3s. 2d.
Oct. 29	Mr. Cripp's, having been a companion and paid half – in pocket £27 0s. 0d. In London.
Nov. 7	Wrote a long report with a drawing annexed, on St. Nicholas Church & Steeple in Glocester, after repeated visits, surveys, drawings to the Bishop of G. – 10.
Nov. 8	Went to Amwell; viewed the G.M. Cistern – work at Bushill – ordered stoppage for the winter.
Nov. 10	Met Mr. King and settled the New Cut near the Red House. Ordered Usborne to do wharfing for the Tump. Trustees. Went to Wormleybury.
Nov. 11	Examined cesspool, drains, smell, smoke etc. and gave advice on the whole and how to treat them. Priveys etc. Returned to London.
Dec. 1	Had a conversation with Mr. Selby and Mr. Stirling on D. of North'ds. interest in the Colne, and a former evening one with Mr. Stirling.
Dec. 12	Began the works of the Sewer in Bridge Street.
Dec. 22	Set out for Portsmouth with Capt. Hin. At Petersfield.
Dec. 23	Arrived at Portsmouth. Met Mrs. Thompson and Caroline. At the George.
Dec. 25	Surveyed Gesop Creek, Gosport lines, etc.
Dec. 26	Viewed shore of Gosport, Charlsfort, New Bridge, etc.
Dec. 29	Surveying Yard etc.

A list of *Mail Coaches* which set out on the Week Days at Eight, and on Sunday at Seven in the Evening.

BATH AND BRISTOL, through Hounslow, Maidenhead, Reading, Newbury, Hungerford, Marlborough, Devizes, Calne, and Chippenham, and continued to Wells, Glastonbury, Bridgwater, Taunton, Wellington, and Exeter; from Swan, Lad-lane.

CARMARTHEN & MILFORD HAVEN, & HUBERSTONE; from Swan, Lad-lane.

CHESTER & HOLYHEAD; through Northampton, Welford, Lutterworth, Hinkley, Atherstone, Tamworth, Litchfield, Stafford, Ware, Nantwich, Taporley, Holywell, Conway, and Bangor; from Golden-cross, Charing-cross.

CARLISLE; through Penrith, Kendal, and Lancaster; from Swan, Lad-lane.

DOVER; through Dartford, Rochester, Chatham, Canterbury, Margate, Ramsgate, Deal, Sandwich, Folkestone, Feversham, and Sittingborn; from George and Blue Boar, High Holborn.

EDINBURGH; through Ware, Buntingford, Royston, Caxton, Huntingdon, Aukinbury Hill, Stilton, Wandesford, Stamford, Witham Common, Colsterworth, Grantham, Newark, Tuxford, Retford, Barnaby-Moor, Bawtry, Doncaster, Ferry Bridge, Milford, Tadcaster (York), Northallerton, Darlington, Durham, Newcastle, Berwick on Tweed; from Bull and Mouth, near Aldersgate Street.

EXETER; through Basingstoke, Andover, Salisbury, Blandford, Dorchester, Bridport, Axminster, and Honiton; from Swan, Lad-Lane.

GLOUCESTER; through Henley, Benson, Oxford, Witney, Burford, Northleach, and Cheltenham; from Angel, behind St. Clements, and Gloucester Coffee-house, Piccadilly.

HULL; through York and Beverly; from Bull and Mouth, near Aldersgate Street.

LIVERPOOL; through Prescot, Warrington, Knutsford, Congleton, Newcastle under Line, Stone, Litchfield, Wolseley Bridge, Rudgeley, Meriden, Coventry, Dunchurch, Daventry, Towcester, Foster's Booth, Stoney Stratford, Fenny Stratford, and Brickhill; from Swan, Lad-lane.

MANCHESTER & DERBY; through Newhaven, Buckton, Stockport, Ashbourn, Loughborough, Leicester, Harborough, Northampton, and Newport Pagnel; from Swan, Lad-lane.

MACCLESFIELD & BEEK; from Swan, Lad-lane.

MARGATE & RAMSGATE; through Dartford, Chatham, Rochester, Sittingborne, and Canterbury; from George and Blue Boar, High Holborn.

NORWICH; through Ilford, Romford, Brentwood, Ingatestone, Chelmsford, Witham, Kelvedon, Colchester, Ipswich, Stoneham, Schole-Inn and Long Stratton; from White-horse, Fetter Lane.

NORWICH & YARMOUTH; through Epping, Harlow, Hockerhill, Littleburgh, Bournebridge, Newmarket, Barton Mills, Thetford, Larlingford, Attleborough, and Wymondham; from Whitehorse, Fetter Lane.

NOTTINGHAM & LEEDS; through St. Albans, Newport, Dunstable, Woodburn, Northampton, Harborough, Leicester, Loughborough, Mansfield, Chesterfield, Sheffield, Barnsley and Wakefield; from Bull and Mouth, near Aldersgate Street.

OXFORD; through Hounslow, Colnbrook, Slough, Maidenhead, and Henley; from Bull and Mouth, near Aldersgate Street.

PLYMOUTH & FALMOUTH; through Basingstoke, Andover, Salisbury, Blandford, Dorchester, Bridport, Axminster, Honiton, and Exeter; from Swan, Lad-lane.

PORTSMOUTH; through Kingston, Esher, Cobham, Ripley, Guildford, Godalming, Liphook, and Petersfield; from Angel, behind St. Clement's.

SHREWSBURY, BIRMINGHAM, KIDDERMINSTER & BEWDLEY; through Southall, Uxbridge, Beaconsfield, High Wycombe, Tetsworth, Wheatley, Oxford, Woodstock, Shipton upon Stour, Henley in Arden, Wolverhampton, Shiffnal, Stratford upon Avon, Chappelhouse, Billstone and Wellington; from Bull and Mouth, near Aldersgate Street.

SOUTHAMPTON & POOLE; through Staines, Bagshot, Alton, Alresford, Winchester, Lindhurst, Lymington, Ringwood, and Wymbourne; from Bell and Crown, Holborn.

SWANSEA & NEATH; through Newbury, Wellington, Marlborough, Devizes, Calne, Chippenham, Bath, Bristol, Newport, Cardiff, Cowbridge, and Pyle; from Swan, Lad-lane.

WORCESTER & LUDLOW; through Hounslow, Colnbrook, Maidenhead, Henley, Nettlebed, Oxford, Woodstock, Euston, Chipping-Norton, Morton in the Marsh, Evesham, Pershore, Tenbury, Broadway, and Bingworth; from Bull and Mouth, near Aldersgate Street.

YORK, NEWCASTLE & EDINBURGH; through Stamford, Grantham, Newark, Doncaster, and Ferry-bridge; from Bull and Mouth, near Aldersgate Street.

1795 to 1799

The Diaries for the years 1795 to 1799 contain the following items of interest: 1795: *Consultations on the Gloucester Canal.* 1796: *Consultations on the Gloucester Canal. Consultations with Rennie on the Maidstone navigation.* 1797: *Death of Mrs. Mylne at Amwell.* 1798: *Death of his son, Robert, at sea on his way to Gibraltar.* 1799: *Prepare schemes for refronting Stationers' Hall, London.*

1795

Jan. 3	Went and viewed the Dockyard. On board the Royal Charlotte, 110 Guns Lord Howe's ship.
Jan. 4	Set off for town at 10. In pocket £34 9s. 6d. Went round by Chichester and Brighton. At Chichester – viewed Cross & Cathedral. Went to Bognor – digned with S. R. Hotham. Viewed buildings, pier, shore etc. Set off. At Arundel all night.
Jan. 5	Went to Brighton. Viewed the place, pavilion, shore. Set off after dinner. At Ryegate.
Jan. 6	In town at one o'clock. Attended Com'ee on E. Brink Petition. 2.
Jan. 14	Wrote Mr. Selby on D. Northumb'ds. opposition to the Padington Cut Bill. 1.
Jan. 15	Called on Mr. Selby at Sessions House, long conversation on the above Cut. etc.
Jan. 23	Corrected a plan for Dep'y. Birch, of an hour garden etc. at Cambridge; to compare and made a new plan thereof to a larger scale.
Jan. 25	Wrote Lord Hardwick and Sr. T's. Page two long letters, on matter of Treaty on E. Brink.
Feb. 11	Portsmouth Harbour; attended a consultation at the Apt. Generals on the Cause, and advising him and the Solicitor General to get a Bill to stop all encroachment whatsoever. 2.
Mar. 4	All day at work, with Sir Thom's. Page on New Cutt, fens, Lynn Harbour, etc.
Mar. 5	Called at Com'ee Room of E. Brink. Reported progress to Mr. York & Creasy. Long Conference.
Mar. 7	Waited on Lord Hardwick in form with one copy on behalf of Eau Brink. Long conference.
Mar. 8	At work on making a plan of the New Cut according to the agreement with Sir T. H. Page.
Mar. 14	Set out for Ware; inspected the Bank over Hornsey Wood and the repair thereof. Viewed works at Bushill, bank, arch. At Amwell – 2.
Mar. 15	Viewed Red House, damages to Bank etc.

Mar. 16	Returned to London.
Mar. 19	Set out for Glocester.
Apr. 1	Left Glocester. In pocket £15 0s. 0d. At Uxbridge.
Apr. 2	In London by 9.
Apr. 8	Went to G. Man C. – Bowes Farm, Bushill, Mr. Mellish's water, and Amwell.
Apr. 13	Went to Ballance Engine, Red House.
Apr. 15	Went to town. In pocket £3 3s. 3d.
Apr. 18	At work with Mr. Ball on Clauses for Bill, and Mr. Cubitt from Sir T. Page. My clerk drew the new lines for the Cutt on 3 small plans, and on the large one which was at Glocester. 3.
Apr. 19	At work all day on sections of new cut, and plans thereof, on new system. 3. Writing Mr. Escourt and Mr. Ball on Clause.
May 9	Went to Ware. Surveyed works at the Green Man Cistern, High Banks, Hornsey Wood, Iron drain pipe, Bowes Farm, Bushill arch etc. and Mellish's water.
May 12	Leave Amwell. In town. In pocket 7s. 6d.
May 16	To Glocester at 11.
May 18	Meeting of Com'ee advertised. Dined at Boothall.
May 21	Leave of absence. Dined with Mr. Fendall. At Matson.
May 22	Came to town.
May 26	Com'ee. Dined at Mr. Raikes. At Maston.
May 27	In Glocester.
May 31	Dined with Mr. Comeline Dr. Cheston.
June 2	In London at 8. In pocket £7 12s. 10d. Expenses up £6 14s. 0d.
June 18	Stationers: Gave Mr. Baldwin 2 plans for leases of Tagg & Lambird's houses in Wood Street, with duplicates for counterpart. Not charged to the Company – Received from Mr. Baldwin afterwards.
June 24	To London. Sworn at H. of Lords, on Sewer Bill.
July 1	St. Paul's. In pocket £21 2s. 0d.
July 2	Set off for Glocester at 2. At Tetsworth.
July 4	At Glocester.
July 6	Shut up St. Paul's.
July 8	Set off for London at 6. At Uxbridge at ½ past 9.
July 31	Centenary Club.
Aug. 21	At Glocester – a meeting.
Aug. 24	A Com'ee; some business done, nequorum. At Matson.
Aug. 27	At London – 9. In pocket £3 13s. 6d.
Aug. 30	At Amwell.
Sept. 6	Opened the Church of St. Paul's. At Amwell.
Sept. 18	Mr. Dadford came to Glocester.
Sept. 23	To town.
Sept. 24	Met Mr. Dance on Mr. Martin's wharf; viewed it and considered his interests.
Oct. 3	Left town at 2. At Tetsworth.
Oct. 4	At Oxford – breakfast. Went round by Marston to Ronsham; viewed etc. Mrs. Coxhead's farm. At Ronsham (see Nov. 8th, 1797).
Oct. 5	Examined roof and witnesses thereon; collected the Bills etc.

Oct. 6	At Glocester at 12 – viewed works and attended a meeting of Committee.
Oct. 11	At Matson.
Oct. 14	Left Glocester at 6. At Uxbridge at 8.
Oct. 15	In town. In pocket £6 8s. 0d.
Oct. 20	Surveyed Lord Fitzwilliams house for Mr. Coutts along with Mr. Whitfoord. Dined at Thatch House, St. James' St.
Nov. 3	Removed to town from Amwell.
Nov. 4	Gave Mr. Coutt's, thro' Mr. Whitfoord, a survey and valuation of Lord Fitzwilliam's house in Piccadilly etc. £14,000. – 10 g's.
Nov. 12	Waited on Mr. Ingram – Sir Clem' Cottrell's business.
Nov. 19	Met Mr. Tupp and 3 other Surv's. on the value of Mr. Tharp's premises. Settled value at £5,000. Signed a Report etc.
Nov. 24	Surveyed house next door, east of the E. India House, belonging to Mr. Gonshaw, and possessed by Mr. Swift, Frank Maker – along with Mr. Cockerel & Tupp, and valued at £2,300. – 2½.
Nov. 28	To Amwell. Bushill – Bosaryuck's Door.
Dec. 14	Surveyed the course of a drain from Stationers Court to Ludgate Hill – examined into Rights etc. – 1.
Dec. 28	To Glocester at 10. In pocket £16 5s. 6d. By the Henley Road. At Oxford at 7.
Dec. 31	Dined at Matson – all night there.
NB	Expenses by Henley Road to Oxford £4 0s. 6d.

1796

Jan. 1	At Matson. Attended a Committee. Mr. Comeline & Dadford dined with me. At Glocester.
Jan. 2	Went on line, beyond Hampsted Hill, to Dr. Lyson's house – and Elsmore Land – setting out the Middle line.
Jan. 3	Mr. Thomas. Mr. Rinkerton & Mr. Pixton. } Did business with them for the Comp'n. all the forenoon.
Jan. 5	Went along the Canal and set out the Central line as far as ½ Mile beyond and South of Russers Lane.
Jan. 10	Set out for London, with Mr. Mills, in his Chaise to Frogmill.
Jan. 11	In town at 4. In pocket £6 18s. 10d.
Jan. 15	Waited on D. of Argyll, on Mr. Campbell's house in Marlboro' Street. etc.
Jan. 19	Called on Mr. Baldwin on Leases of Stationers Comp'y. Met Mr. Dann, on No. 11. Gave Mr. Baldwin the 2 Schedules of Mr. Tagg's, No. 12, and Mr. Bolton, No. 11.
Jan. 23	Sent Mr. Baldwin 2 Schedules of Mr. Lambert's and of Mr. Fuller's premises, Wood Street, and returned the general plan of the estate altered, as now built and devised.
Feb. 1	Waited on D. of Argyll; gave him a drawing of iron railing for lawn at Inverary. 2.

Feb. 10	Met Mr. Fisher, a long consultation on Mrs. Campbell's house – could not agree. Postponed the Conference. Met Sir Clem'. Cotterel at Mr. Ingram's Chambers – long conference on his law suit – gave advice etc.
Feb. 22	Wrote Mr. More a long letter on Aberdeen Harbour in answer – 2. Making a copy of Mr. Smeaton's report thereon. 1.
Mar. 7	Attended with Mr. Baldwin at Stationers Hall. Saw all the Leases of estate in Wood Street executed. 2. Settled schedules and disputes of various kinds.
Mar. 9	Waited on D. of Argyll. Made further report on Mr. Campbell's house.
Mar. 14	Went to Amwell – called at Bushill, Bulls Cross, Mr. Bosanquet's etc. At Ware.
Mar. 15	Ordered works at Walksman's house and Bridges Yard etc. Returned to London.
Mar. 22	Attended Court at Stationers Hall on Sewer, and passage in Stationers Court Petition etc. ½.
Mar. 24	Set off for Glocester at ½ past 1.
Mar. 25	At Glocester at 2.
Mar. 27	Easter Sunday. Went to Matson – all night.
Mar. 28	Easter Monday. General meeting at Glocester. Attended all day – Dined.
Apr. 2	Set out New Bridge & its roads. Set out Hampsted Avenue etc. Sounded the river. Dined with Mr. Mee.
Apr. 3	Attended Mr. Whitworth at office. Explained the plan and the execution. Surveyed the line to Hardwick Court. Dined Kingshead – Whit & Dud.
Apr. 4	A Com'ee held. Laid the 1st stone.
Apr. 5	Set off at 6. In pocket £11 13s. 6d. At Cirencester.
Apr. 6	Set off at 6. £7 15s. 6d. coming up. In town at ½ past 7. In pocket £3 18s. 0d.
Apr. 9	To Amwell. Surveyed works at Bulls Cross.
Apr. 10	Examined from Amwell up to Ware – work at Walkman's house, yard, Tumbling Bay etc.
Apr. 11	Set out work at Bridge's Yard. Tom Wick's began. Letter on St. Margarett's Bridge. Returned to town. In pocket £1 11s. 7d.
Apr. 23	To Amwell. Various Business on the road with Mr. Treacher.
Apr. 24	Examined Mrs. Lake's bridge at St. Margaret's; measured construction – 5 feet.
Apr. 25	Returned to Islington.
Apr. 29	Attended on Sir C. Cotterel's affairs of roof etc. – at Messrs. Ingram & Brinley.
May 7	Went to Amwell – by the way New Drain near Newington – business at St. Margaret's.
May 12	To Glocester. Set off ½ past 2 o'clock, Mr. Jessop in company. Sleep at Tetsworth.
May 13	At Glocester at ½ past 4. Went and viewed bason etc., line of Canal to Hampsted and ½ a mile further.

May 14	Examined plans at office. Set off on river, along line to Lord Hardwick's to Pagthorne Hill, Stroud Mill, Stroud Canal, Whitminster, new line – to Frampton – Luncheon – To Paul's Wharf, to Cambridge Brook, to Berkely, To Newport – stopt.
May 15	Went to line at Berkly, along it to Bason, Pill Mouth etc. Returned to Colateral Cut – Luncheon, along line the whole way to Cambridge Brook. Returned to Glocester.
May 16	Consultation with Mr. Jessop. Attended meeting of Com'ee. Mr. Jessop made a report – viva voce. Dined with Com'ee.
May 20	Attended a Com'ee. Received letters and plan from Portsmouth. Wrote 4 letters on that Harbour to Jessop, Huddart, Knight & Gratham, on the subject. 2.
May 21	Went along the Canal line; set out Well for engine near the stone bench. Went cross over to Matson.
May 22	Finished estimates. Surveyed house etc. at Creed Place. Dined. At Matson.
May 24	Bored 24 feet below Bason. Dined with Mr. Howard. Left Glocester. At Frogmill.
May 25	Set out ½ past 6. At home 9 o'clock. In pocket £5 17s. 3d.
May 28	To Amwell. By the way – Mr. Seele's Water Rent, Mr. Mellish's – deepening his water.
May 30	Returned to town.
May 31	Wyat – Dinner. Washed at the Globe, Fleet street.
June 3	Set out on survey of Hoe Mill. In pocket £6 5s. 8d. At Chelmsford & 8 miles to the Mill. Surveyed Mill Meadows, New Cut, etc. Returned to Chelmsford. Marriage.
June 4	Consultations with Mr. Mass (?) Met Mr. Coate's – waited on Mr. Tindall. Returned to London. In pocket £4 7s. 0d.
June 8	To meet Mr. Jessop; did not come; confined to Newark. Met Messrs. Huddart, Coates & Marriage, on Hoe Mills – Long conversation – postponed; some Dic. Waited on Mr. Wall on Hackney Mills etc. long conferences.
June 10	Meeting with Lessees of Hackney W. Works at Kingshead, Holborn.
June 11	Attended Mrs. Coutt's in Piccadilly on the proposed improvements to her house.
June 13	Set off for Maidstone. In pocket £12 6s. 6d. At Maidstone – an election – nobody to be found. Surveyed river a mile down with Sr. Will'm. Bishop.
June 14	Went down the river to Aylesford – surveyed it; Mills, Bridge, Shoals, etc.
June 15	Attended a meeting of the Hall; made a long report viva voce; satisfied all parties on a proper plan. Set off for town – dined at Farningham. In town. In pocket £7 7s. 8d.
June 17	Set off for Portsmouth. In pocket £17 17s. 0d. By Gosport. At Portsmouth.
June 18	Examined the Harbour all day.
June 21	Dined with Sir Char's. Saxton.

June 22	Set off at ½ past 6. By Petersfield and Guilford. Returned to town.
June 29	Meeting of B.B. Com'ee. Viewed the Bridge, and dined. Met Messrs. Huddart & Jessop; read fair copy of report – signed it and settled it finally.
June 30	Waited on Mr. Wall; Hackney W. Works.
July 4	New River – survey of the head, N'n Field, Main etc. All day at work.
July 6	Luncheon at Amwell. Dined at Hertford. Returned to London.
July 8	Finished report on Portsmouth Harbour and plan, and sent it to Mr. Greetham etc. A long conversation with Mr. Rennie on Maidstone Navigation etc. A long conversation with Mr. Rennie on the Chelmer Navigation and Hoe Mill. Wrote Mr. Marriage, and sent a draft of the fit parts of new Bonds etc.
July 29	Signed the Award along with Mr. Jessop, in the disputes between Chelmsford Navigation & Mr. Marriage.
Aug. 11	Left town for Glocester – at 2.
Aug. 12	At Glocester at 3. In pocket loose £2 0s. 6d. Attended meeting of Com'ee.
Aug. 13	Went a survey of the Works in hand.
Aug. 20	Set off. Went to D. of Norfolk's in Herefordshire. Returned. Expenses to & return halved with Mr. Greenaway. £1 8s. 3d. – £2 16s. 6d.
Aug. 23	Set off at 6. At Frogmill.
Aug. 24	Set off at 6. Returned to town at ½ past 8.
Sept. 3	To Amwell – called at Bushill at work on the foundations.
Sept. 17	Went to Amwell – at Bushill sluice. etc.
Sept. 20	Went to town – called at Lewes's about Wharfing, and at Bushill sluice.
Sept. 22	Set off for Glocester at ½ past 2. Tetsworth at ten.
Sept. 23	Off at ½ past 5. At Glocester at ½ past 2. In pocket £13 1s. 0d. At Com'ee held at 7.
Oct. 2	Went along line to far end of works, then to Standish Park. Dined at Mat; slept there.
Oct. 4	Set off at 6. At Frogmill.
Oct. 5	Set off at 6. Returned to town at 8. In pocket £17 14s. 11d.
Oct. 15	Went to Amwell, called at sluice, Bushill.
Oct. 17	Left Amwell at 11. Went to town, with (?) Not at Amwell – fences cut down at Bushill sluice etc.
Oct. 29	Went to Bushill; examined work at Stop Gate. At Bushill, Broxburn Bridge etc.
Nov. 12	Went to Amwell – examined works of Stopgate, Bushill etc.
Nov. 15	Returned to town. At Bushill etc. etc.
Nov. 17	Sent Mr. Baldwin a survey and valuations of the Morley Estate in Lincoln's Inn Fields – at £4,250; and also the estate at Whitefriars Dock at £13,332, with an accurate and minute plan of the latter.
Dec. 26	Set out for Glocester at 10. In pocket £38 8s. 1d.
Dec. 27	At Glocester at 2.

Dec. 31 Settled the proposals for Messrs. Sharpe & Tyler. Walked to Matson – dined there. Stayed all night. } Wrong, it was next day.

1797

Jan. 1 At Gloucester. Dined at Matson. Stayed all night.

Jan. 3 Settled explanation of Contract with Messrs. Strand & Cooke.

Jan. 5 Went the survey of the whole line as far as Hardwick Court.

Jan. 10 A Com'ee held; set off for town at 4. Burford – ½ past 8.

Jan. 11 Off at ½ past 6. In town at 6. In pocket £28 7s. 0d.

Jan. 14 Wrote D. of Argyll a letter and Mr. Ryder on a ground rent to be sold, Argyll House, and opinion thereon, for £150. (1).

Jan. 21 Wrote D. of Argyll on purchase made of ground rent. ½.

Feb. 24 Waited on L. M. Duncan relating to a water closet, and the Chandelier etc. Attended and gave evidence on Petition of G. & Berkeley Canal, at H. of Commons.

Mar. 3 Went to Ware – examined at Bushill, New Stop Gate, and all its works etc.

Mar. 4 Making preparations for trials, of 2 actions.

Mar. 7 Trial at Hertford Assizes, Judge Heath. Referred my own case to Serj. Runnington, a verdict for me on the Island Cause.

Mar. 8 Returned to town – ordered works at Bushill.

Mar. 25 Waited on Mr. Hayton and received instructions on an estate in King Street etc. Renewal.

Mar. 28 A long Conference with Mr. Hume and Mr. Worthington on Manchester Water Works etc. Attended a Committee of Commons on new Bill for Glocester Canal – when it passed – furnishing, plans, estimates etc.

Apr. 8 Wrote Mr. Hayton on his estate, St. James's, a long letter, by way of a partial report thereon.

Apr. 26 Stationers – waited on the Stock Board; gave advice and opinion on a window etc., fireplace, in house of the person who is porter to Presid's. houses. – ½.

Apr. 27 Sworn at Lords – Gloc. Bill.

May 1 At House of Lords – Gloc'ster Canal Bill passed. Surveyed further on Mr. Hayton's estate.

May 3 Award – Mr. Long.

May 11 Set out for G'r. at 2. At Tetsworth ¼ past 8.

May 12 At Glocester ½ past 3. A Com'ee. In pocket £26 6s. 0d.

May 14 Breakfasted – Mr. Dudford went with me along the whole line; examined fire engine. Mr. Dad dined with me. No supper.

May 17 Went to Whitminster – set out crossing etc. made views. Went to Frampton Pill; considered access to Slimbridge warth, Mouth of Pill, etc. Dined at F'n. Green – carried Mr. Bailifs. Returned to Glocester.

May 25 Went on survey, Frampton Green, Framiloads, Epney, Whitminster, Frampton Pill, etc.

June 26 Col. Will'm. Duncan married to Caroline Mylne at St. James's Church, Clerkinwell.

June 28	Went with Mr. Hayton and surveyed his 4 houses in King Street & Ryder Street, treated with tenants etc. 2.
June 30	Went to Richmond with Mr. Sayer to inspect D. Clarence's house and repairs necessary to it.
July 1	Went to Amwell – called at Bushill and Broxbourne B.
July 3	Returned to town. Called at Brox. Bridge and Bushill sluice.
July 8	Went to Amwell. Removed Mr. Mylne and all the family there. Called at Bushill and at Broxbourne Bridge.
July 11	Returned to town. Called at Bushill and Brox. Bridge.
July 13	Mrs. Mylne died at Amwell at 7 in the morning. Went to Amwell. Sent family to town.
July 14	Returned to town.
July 17	Son Robert set off for Gibralter.
July 20	Mrs. Mylne interred at Amwell ½ past 6.
July 21	Robert embarked at St. Helen's for Gibralter, on board a Transport.
July 22	Mr. Douthwaite returned after paying Robert's whole expenses and putting 10 guineas into his pocket.
Aug. 15	Called at Dr. Baillie; took the sizes and extent of all the Bookcases, presses, preparations, books, pictures, etc. of Dr. Hunter's Museum – for Glasgow.
Sept. 12	After several letters, Mr. Mony called in, had 5 hours consultations on a Bridge at Northam, near Southampton, over Itchin River.
Sept. 16	Trustees of Dr. Hunter's Museum dined here. Long consultation on the site and plan for it, at Glasgow. Long letter on this to be sent to Glasgow.
Sept. 18	Mr. Moneypen called – short conversation – reading the Act & papers etc.
Sept. 19	Went with Mr. Money: again – long discussion on foundation piling etc. 3 hours.
Sept. 21	Set out for Gloc'ster at ½ past 2. At Tetsworth at ½ past 8.
Sept. 22	Off at ½ past 6. Thro' (Cheltenham). At Gloc'ster at ½ past 4. No Com'ee as expected.
Sept. 23	A Committee held, totally on my salary etc. Committed it into an allowance of 4 guineas per diem.
Sept. 24	Dined at Matson. All night.
Sept. 25	Breakfasted with self. A Committee. A General Meeting. Dined with (?) without being there.
Sept. 26	Breakfasted – self. Went along the line on foot to Hampstead Bridge – home.
Oct. 2	Home. Sir G. Paul all forenoon. Mayor's feast – Dadford broke out. Home.
Oct. 3	Home. Apology & pardon by Dadford. Mr. Comeline. Not home.
Oct. 7	Set off to Berkeley – there at ½ past 3. Viewed Berkeley Pill again. At Berkeley.
Oct. 8	Breakfasted. Rode to Pierton passage; walked to Kingston Pill; rode back, then walked to Sharness point, and rode home. At Berkeley.

Oct. 9	Set off and walked 1½ mile to Newport, and to Crosshands & Bath by ½ past 2. At Parade Coffee house. In pocket on getting to Bath – £17 8s. 0d.
Oct. 13	Went with Mr. Connaught to Comb-haye to see the caisson etc. on the Dunkerton Cold Canal. Dined with Mr. Brett & Capt Phillips. Payed Bill – £3 7s. 6d.
Oct. 15	At London at 3 o'clock. In pocket £10 12s. 8d.
Oct. 17	For D. of Argyll – examined Mr. Clavering's house etc. for repairs.
Oct. 18	Wrote D. of Argyll report and estimate of repairs of M.C. House – £150., and also a duplicate thereof to Mr. Clavering.
Oct. 23	Waited on Mr. Cowper; long conversation on altering a River at Tewin Water, Herts.
Oct. 24	By Loydd's list the Kingston Canal Morrison was taken by the La Hooke Privateer and carried into L'Orient.
Oct. 25	Called on Messrs. Brown & Co. at their wharf; went and viewed their wharf. Met Mr. Anderson – conversed him and treated for an accommodation etc.
Oct. 30	Set off early for Mr. Cowper's at Twin Water. Own chaise to end highway. Post chaise to Hertford – saddle horse to Tewin. Examined ground, piece of water, river, intended alterations, house levels, etc. Returned to Hertford and went to Amwell.
Oct. 31	Returned to town.
Nov. 7	A long conference with Mr. Sloane on the question of Draw B. in Northam Bridge.
Nov. 8	Waited on Mr. Long at the Treasury with my two Demands of – £116 5 0 ⎫ £179 5s. 0d. and: £63 0 0 ⎭
Nov. 15	Waited on Mr. Sloane – a long conference – left with him two drawings of Bridge and of Drawbridge. Meeting with Mr. Edighton on Anderson's wharf.
Nov. 21	Sent to Gloc'ster estimate of swing bridge and particulars thereof and 2 letters.
Dec. 3	Set off for Southampton at 10. Emily & Charlotte. At Hertford Bridge at 4.
Dec. 4	Set out at 10. At Southam at ½ past 3.
Dec. 5	Went and viewed and inspected the site works at Northam; crossed the water and considered of various propositions.
Dec. 7	Met Mr. Taylor and son with Mr. Lance, Fitzugh, at Admiral Thompson. A long discussion when Mr. Taylor agreed and gave his full consent to the omission of a Draw Bridge, provided Mr. Sloane acceded to such a proposition. (– and viewed the site at L. Water, at Northam).
Dec. 8	Made a report to the Com'ee viva voce of a total direction of the design and proposing a new plan, method etc. In pocket £3 9s. 6d.
Dec. 10	In town at 10. – Cost up £5 9s. 10d.

Jan. 27	Went and viewed the Smith's house, part of Mr. Hayton's estate; examined part of wall foundations and general state. Wrote Mr. Hayton thereon.
Feb. 18	A visit and a long conversation with Mr. Sloane on Northam Bridge, and his situation in respect thereof.
Feb. 22	Set out for Norwich etc.
Feb. 23	At Norwich at 7.
Feb. 24	Viewed Water Works, Mills, etc. (Emilia died in the morning at South). Made a report on the state of the works to the Aldermen, etc. viva voce. Do. to the Commons.
Feb. 25	Went with Mr. Lawson and viewed the works etc. of Mr. Patesson's Brewery. Consultations on engines etc.
Feb. 27	Left Norwich for Yarmouth. Went North, round by Pawling, Winterton, Caister etc. 35 miles. There at 5 o'clock; viewed Shoar, landing place etc.
Feb. 28	Surveyed Yarmouth River, Bridge, Quays. Went down N. Side and sounded Harbour Mouth etc. over the Bar at several places and in different directions. Viewed and examined Mr. Patteson's tower etc.
Mar. 1	Mr. Patteson went to Norwich. Set off for Lowestoft and town. At Wickham.
Mar. 3	In town at 12. In pocket £18 9s. 3d.
Mar. 13	Received a letter from Robert – in France.
Mar. 19	Sent Mr. Wheeler, Glocester, a letter in answer on the N. Wharf wall which has failed. 2. Sent by the Mail C. my report in writing on the lease and works on the Lease & Works of the Mills, Water Works, etc. Norwich.
Mar. 24	Set out for Ware with Mr. Riveley. At Bushill – Bridge, Stop Gate. At Mrs. Phillips – wharfing.
Mar. 26	Went to Ballance Engine, Hertford etc.
Mar. 27	Settled Rent for Mr. Usborne's son in Chadwell Mead. Do. for Mr. Wilson's – part of A. Green's. Returned to town without Mr. Riveley who stayed behind to attend a meeting of Lea Trustees.
Apr. 18	Robert will get to Matson.
May 7	Miss Godin came as Governess at 40 guineas salary.
May 10	Set out for Exton, to meet Mr. Edwards along with Mr. Burley. At Bugden.
May 11	At Exton. Went and surveyed the head of water above the house, then down the valley, to point of junction and to Horn Mill, then up the North valley to heads of waters, two, there.
May 12	Went to New Road, intended thro' the Park woods etc. Surveyed upper water and site of a Bridge & Boat house etc. Dined at the Lodge.
May 13	Went to Oakham. Viewed house and Riding House – returned to Burley, Lord Winchilsea's.
May 13	In town at ½ 3. Mr. Burley paid all the expenses of journey.

May 17	Wrote Lord Bredalbane on the stone for his intended bridge, in his Park.
May 18	Altered Bill for Northam Bridge, and wrote Mr. Sloane thereon.
May 25	Stationers Co. – By desire, inspected the floors of warehouse under the Great Room, which were rotten, and reinstating at the Hall. ½.
May 29	Earl Bread Albane – Wrote Lord B. long letter with directions and advice on a bridge, and sent by the Mail a design for it of 2 drawings washed of elevation, section and plans of foundations and superstructures. £17 17s. 0d.
June 4	Passed Bill for works at C. Clavering's house for £242 17s. 0d. Monsieur Faisant began with French and Latin, Willy, three times a week at 21 sh. for 12 lessons.
June 11	Made and sent Mr. Patteson a design for the tower at Yarmouth – elevation, 5 plans, section etc. and long list of directions for the works.
June 12	Waited on Mr. Campbell relating to the estate, late Lord Bute's, near Christchurch. Waited on Mr. Hayton, Adelphi.
June 13	Wrote the D. of Argyll on the repairs of C. Clavering's house of £242 17s. 0d. Wrote another letter also on Mackingtyre's house and his desertion of it.
June 15	Examined state of Macintyre's house; cleaned.
June 16	Set out at Hants, with Messrs. Campbell's for Christchurch.
June 17	At Christchurch.
June 18	Returned to High Cliffe – made survey of house at Lymington – lands, gardens etc. and state thereof. Went by water to Southampton – at Lady Thompson's.
June 19	Called on Mr. Galpine – some conversation with Mr. G. Mr. M. called – some conversation with him. Set out. At Fareham. Made survey of Sir C. Thompson's house etc. At Farnham.
June 20	At London – 3 o'clock – In pocket £17 2s. 6d.
June 22	Surveyed Mr. Hume's house.
June 27	The Com'ee visited the Bridge, viewed etc. Made a report to Mr. Campbell on High Cliffe – its situation, value, plan, state of repair etc. etc.
July 1	Went to Amwell. Removed family there. Called at B – gave directions on Sewer and Malters; the sluice gate, Mellish's water etc.
July 2	Began with Tom Wicks & Phillips. Family came down to Amwell.
July 3	Went to town.
July 14	Wrote to Lord Bread Albane and sent drawing in line of an elevation of the Bridge, with a new scale, was to make it 45 instead of 60 feet wide, new figured etc. Went to Amwell.
July 19	With Mr. Hoare – examined roof and rainwater pipes of his house, and also the course of the drains and stink traps. Glocester Canal.
July 21	Went to Amwell.

July 23	Altered the Church, the seats, and put up new Pulpit.
July 24	Came to town.
July 26	Queen Street.
July 27	Went to Amwell.
July 30	Mr. Timpson came and surveyed house, windows, settled windows at 31 in all – when Library finished, but 29 for the present. And the house, garden and outbuildings at £18. per annum for taxation.
July 31	Went to town.
Aug. 30	Mr. Evans. Surveyed his house and others adjoining as to its stability and security; gave opinion and directions for some works to be done in the cellar storey.
Aug. 31	To Amwell.
Sept. 1	Tried at Ballance Engine – dam did not prove large enough, being made by the Stop Gate. Gave it up.
Sept. 4	To town.
Sept. 5	Took survey of mains etc. with Mr. Cockerel from 9–5 afternoon.
Sept. 14	To Amwell.
Sept. 19	Broke the chaise – Horse restive and ran away. To town, by a chaise from Hodisdon.
Sept. 20	Stationers Co. Waited on Messrs. Warden Bate & Stephens with a drawing of new windows and estimate of work to be done at Court Room, Stationers Hall. Viewed and approved the works at Mr. Evans in the Poultry.
Sept. 26	Surveyed, with Mr. Cater, and took delapidations of house in Kerby Street, for Mr. Hoare etc. Self and Clerk for 2 hours. – Mr. Hensley, his surveyor.
Sept. 29	Mich's day. Went to Amwell (chaise Fetter Lane). Examined works of Breach and set out Mr. Gray's land for digging – Clay etc.
Oct. 9	Returned to town – post chaise – Ware.
Oct. 19	Si Abr. Hume's. Went to Wormleybury. Examined water engine – loss of the moving water. Defect of several ponds to hold water – directed various searches to be made.
Oct. 21	Robert landed at Dover.
Oct. 23	To town. Ware – chaise. Examined works at Hornsey Wood.
Oct. 26	Robert came to town.
Oct. 27	Returned to Amwell. Examined works at Hornsey Wood.
Oct. 29	Went to Wormleybury – inspected Springs, the machine, ponds etc.
Oct. 31	Phillip went away.
Nov. 5	Made out and sent Sir Abr. Hume a report on his ponds, supply of water and engine etc. in consequence of the late investigations. Went to town for good this season with family. Visited works near Hornsey Wood. (2 chaises from Ware).
Nov. 16	St. Paul's meeting, at desire of Mr. Banks.
Nov. 17	Robert set off for Portsmouth and Gibralter with £25 in pocket and £40 in agents hands.
Nov. 18	Embarked aboard the Minerve – C'p. Cockburn.

Dec. 1	Sent Capt. Scott 2 sketches or ideas for restoring Kelso Bridge, with paper of explanations.
Dec. 8	Robert died at sea aboard the Minerve Frigate, on the passage to Gibralter.
Dec. 17	Wrote and sent Mr. Sayer draft letter to his landlord on house in (?) Square, and also paper on the repairs and alterations necessary to be made thereon. Estimated – 396.
Dec. 21	Called on Mr. Sayer – went and examined a house in Bedford Row. Lease 13 years to be sold.
Dec. 31	Going to Guildhall; settled proportion of Land Tax of Dark-house Lane House at £5 6s. 0d. to be purchased by the writing, Mrs. Baldwin etc. Stationers Co. (£1 1s. 0d.)

1799

Jan. 25	The news of Robert's death.
Feb. 4	Stationers – altered Court of Assistants. Made report on divisions of land tax for house in Darkhouse Lane. Report in writing on tenant and party wall, on doorway in Crosby's house etc.
Feb. 24	Argyll – Meeting with Mr. Cameron; long treaty on lease of house, Mar. Street. Made an Agreement at £45 an annum etc.
Feb. 26	Stationers – waited on Mr. Warden Bate on the subject of the new roof for Hall etc. ½.
Mar. 25	Delivered notices at Mr. Hoare's house for Mr. Cator to repair, Mr. Lupton's 2 copies. Examined Lease of Marlb. Street House for D. of Argyll and sent it to Cameron.
Mar. 30	Pulpit placed.
Apr. 4	Architects – St. Paul's.
May 3	At Dr. Baillie's; attended a meeting of Trustees of Dr. Hunter's Museum, as to the building to be directed at Glasgow – on plans of ground etc.
May 10	Waited on Com'ee of Stationers Co. on a new roof, new façade, and new sashes for their hall – 3 estimates, report on state of hall etc.
May 19	With Mr. Evans – consultation on purchases of his house, belonging to Mr. Sikes, and the price set of £1,000.
June 21	Waited on Co. of Stationers for Roof, and new design for front.
June 24	Went to Twickenham; viewed, examined and surveyed a house etc. for L. M. Duncan. Returned and made report to her thereon.
July 4	Attended sale of villa at Twickenham for Lady M. Duncan. 1900 g's. Wrote her on that and Mr. Sayer's house at Richmond.
July 15	Wrote & sent Messrs. Blake & Whale a schedule of fixtures to Mr. Hoare's house, 41 Kirby Street, Hatt: Gardens.
July 31	Went to town in Whiskey – Cheapside.
Aug. 16	Waited on Com'ee of Alterations at Stationers Hall to report, and considered further of front railing, steps & yard. Went to Amwell.

178

Aug. 21	Went to town; set out bridge at Bulls Cross.
Aug. 23	Went to Amwell.
Sept. 4	Went to London.
Sept. 5	Waited on the D. of Northumberland. Long conversation on Powder Mills, next Baber Bridge, its Water Courses, lease to Taylor & Co. and proposed variations etc. (hire 4s. 6d.).
Sept. 6	Waited on Taylor & Co., Broad Street, long conversations with Mr. Gardiner on proposed alterations of the Mills, on rebuilding the same. Went to Amwell.
Sept. 13	Returned to Amwell.
Sept. 25	Went to town & Cheapside.
Sept. 27	Returned to Amwell.
Oct. 18	Called at Wormleybury – staid all night – consulted on pond & water wheel. Viewed Flash for Co. – ordered work. Got to Amwell.
Nov. 8	Called on Mr. Hoare with paper of delapidations of Mrs. Lupton's house – settled with Mr. Chapman after a tedious negotiation at £24. Wrote report thereon to Mr. Hoare at Bath, and also on his proposed new sewer in Fleet Street, and also on Mrs. L's. repairs.
Nov. 12	Meeting of Com'ee on timber.
Nov. 22	Bethlem – meeting at building with Lewis, Hollend, & Ward – surveyed one half.
Nov. 27	Went to Lyme House with Dance, Peacock & Wright – surveyed 6 wharfs – then to Blackwall on Mr. Proston Cooperage etc.
Nov. 28	Waited, by desire of the D. of North'land, and gave advice on Buchan's place and Mill next the D's stream at Hermandsworth, and the purchase thereof. 3.
Nov. 29	Met again at Bedlam – surveyed other half of building with Lewis, Ward & Wright.
Dec. 1	New cloaths to servants.
Dec. 11	At Dance's office, Guildhall – compared notes on valuations.
Dec. 16	Meeting at Mr. Dance's office, with Dance, Peacock & Wright; compared estimates – consultations etc.
Dec. 17	All day at work at home on Dance's lands and Wharfs at Limehouse.
Dec. 21	Attended all day, from ½ past 10 to 7 o'clock at Hicks Hall, and gave evidence on value of 4 wharfs – Steward's property at Limehouse. 2 guineas.

1800 to 1804

The principal items of interest in these diaries are as follows:
1800: Various meetings with architects and engineers including
Dance, the City Architect. Makes a plan for a new London Bridge.
1801: Meets Council of the Royal Academy in St. Paul's Cathedral
to decide sites for monuments. Designs new ceiling for Stationers'
Hall. 1802: Examines Rochester Bridge with Daniel Alexander.
1803: Designs a boathouse with a temple over it for the Duke of
Northumberland at Isleworth. 1804: Travels in East Anglia.
Visits Henry Holland's house in Hans Place for Lord Stair.

1800

Jan. 21 Sessions House – attended on leasehold; interest of Satchell, Reeves, & Whitlock. Gave evidence on all.

Jan. 25 Dance's office at 3. Met Peacock, Wright & Rob. Considered plans, property, at Limehouse, Blackwall etc. Dined – Consulted.

Feb. 1 Went to Lymehouse and Blackwall with Peacock, Wright, Robinson & Montague, on survey of Mr. Lyniey's Rope Ground – Mr. Granger and Mr. Garvey's premises for West Docks etc. All day.

Feb. 6 Architects – Proposed New Rules – not approved.

Feb. 10 Went to Blackwall with Messrs. Peacock and Fellows – surveyed Govey's, Granger's and other premises for West Docks etc.

Feb. 13 Meeting with Mr. Lewis and Messrs. Holland & Wyat, and Ward – Considered, agreed on Report, and signed. – At G. Inn Tavern.

Feb. 15 Meeting at Dance's office to settle business of Mr. Granger's premises. Worked from 12 to 4 on calculations, and the value of the whole with Peacock and Robinson.

Feb. 18 Received from Mr. Bremner a Bill, at 3 days, for £1980, in part of price of £2,000 for Pouderhall.

Feb. 19 Bridewell.

Feb. 21 Attended at Mr. Dance's office. Met Peacock, Wright & Robinson – finished Mr. Granger's premises and settled Mr. Lyney's.

Feb. 22 Worked on Mr. Granger's premises for trial.

Feb. 24 Attended all day at Sessions on trial of Granger's premises, gave evidence etc.

Mar. 3 Attended L. M. Duncan and delivered Bills. Attended L. E. Tufton – viewed 3 houses to be taken by her – gave advice thereon etc.

Mar. 4	Attended Com'ee of Repairs, Stationers Hall. Received instructions for new front, sashes, etc. Consultation on Mr. Leache's premises.
Mar. 7	Sent the Duke of Argyll copy of 2 plans and 2 elevations in lines, for Inverary Church, the former having been lost by the Mail Coach.
Mar. 8	Waited on L. E. Tufton – viewed 2 more houses – they would do well. Made Agreement for large house, Hinde Street, at £125 a year etc. Coach hire 5 sh. – 5.
Mar. 25	Put by in the Drawers, 2 designs for a bridge at Exton, intended by desire of Mr. Noel, but he altered his mind and would not build any at all.
Apr. 3	Architects met and settled their Constitution by ballot. Went with Mr. Nares to Games Street etc. Pimlico.
Apr. 5	Went to Lymehouse and Blackwall – Examined Mr. Lyney's Rope Walk and premises. Conversation with him on his interest. Went on to Blackwall – examined great part of Stewart's Cooperage, buildings, ground, etc. Adjourned it to another day.
Apr. 11	Went to Mr. Williams at Moor Park—considered with him the purpose of our visit.
Apr. 12	Went with Mr. Earle & Salter ; viewed at Cottage Mill Stream & ordered etc. Then Milldown & New Cut, Swingbridge, Strutt's Wharf, Williams trunk, Tumbling Bay, River, 1st Loch, Meadows, Cut Tunnel, etc. At Moor Park.
Apr. 13	Returned to town at 4 o'clock.
Apr. 15	Wrote to Mr. Williams on his dispute of water with G.T. Canal, and the draft of a letter from him to the Company, Postage etc.
Apr. 22	Surveyors Office, Guildhall, met Wright & Robinson—made great progress in the valuation of Steward's premises, Blackwall, all day.
Apr. 25	Attended all day, on trial, at Sessions House, on Lyney's property of Rope Ground at Limehouse.
Apr. 28	Attended all day at Surveyors Office, Guildhall, forming valuations of Mr. Steward's and Mr. Fenwick's premises at Blackwell etc.
May 1	Attended all forenoon on Trial of Stewart's and Fenwick's premises etc. at Sessions House. Verdict by Consent. Architects.
May 12	Surveyed Argyll House by desire of L. F. Campbell. Made an estimate of 100 to £120. Wrote a report to L. Frederick thereon, to be submitted to D. of Argyll. 2.
May 14	Attended a Com'ee of Stationers Hall on a request of Mr. Fuller, for a doorway to be made into Clement's Court, from Robinson's G: and also upon Leach's proposal at the back of his premises. 1.
May 19	Examined London Bridge.
June 5	Report to House of Commons – a long paper with drawings amended. Attended the Select Committee on Port of London etc. therewith.

June 8	Wrote to D. of Argyll on Colonades proposed to be added to Inverary Church. 1.
June 23	Sent a plan or scheme for a new London Bridge – a plan for improving the legal Quays, Custom House, etc., and for a new set of streets etc. to both – in writing to the Com'ee on the Port of London.
July 16	Examined works at Stationers Hall.
July 18	Went to Amwell – Bursop's horses, a pair, which had gone a 9 mile stage to-day, and 2, 12-mile stages yesterday, quite worked up – 4 miles.
July 19	Wrote D. of Argyll a long letter on Round porches to each side of Church at Inverary, and sent a drawing (copy) of the plan of the town, Square, Church etc. in lines.
Aug. 5	Harriet set off for Isle of Wight with Col. Home. She was in Sackville Street.
Aug. 6	And at Ryde, Isle of Wight.
Aug. 19	A thunderstorm at 5 o'clock. Examined and altered a lease of a Doorway to Mr. Fuller, in Friars Alley – Stationers Co.
Sept. 15	Went to Ballance Engine – took off the water – works done 2 years – agree all right.
Sept. 18	Stationers Dinner – Venison etc. Made report to Com'ee on Mrs. Montague's house – $\frac{1}{2}$ G.
Sept. 24	Sent D. of Argyll 2 plans and 2 elevations of the side of Church at Inverary, in lines, with the plan and elevations of Portico's attached to the side thereof, washed and neat, one design being for a circular porch, anyway – the other square.
Nov. 16	Held a long conference with Mr. Jessop on the matter in dispute at Rickmansworth, between the Navigation there and Messrs. Williams etc., on the Mills, Gauge Waters etc.
Nov. 19	Conference with Mr. Alexander on Docks etc.
Nov. 23	Set out with Mr. Jessop to Rickmansworth on dispute etc. between Messrs. Williams, Early & Salter, on one part and G. Canal Co. and Messrs. Strutt's on the other. Begun at Mills – viewed Millhead, tail, round wharfing below, asked for pipe. Requested head to be lowered – refused – then granted in part but not done to all its parts. The water, when lowered, was stopt at sluice or opening; went thence up to Tumbling Bay, then to Tunnel, then to Loch, then to Mr. Weard's water courses etc.
Nov. 24	Water pent up to highest. Went to Mr. Earle's; then up his meadows, down the Coln to the Bridge, then in his lower grounds. Then down to Wear's loch and Tum: Bay & Mills; then into Pleas: Ground and Cottage. Examined Wittingfolds, Mr. Salter, Gardner, and Swannale.
Nov. 25	Mr. Jessop went away and left me – writing particulars, making plans, examining drawing, documents etc. Mr. Holland present; examined Swannale etc. Rained hard, could not go out.
Nov. 26	Returned to London in Mr. W's, chaise, Edgware, and then chaise to N. R. Head.

Dec. 2   Went to Wapping, and asked Mr. Alexandre's attendant. Viewed Night in the Lane, Hermitage, Bridge, Dock, etc. etc. then to Wapping Church, Ball Dock River, Middle Ground, Perr (?) Street, etc. Returned.

Dec. 5   Waited. Com'ee at Stationers Hall, on Mr. Fuller's door, Mrs. Montague's window, Leach's Treaty etc.

Dec. 24   Made out a drawing etc. of the North End of Stationers Hall, with figure etc. of present window therein, plan, scale etc. and wrote Mr. Sheriff Cadell thereon. 1.

1801

Jan. 3   Wrote a 2nd time to Mr. Golborne on the New Cut and the dimentions etc. thereof, for the meeting of Com'rs. on the 8th instant.

Jan. 10   A long conversation with Mr. Vaughan and Mr. Alexander on Wapping Docks, and the mode etc. for forming a plan to execute the same.

Jan. 11   Mr. Rennie called – conversation on the mode of proceeding on the above mentioned.

Jan. 14   Birth Day – 68! Held a long conference (the 1st) with Mr. Vaughan & Capt. King, with Mr. Rennie, Capt. Huddart, my Brethren in the Commission, on Wapping Docks – for 3 hours on the question stated by the Com'ee of Directors; Mr. Alexander acting as Clerk and Mr. Chapman being ill at Newcastle.

Jan. 17   1st Meeting of Com'ee of Engineers on Wapping Docks held at Mr. Alexander's office, when the whole scheme was entered upon, and various matters discussed, and some letters settled. – Adjourned.

Jan. 23   Meeting on Wapping Docks, went by myself, (all the others being engaged) to Tower Hill, Herm. Bridge down the South Side, examining wharfs, shoar & street to Old Grav. Lane, thro' do. Ratcliffe Highway etc. – and returned.

Jan. 31   Worked all day with Mr. Golborne, and formed a new estimate of £40,000 to execute the Eau Brink Canal, for his carrying same to the Committee next meeting.

Feb. 1   Mr. Golborne came – compared estimates and agreed on them. Gave some good advice for the Com'rs.

Feb. 2   Wrote D. of Argyll and sent an Abstract of the Bills at Argyll House £86 1s. 6d. Wrote also a long letter on a proposition for Colonades, porches etc. by the Nasmyth. 3.

Feb. 9   All day with Chapman, Huddart, on Wap. Docks at Mr. Alexander's. Went and viewed legal quays, St. Catherine's, streets etc. and G. Hermitage Street, Allen's Brewhouse Foundry, and Pennington Street etc. Dined at Fould's. Expenses of coach-hire – 15 sh.

Feb. 10   Waited on Sir G. Evelyn on an addition proposed to house at Buxted – 2 hours.

Feb. 11	Met at Mr. Alexander's – Rennie, Huddart & Chapman. Received a letter from Mr. Vaughan, and Dep'y of 2 members from Com'ee – proceeded on various parts of Canal etc.
Feb. 14	Made a new plan for entrance at Bell Dock for the use of Engineers.
Feb. 17	James Harris, fished ponds at Amwell with a casting net, by order of Major Brown. Lady M. Duncan's, Argyll for money – Islington for Company and Nares.
Feb. 20	Meeting at Mr. Alexander's – Mr. R. and Huddart attended. A Bridge – sub-committee. I came too late at ½ past 2 – did some business with Mr. Alexander. Met at the C. & Anchor.
Feb. 21	All day at work on London Dock drawings and calculations.
Feb. 25	At Mr. A'sns. With Ren: and Hud. All forenoon at work. Went to Wapping stairs – examined sites, 2 for fire eng. Dined at London.
Feb. 27	At Alex'drs. with Rennie and Huddart. At work all day. Dined with G. & Valture – expenses 15 sh. (dinner & coach).
Mar. 3	At work at Mr. Alex'rs. with Rennie & Huddart all day on London Docks.
Mar. 4	Met at Trinity House and down to Shadwell. Viewed that scene of entrance – streets adjoining – all thence we stroard to S. West Corner. Ended at 4 o'clock.
Mar. 7	Dined with Mr. Vaughan. Present: Capt. King, Mr. Baynes, & Co. Mr. Huddart, and also Rennie and Alexander. Much conversation on the Docks etc.
Mar. 10	All day on Docks. Drawing Report – self and 2 clerks, 3 days making drawings, calculations etc.
Mar. 13	At Mr. Alexander's, with Mr. Rennie & Huddart. examined my draft report – amended it etc. signed it and a plan and 2 sections relating thereto; all this on the best plan for a Dock at Wapping.
Mar. 16	Went to H. of Commons. Examined the Votes; Found a Petition of G. I. Canal on the matter of dispute at Rickmansworth. etc.
Mar. 17	Waited on M. of Lorne – could not see him. Wrote Mr. Swanell on dispute at Rickmansworth.
Mar. 18	Mr. Hoare went and surveyed a house of his in lease to Mr. W. Wright. Rent £30 in Hatton Garden, for a renewal thereof went over the whole premises.
Mar. 26	Attended a meeting of Delegates at G. I. Canal in Fludyer Street, on the dispute at Rickmansworth. Stated the whole matter; heard a proposition from them. Agreed to see Mr. Barnes on it, by way of trial. Waited on Mr. Baker on all this etc. Coach-hire – 5 sh.
Mar. 27	Surveyed a house in Queen's Square with Mr. Frazer, on lease to Mrs. Stevenson. Gave him advice thereon and adjourned it. Surveyed with Mr. Hoare the estate of Mr. Cole and of Mr. Macklin therein, of large rooms – freehold premises in Fleet Street. Considered of value etc. and adjourned it to next week.

Mar. 30	Attended at Mr. Alexander's, a Meeting of Engineers and the Delegates from the Dock Prop'rts. Considered of the 2 acres made by the Directors to our Dock and got them to propose the reseinding that idea on Bell Dock, and the best means etc.
Mar. 31	Waited on Mr. Hoare – made a report on the value of Mr. Hoare's premises proposed to be purchased off Mr. Cole etc. at £5,000 valuation.
Apr. 2	Called at G. I. Canal – Conference Mr. Gray there. Then again at H. Commons with him and Mr. Baker, on Mr. Williams' business.
Apr. 7	Attended a Select Committee of Bridge House lands at Guildhall – on London B: and its repair etc. 42 acres proposed by them – took time to consider etc.
Apr. 11	Stationers – Com'ee of Repairs – attended all day and settled the accounts of last year and the work of the ensuing season.
Apr. 22	Called on Mr. Hoare etc. Attended at the H. of Commons on a Com'ee of the Great Junction Canal, and Mr. Willeage & Co's. interest therein. Presented my Draft of Clauses.
Apr. 29	Attended Com'ee of Commons on Mr. Wittram's business.
May 1	At Wapping all day for Duke of North'land. Went to Isleworth and surveyed the River and walls. D. of North: to say what occurred at Messrs. West & Co.'s establishment of a Calicoe works, the Waters, Spring, Penstock's etc. etc. Mr. Raine, Counsel.
May 2	Went over to Richmond – surveyed Lady North. villa and situation for L. M. Duncan. 2.
May 3	Waited on Lady M. Duncan and took her instructions for buying a house or villa at Richmond etc.
May 4	Went to Richmond – attended sale of Lady Northampton's house etc. Bid £3,000; went at £4,000.
May 9	Attended Mr. Caddell at Stationers Hall, on his proposed painted glass window.
May 11	Attended a Com'ee of repairs at Stationers Hall on a new ceiling and on Mr. Sheriff Cadell's painted glass window. Attended Mr. Raine at Chambers, on Duke of Northumberland's suite & river etc. 1.
May 17	Wrote the D. of Argyll on a Bath at Rosneath, and all the waters works for the same.
May 20	Com'd. for the Duke of Argyll, 2 plates of looking glass, value £11 15s. 0d. and wrote His Grace thereon, to go by Lea from Lanc' to Rosneath.
June 1	View of Bridge – expenses, waterage etc. 3 sh.
June 3	Waited on Mar. of Lorne – long consultation on a covered way for Inverary town etc. at or near the Church. Left a drawing and front. 2.
June 8	Met Mr. Rivington on the purchase of Mr. Templar's drain, in Mr. Mile's house, and also on Mr. Bloore's vault, door, etc. at the place; consultation etc. 1.

June 20	Attended Mr. & Mrs. Coatts, 2 hours on house in Piccadilly – gave plans, one of each storey.
June 22	To Amwell with family. Called at Edmonton, and attended Com'rs. of Enclosing waste etc. in that Parish. Went and examined Bushill works, and then to Amwell.
June 29	Began works at Amwell. 2 carpenters came from Cheffin at 10 o'clock. Butler came from town. 2 carpenters came from Cheffin at 10 o'clock.
June 30	To town – alone, Mr. Fairfaix chaise in $2\frac{3}{4}$ hours.
July 2	Architects' meeting – Cockerel Charge, Judgment, etc.
July 3	Went to Amwell – Fairfax's horses: $2\frac{1}{2}$ hours.
July 4	Finished hay-making after deal of rain.
July 9	Went to town at $\frac{1}{4}$ before 7. At New River Head at quarter past 9. Mr. Fairfax's horses. Duke of Argyll – paid the Assoc. of 2 plate glasses after despatching them etc.
July 17	Wrote out and sent Mr. Hoare report on houses in Wapping, belonging to Newman's Charity, as to lease, repair work by the year etc. 5. Wrote Mr. Hoare a report etc. on one house of his own at same place. 2. Returned to Amwell – F – horses, $2\frac{3}{4}$.
July 23	Wrote and sent Mr. Hoare a letter and report on his house in Hatton Garden (Mr. Wright's), on the state of it, and purchase of a stable yard. Went to town and returned in the evening with Mr. Fairfax's horses – $2\frac{3}{4}$ hours.
July 27	Old smith and labourer absent and likely to be all week. Endfield Chase Meeting for dividing etc.
July 29	To town at 6. Met Mr. Ford & Bailey, Windmill Street, at 3. Viewed walls etc. for Toust Estate. Mr. Robinson before 4.
Aug. 8	7 days a week, not to be allowed after this, Notice thereof given.
Aug. 10	Cheffin's, Carpenter, absent – Drink.
Aug. 11	Carpenter sent away because had been drink'ing and was not fit for work.
Aug. 14	Set Mr. Norris to work to finish at Stationers Hall. Returned to Amwell – in Fairfax's chaise – 3 hours full.
Aug. 15	2 daughters went to Fareham to Lady Thompson's.
Aug. 19	Gave for Mr. Hoare, to Mr. Blake, a Report and survey of the estate in lease to Mr. Macklin, with a particular of repairs to be done thereto. To London by 9.
Aug. 20	Sold old house at Mr. Hoare's to Mr. Fidler for £120, to be taken down and certain parts reserved.
Aug. 21	Went by Endfield – examined Mr. Price's wharf and encroachments. Returned to Amwell.
Aug. 31	Began to rain a little. Cleared up glass house. Smith lost $\frac{1}{2}$ a day and his labourer was idle for want of him – scorch'd both.
Sept. 3	Went to Beckenham – surveyed Messrs. Hoare's house, premises of offices, garden, pleasure ground, and 2 fields. Returned to London.
Sept. 10	Delivered survey of house offices etc. at Beckenham in Kent, belonging to Messrs. Hoare's with paper of particulars, valuations etc. (5)

Sept. 11 Returned to Amwell at ½ past 8.

Sept. 12 Set out for Eau Brink, at Lynn. At Cambridge at 5. Called on Mr. Davy – manuscript. At Ely at 8. In pocket £28 12s. 6d.

Sept. 13 Dined with Mr. Jeffory. At Lynn at 6.

Sept. 14 Begun our works of surveys etc. Set out middle of Cut at lower end.

Sept. 19 Packet from town. Finished Middle Line, in the straight part.

Sept. 24 Left Lynn at quarter before 8. In pocket £11 12s. 6d. At Ely at ½ past one. At Newmarket at 4. Went to Kirthinge, examined all the materials etc. to be sold, if any part would do for Mr. Coutt's; furniture etc. Returned to Newmarket.

Sept. 25 At Amwell ½ past 3. In pocket £4 5s. 0d.

Sept. 29 To London – at seven. Waited on Mr. Hoare's. Do. Mr. Coutts.

Oct. 1 Surveyed a house in Berkeley Square for Mr. Coutt's, belonging to Mr. Bligh; made a report thereon.

Oct. 2 Returned to Amwell at 6.

Oct. 6 To town, by 1¼ before 10. Attended Court of Assistants – Stationers Hall. Gave Mr. Coutts a letter or Report on the value of Mr. Bligh's house, Berkeley Square – its· . . . .

Oct. 10 Went on survey of Grand Junction Canal. Began at Padington; went along Canal to Greenford Green. Left off there; crossed over to Brentford Cut, near B. Bridge. Went down the Canal to Brentford Bridge. Returned to London.

Oct. 19 To town – agreed with Mr. Fairfax for his chaise and horses to go the Round.

Oct. 20 To Greenford Green. Uxbridge all night.

Oct. 21 Rickmansworth and Watford, all night.

Oct. 22 Tring all night.

Oct. 24 At Amwell at 12 o'clock.

Oct. 26 To town by Fairfax's horses. At 10 o'clock – carried Cook and sent Lewis by stage.

Nov. 1 All day at home, settling finally report on London Bridge.

Nov. 4 Waited on Mr. Newman on London Bridge, for the Select Committee of Bridge House Lands.

Nov. 13 Went to Sion House and Isleworth with Mr. Stirling on Duke of Northumberland's business of the Calicoe ground. Examined, surveyed, and stated all the premises and facts. Made a sketch of the whole.

Nov. 14 Left town. Went to Bushill – viewed Mr. Mellish's ponds – Garden Banks, and piece of ground let to him. Arrived at Amwell at 3 o'clock.

Nov. 16 Went to town at 1 o'clock.

Nov. 17 Went to a meeting at Hounslow, of the Millers on the Colne etc. Made a long report viva voce, on the G. J. Canal – the deficiency of water, the trade etc. very long – minute etc.

Nov. 21 Dined at Mr. Coutts. Met Sir Erskine, afterwards a Cardinal.

Nov. 27 Conversation with Mr. Stirling, on late transactions at and near Longford partition of Duke of North'ands River, and part ditto on Tuesday eve. last at home.

Nov. 29	Went along with Messrs. Stirling & Browne to a meeting at Longford, of the D. of Northumberland's tenants on his stream, relating to an alteration of a point of partition, below Drayton Mill. Said to be altered by intimation from Mr. Williams of Wraysbury Mill.
Nov. 30	Gave notice to the servants at Argyll House of the Duke's intention to sell the whole of that property.
Dec. 1	Sale at Hoddesdon of Chapman's land.
Dec. 7	All the forenoon at work with Sir T. Page on the breadth of the Cut at Lynn, the middle line being settled and allowed.
Dec. 9	Waited on Mr. Vansitart and Bishop of Lincoln to St. Paul's, on subject of monuments.
Dec. 11	Attended the Bishop of Lincoln to the Lords of Treasury, on the models proposed for St. Paul's for Sir R. Abercrombie, Lord Howes etc.
Dec. 22	At a meeting at St. Paul's, with the Com'ee of the Royal Academy; settled the situation of all the former and late monuments and voted by the H. of Commons. Stationers Company – Examined a complaint in Mr. Law's House, of water from the pump into cellar.

1802

Jan. 1	A great and sudden loss in the River – water in ponds down 2 feet. Set off for Ware, Amwell, Endfield etc.
Jan. 2	Examined works on River, post and rail, at Amwell end – wharfing etc.
Jan. 3	Set off at 12 for town. Past thro' Endfield – examined Mellish's Law and New Cut. In town.
Jan. 5	Wrote Mr. Ferrier on Argyll House. Wrote Lord Breadalbane on do.
Jan. 25	Wrote Mr. Lovedon a long letter on Thames Navigation, from Lechlade to Waplederham. 1.
Jan. 30	With Mr. Coutts, Lady Bute, and Mrs. C. to Richmond. Viewed and examined Mr. Sayer's house etc. for the purchase thereof. Then to Petersham; viewed etc. Lord Bute's villa; then to Wimbledon etc.
Feb. 1	A long conversation with Mr. Alexander on a defect in Rochester Bridge. 2.
Feb. 2	Went with Mr. and Mrs. Coutt's; viewed Lady Bute's villa at Brompton; advised the sale of it. Waited on Lady Bute in S. Audley Street; viewed the house all over – all the plans of Luton Park house etc. – selected some for a view. Advised the sale of Petersham House if Lady Griffon should not take it. Settled with Mr. Coutt's to offer £10,000 for it – n-house. Called on Mr. F. and Atkinson and gave them a commission to that amount. Coach-hire 6 sh.
Feb. 4	Attended sale of Littleton House for Mr. Coutts, which he bought at £10,521 – afterwards on Mrs. Coutts thereon, and alterations proposed.

Feb. 5	Wrote Mr. Starling, for Mr. Coutts, a letter on the stones of the bow window at Kittlinge and matters of some barns. ($\frac{1}{4}$).
Feb. 10	A long consultation with Mr. Millard on the upper districts of the Thames, the works proposed in 1791 – the parts thereof not done – and on 3 new propositions and improvements.
Feb. 14	Wrote a long letter to Mr. Coutts on Rawlinson's estate on Littleton House, and the fire store. $\frac{1}{2}$.
Feb. 15	Called on Messrs. Lorne – long conversation on the sale of Argyll House.
Feb. 16	Waited on Mr. Coutts – long conversation on house, stables etc. near North, in Stratton Street, on Littleton House etc.
Feb. 19	To Rochester. At the request of the Wardens and Mr. Alexander. Examining the Bridge in all its parts, particularly the 1st pair, next Rich. rebuilt in 1740.
Feb. 21	Examined the works of the Tunnel, under the Thames, at Gravesend. Returned to town with Mr. Dance.
Feb. 23	Waited on the D. of Northumb: – a long conversation etc., on his dispute on the Printing Ground, waters etc., the G. J. Canal, the Millers question, the division of the River Colne near Drayton etc. 2 hours.
Feb. 27	Dance and Alexander at dinner. Consultation on Rochester Br. Settled provision and Report thereon on the defective pier.
Mar. 4	William Boucher came as footman at 18 G's. D. of Northumb: – a long conversation by appt. on Penny & West's encroachment on his river near Queen Bridge, Twickenham. Gave His Grace a sketch of the place, works etc. 2. Gave also a copy of drawing of the London Canal, to shew his river in all its parts and connections, and particulars added thereto. 7.
Mar. 11	Mr. Coutts. Went to Littleton House – examined the large glasses, with a friend – their size, quality, and value.
Mar. 12	D. of North'd. Went to Worton. Met Mr. Penny and West – examined their plant and manuf. – the springs – use of. At Twickenham – waters etc. advised them to alter certain parts thereof, and to see it and them again. Went to Hounslow – Met a Com'ee of the Gent'n. on the Duke's River. Discussed the position at Drayton. Appointed a meeting at Longford on the 30th.
Mar. 16	Mr. Coutts, sometime etc. about things proposed to be bought at Mr. Munday's sale.
Mar. 19	Went to Rochester with Messrs. Dance & Alexander. Surveyed the bridge again – examined drawings etc.
Mar. 20	Went – and at Rochester by 2 o'clock. Surveying the Bridge, over and under; going to Chatham Dock; writing Report.
Mar. 21	Settled and signed report etc. Returned to town by 3 o'clock.
Mar. 22	Wrote Mr. Starling on Mr. Coutt's bow w. Sent Mr. Trotter 4 plans, 3 elevations and 1 section, of a house for Durham Park, on a small scale etc.
Mar. 25	Meeting at Cambridge, held at 12 o'clock. At Cambridge.
Mar. 26	Set out at 12 o'clock, by Royston, the Dock, Hitchin, to Luton Park. At 7 o'clock at Lord Bute's.

Mar. 28	Set off at 8 o'clock; went by St. Albans to Durham Park – found it in ruins, burnt down last Wed. night. To town at 2 o'clock.
Mar. 29	Waited on M. of Lorne and Mr. (?) at Argyll and settled that the house is not to be sold, and to get it cleaned. C. Hire 4 sh.
Mar. 30	Went with Mr. Stirling to Longford. Met Com'ee of Millers. Went to Drayton. Set out the point of partition of both streams, leading thence down to the Dukes, the King's, and Stanwell Streams. Many persons present – called witnesses. Returned in Stirling's chaise. C. Hire 5 sh.
Apr. 7	Went to Penny & West's at Norton; examined works done, to reinstate the old order of things. Gave them more work to do. Went then to Hampton Court. Took L. M. Duncan. Examined etc. Sir G. Young's villa; ½ of it let off. Went on with Messrs. Stirling & Brown to the D. of North'd.'s river; viewed it etc. from Perry Oaks to Longford. Did other business thereon.
Apr. 9	Stationers Hall – Waited on Com'ee of repairs. Settled the works of this season. Made a report on Mr. Law's cellar, and house to be let in the Alley at £20 a year – without repairs. Waited on Mr. Hoare, on all his business.
Apr. 10	Dr. Baillie.
Apr. 14	Blackfriars Bridge.
Apr. 15	N. River Board adjourns to the 29th. Set out for Lechlade on a survey of the Thames but made a view of part of the G. J. Canal. At Amersham all night.
Apr. 16	At Wendover at 9. Surveyed Hoare's mills etc. and Cut to Tring etc. Passed thro' Aylesbury, Thame and Oxford. And at Buscot Park, Mr. Lovedon.
Apr. 20	Meeting at Ely. At Ensham town.
Apr. 21	At Oxford.
Apr. 25	At London 9 o'clock.
Apr. 28	Waited on Duke of Northumberland by appt. on his River business. Waited on Mr. Hoare – gave him 2 estimates of works to be done.
May 5	Waited on Mr. Hoare – gave 2 estimates on offices and room.
May 7	Went out to East Skeene; looked at Lord Palmestone's villa for Mr. Coutts. Inspected the whole; the house, offices, gardens, out-buildings, and pleasure ground.
May 8	Made a report to Mr. C. and Lord Bute on the state of the said villa, and for the tenure of 3 years only. Made a report to and attended the Building Com'ee on the subject of the large window at Stationers Hall, when I resigned the same.
May 11	Met Mr. Dance; dined on Lord Noth'ds. business.
May 12	Waited on Mr. Hoare; gave an estimate on his warehouse. Waited on Mr. Coutts; gave a proposal for the works in Littleton and his own house.
May 14	Waited on Lord Bute at Brompton; gave him on one sheet a design for New Modelling his present house and offices at Luton – to convert the same into a tolerable dwelling.

May 15	Went to Hounslow – meeting of Gentlemen Millers; made a report of the whole business of the G. J. Canal – the complaints and the cause thereof. Very long, many calculations, much matter.
May 21	Waited on Mr. Coutts; Examined 4 Bills of Work at Argyll House, not taken care of by me. 1.
May 31	For Mr. Bushman, Solicitor to the City; perused deeds, papers, Bill in Chancery etc. and made a double plan of Gevew's estate, black, of great trouble. Difficulty from my own plan – waited on him twice. 10.
June 1	Mr. Coutts acquainted me, he had agreed for Rollinson's estate at 10,000, 3 per cent, that is, as the funds are at £7,500. This was done in consequence of a valuation by me 2 different ways, and making a plan etc. He gives £1,500 more than a very moderate value specified; the reason is obvious.
June 3	Gave Mr. Lovedon, for the Com'rs. of the 5th & 6th Districts, a special Report on 4 New Cuts proposed, long and particular, with 4 drawings annexed thereto.
June 7	Waited on the D. of North'd. and read to him my report on the G. J. Canal; the effects of it on his River – promised a copy.
June 10	Visited Mr. Craign and others, the vaulted spaces in West'r. Bridge, over the pier which sank and failed, before the Bridge was opened.
June 11	Gave to Mr. Lovedon the first part of a long report on the Thames Navigation between Lechlade and Abingdon – to be continued in 2 parts, and also 3 drawings, being fair copies amended of the 3 Cuts stated in the special report. 15.
June 21	Went to Bushill and Ware, Hoddesdon chaise. Examined works in New Cut, in Mellish's ponds, at Ware Mill – took dimentions of Hawkins' new sluice etc.
June 23	Made out 2nd part of Report and sent it to Oxford by the mail, being the end of all the surveys on the Thames.
June 26	Went to a meeting at Honslow Millers on the complaints against the G. J. Canal. Consultations – gave advice etc. on measures to be pursued – on Mercers Millhead and tail. Went also to Mr. Penny & West – examined parts and gave directions for order to be done.
July 25	Went to Amwell – stop't at Bushill – gave directions about New Cutt and several matters in Endfield.
July 29	Went to town – Mr. Fairfax's horses; at head 9 o'clock. N.R. Venison – Mids'r. Dividend.
July 30	Long conversation with Mr. Lintal on behalf of D. North. and Millers, relating to his duty on the G. J. Canal.
Aug. 2	Went to Amwell from Balls Pond – Fair-Chaise – with Mr. Williams.
Aug. 5	Viewed works at Hawkins Mill.
Aug. 10	Went to town – Fairfax chaise – alone, by 9 o'clock – the straight road.

Aug. 14	Went to Br. of London's; got accounts settled. Went to Duke of Northumberland's. gave him a report of the Grand J. Canal. 2. Examined place for a Boathouse and Temple over it. Took directions of site and orders for a design. Viewed the water etc.
Aug. 16	P. Clerkenwell. Attended meeting of Com'ee of Vestry Clerk. Plan approved of.
Aug. 23	Wrote to the Port Comm'ee on Blackwall Rock: from Amwell.
Aug. 26	Surveyed the Lea navigation from B. Engine thro' Ware to the Loch. Examined the Mills, Pound Loch, and Hawkin's proposition for a New Waste Gate.
Aug. 30	Went to town (Mr. Fairfax) by Bushill. Called at Bosanquits – Mr. Mellish's Cutt, and do. at 8 Mile Stone.
Aug. 31	Mr. Biggs called – gave notice of the London Canal proposition. Mason came back, carried off his tools and went to town next morning.
Sept. 1	Surveyed a house in Stationers Court, of Messrs. Want & Co. – made a report on value thereof for Company at £750.
Sept. 2	Attended the Com'ee for the removal of the Rock at Blackwall and explained full the method of blowing up.
Sept. 5	Went to Amwell, Nony and Miss Godin. Burnet, mason, carried down from Nutt and left his tools at Hodesdon.
Sept. 7	Duke of North'd. Wrote a description of an allowance of water, to the Duke of St. Albans, for the Duke's River for a base thereof. 2. and wrote Mr. Morris thereon.
Sept. 27	Came to town before breakfast, Fairfax's horses. Set out part of Cutt, at 8 Mile Stone. Met Mr. Boucher's agents on fixtures and delapidations in Stratton Street. Attended a meeting of Clerkenwell Parish on new plan.
Oct. 2	Went to Syon – gave D. of North'd. 4 drawings, washed, for a Summer House, and boat-house. Went to Penny & West's – surveyed minutely. Required the back stream and trough cut off, and the ditch covered to be stopt at one end. Final.
Oct. 11	3 children went to Fareham. Went to Dr. Pitcairn's – viewed Hawley House, ground and land, etc. for purchase – valued at £2,000.
Oct. 19	Sent a Report on Blackwall Rock, 6 pages, to Com'ee for improving the Port of London.
Oct. 25	Set Monument in Fareham Church, for Sir Ch. Thompson.
Oct. 30	Went to Rochester Castle – examined an Oct'n. kitchen for troops.
Nov. 15	Went to Blackwall with Mr. Dance on the subjects of the Rock and surveys, etc. proposed.
Nov. 28	Open St. Paul's.
Nov. 30	Royal Society.
Dec. 6	Waited on Mr. Brogden and Raine, 2 or 3 times, at the House of Commons, several times on the D. of Northumberland's business – could not find them.
Dec. 11	Waited on Mr. Raine and Mr. Stirling, for D. of Northumb. on the new Bill of the G. J. Canal, and on a remedy for the old one – Long Consultation.

51 CROYDON: ADDINGTON LODGE. Entrance front

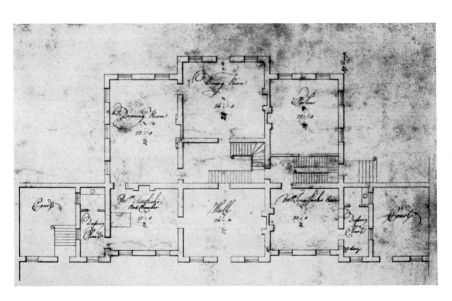

52 CROYDON: ADDINGTON LODGE. Ground-floor plan as
designed originally

53 DESIGN FOR MR. ROBINSON'S HOUSE IN WALES:
Entrance front

54 DESIGN FOR MR. ROBINSON'S HOUSE IN WALES

Dec. 23   Gave Mr. Coutts, house, valuations for making insurance on 78 Piccadilly, and his estate in Stratton Street.

1803

Jan. 12   Went to Cambridge.

Jan. 13   Attended meeting of Com'rs. of E. Brink held at Cambridge – Made a report that I could not agree with the plan marked on the ground near Lynn, for the New Cutt. Whereupon the Com'ee made certain orders to compel an umpire being named to settle all differences.

Apr. 19   Meeting of Eau Brink, at March in Ely.

May 25   Harriet's share at this time in the 58 Annuities and the last dividend at 5 April, was valued at £155 10s. 4d.

July 4   Went to Amwell, with family, by the Lanes; examined works at 8 Mile Stone and Bushill.

July 5   – Or this day rather.

July 12   Meeting of Eau Brink Com'rs. at March Isle of Ely, when an order was made to apply to the King's Bench.

July 13   Went to town and round about, by Endfield Chace, Bushill etc. Set out works at both places, for fences, drains etc.

July 19   Went to Lyon; examined site and measures of Trinkle and Boat houses, Duke of North'd. Set out foundations etc.

July 21   Went to Amwell after Board.

July 25   Attendance at Hertford by Subpaena of Mr. – to give evidence against Strutt's action, and on behalf of Bovington and Caius College, Cambridge, relating to the use of waste of water at Bacher Mill, Rickmansworth. Not called.

Aug. 4   Left Amwell at 6 o'clock – alone (Expenses by N.R.C. by Turnpike road – £1 5s. 0d.) Breakfasted in town. Attended Board.

Aug. 6   Went to Isleworth and set out foundations, levels and site of D. of North'ds. boat and summer house, with Mr. Donaldson.

Aug. 10   Attended at Mr. Dance's office on Mr. Montague, and gave directions to Mr. Sleight to complete the survey of River above and below Blackwall.

Aug. 11   At N.R. Board. Went to Amwell, by Turnpike Road.

Aug. 18   Absent – from Board. Visited Mr. Walker, at Haley – coming home, the Metior.

Aug. 25   Went to town at 6, and along the river by Endfield, Bushill etc. Surveying waters for End. Chase, Bushill, 8 Mile stone, Tunnel etc.

Aug. 27   Went to Isleworth, with Mr. Don'n.

Aug. 28   Mr. Williams went for Scotland, by sea, in a Leith Cutter.

Sept. 1   Went to Amwell, by Turnpike Road, carried Miss Cuming. Examined Mr. Dixon's wharfing and complained against Mr. Bos. her landlord – Gate etc.

Sept. 14   Went to town alone by Endfield – works at Bushill, at 8 Mile Stone; inspected. At Chitt's Hill – viewed etc.

Sept. 16	Waited on Com'rs. of the Navy: made a partial report on the Main, to supply Plymouth Dockyard, and a long discussion thereon. With Com'rs. 2 hours.
Sept. 19	Sold at St. Paul's – Old materials. Called at Mr. Dance's office, at Guildhall, met Mr. Wadd – conversation on the Black: Rock etc.
Sept. 22	Wrote the D. of North'd. on his building – Isleworth. Wrote Mr. Coutts on the Ede leases etc. Went to Amwell – Mr. Cuming in comp'y. A letter from Mr. Woodthorpe on Blackwall Rock.
Sept. 27	Com'rs. of the Navy. Wrote out and sent a long report, the main pipe for supply at Plymouth Dockyard, with water; – its bore – a gauge thereon – crooked elbow joints etc. 15.
Oct. 5	Went on the Com'ee for the Port of London, and gave a long report on the Rock at Blackwall on the course of the River, tides, eddies etc., with a map annexed. Made by *Slight* by directions and a small drawing also, of the manner of fortyfying that place in 1588.
Oct. 8	Went to Isleworth on the D. of North'ds. Boathouse – Donaldson and Stirling with me.
Oct. 13	At Board. Went to Amwell by Green Lane's Road. Examined 8 Mile Stone etc. – Bushill – Bridge to be taken up.
Oct. 28	Coutts. Settled with Mr. Coutts Trotter the Insurance to be made on the house bought of Mr. Rolleston – on 3 sets of chambers in Albany building – valueing them etc.
Oct. 31	Went to Isleworth, D. of North'ds. Banqueting House.
Nov. 7	Gave a small plan to Stat's. Company for a new passage from the Old Baily, and a copy thereof to Surveyor's Office, to aid the application for the same. Wrote Mr. R:
Nov. 9	To Amwell. Sent – the Return – of the Property Tax to Clerkenwell and to Amwell. Went to Amwell by Turn. roads – Miss Godin.
Nov. 12	Affidavit by Messrs. Suffery & Wells, relating to E. B. Cutt.
Dec. 18	Mr. Coutts – wrote him on his business, bills, etc.
Dec. 27	Read over, considered, and took Minutes of a Bill in Chancery, to be filed against G. J. Canal by the millers and on the Colne. 52 sheets.

1804

Jan. 7	River Colne. All day at work on a Bill to be filed against the G. J. Canal Co. with Mr. Stirling and Clark; altering, correcting, etc. etc. the draft thereof made by Mr. Stanley.
Jan. 11	D. of Northumberland. With Mr. Stirling, settled the ground of action against Messrs. Penny and West.
Jan. 12	Son introduced to N. R. Board as assistant surveyor, etc.
Jan. 28	Attended all day in C. of K's. Bench on the business of the E. Brink, with Mr. Adam, Counsel, and Mr. Athoe as Solicitor – letters, coach, clerks, etc. hearing had.
Feb. 4	Attended a consultation with Mr. Atho: on Mr. Adam – some discussion on Eau Brink. Put off.

196

Feb. 5	Attended all day on Mr. Adam on the Eau Brink, in consultation for the hearing coming on.
Feb. 8	Attended K.B. Court. Hearing came on – the Counsel in 3 parts – Decision by the Judge in 4 distinct speeches – all for my interpretation for the Act of New Brink Cutt.
Feb. 11	All day at Lymehouse on Capt. Huddart's machines, and specifications.
Feb. 15	At Mr. Burley's chambers, in consultation with Messrs. Perry, Dingwall, on an opposition to be made on the Portsmouth Canal, etc.
Feb. 16	Went to Clerk of the Peace's office for Surry in the Temple; inspected plans, maps etc. for the Croydon and the Portsmouth Canal etc.
Feb. 18	Got plans from Mr. Fasten of the G. Surry Canal and of the Croydon Canal, and of the Portsmouth Canal.
Feb. 19	Went to Croydon with Mr. Burley, to Mr. Dingwall's at Croydon. Consultation on the plans – took a view of the termination, of the C'n. Canal; then the Junction of the Portsmouth Canal with it, and then the line recommended by Mr. Dingwall; then the mode of opposing and the objections to be made to the scheme etc.
Mar. 2	Wrote to Sir Tho. Page on the subject of an Umpire to be appointed for Eau Brink business.
Mar. 7	Another letter from Sir Tho. Page dated the 6th received, proposing a Ballot between Mr. Jessop and Capt. Huddart. Wrote him an answer – to meet again on Friday next.
Mar. 8	Received answer – he would meet.
Mar. 9	Held a meeting of 2 hours with Sir Tho. Page. Discussed the business – gave an answer to his proposal – Could not agree.
Mar. 10	Stationers. I mentioned in default of Huddart, Mr. Watt, but absolutely refused. He mentioned Jessop and Rennie first, then Dance & Alexander, and lastly G. Bentham.
Mar. 12	Mr. Dingwall of Croydon called – a long consultation on the Portsmouth Canal; repairs stated and examined, etc. – to oppose.
Mar. 15	Attended Com'ee of opposition to the Portsmouth Canal in Palace Yard – long discussion – gave opinions – stated objections to it. Attended H. of Commons – members – Bill thrown out. C.H. 6sh.
Mar. 21	Attended with Mr. Rivington on the sub-committee of City Lands, at a view of the grounds in Old Bailey, for Stationers Company.
Mar. 24	Waited on the Master (Domville) at Stationers Hall. Reported progress on the Treaty in the Entrance from the Old Bailey – a long conference.
Mar. 27	All day writing and a narrative of proceedings by writing and conference with Sir Tho. H. Page to choose an Umpire on the matters in dispute on the Eau Brink Canal. Cutt. And writing him a formal letter to agree on naming (Cop'n. Tos. Huddart').

197

Apr. 3	Set out for Amwell by the Green Lanes. Examined ground at 8 Mile Stone, and then Bushill sluice, New Road, Bridge, when up – then Mr. Hill on Elm Timber and oak plank, and land on Enfield Chase, etc.
Apr. 4	Went to Mill. Measured & examined lands, Pound Loch, buildings, etc.
Apr. 6	Went to Hertford; called on Mr. Ellis, Andrews & Millard – elm timber – and on Mr. Nicholson on chalk pit etc. of Mr. Couper.
Apr. 7	Returned to town by post road. Expenses by New R. Company £11 10s. 0d. for a finished survey etc.
Apr. 14	Wrote Sir Tho. Page by post to Chatham. Harriet brought to bed of a son.
Apr. 21	Waited on D. of North'd. on appointment of Grand Junction Canal; Penny & West's suit, on his River and cottage and on the Temple and River.
Apr. 23	Waited on Mr. Coutts relating to Ede's leases, Littleton House, the water closets, accounts etc.
Apr. 24	Northumberland – Met Mr. Stirling on a consultation with Mr. Raine, Bedford Row, on the Bill again – the Grand Junc. Canal, and on P. & West's suit. 2.
Apr. 29	Conference with Mr. Saffery on the instrument for authorising the Umpire, of differences on the Eau B. Cutt etc.
May 7	Went to Isleworth on the D. of North'ds. building, and then to Petersham – viewed and examined Lord Bute's villa, its offices, and then for additions etc. – changes to be made thereon. Expenses – 5 sh. waterage.
May 10	Sent Mr. Coutts, for Lady Bute, an answer to her quere's on the house at Petersham, with many improvements to be made thereon.
May 14	Received the apointment, signed & executed for Capt. Huddart as Umpire on the Eau Brink.
May 16	Wrote Mr. Coutt's for Lady Bute's information, with an estimate of works to Petersham House, at £800.
May 18	First meeting with Capt. Huddart as Umpire on Eau Brink Cut; showed him maps, books etc.
May 21	Went with Lord and Lady Bute to Petersham – long consideration. Examination of the whole house, offices, gardens etc. and settled a general plan of alterations, improvements etc. Went to Tedington Grove House and viewed it. Coach-hire 9 sh. to Brompton.
May 22	Reading over the Draft of an Affidavit against the G. J. Canal Bill – letter from Mr. Clarke etc.
June 9	Went to Petersham – examined plan – opened all the drains, wells, cesspools etc – took many measures, levels etc. Had bricklayer, carpenter etc.
June 14	Blackfriar's Bridge viewed by Com'ee. Nothing seen under the Bridge as it rained so – much all day.
June 15	Family moved to Amwell by a chaise. Architects were with me at St. Paul's on Sir Christopher Wren's statue.

June 16	Waited on Mr. Coutts and Lord Bute, to view Mr. Holland's house, lands etc. at Hans Town. Then went with Lord Bute to Petersham; viewed and examined house, offices, drains & garden – Coach hire 5sh.
June 17	Set off for Lynn with Capt. Huddart. Called at Amwell. At Cambridge at 6. .
June 18	With Messrs. Colborne at ½ past 8. At Ely at 6 o'clock.
June 19	Set off at ½ past 8. At Downham.
June 20	Set off at 9. At Lynn.
June 21	Leave of absence. At Lynn.
June 25	At Lynn – Capt. Huddart at St. Germans.
June 28	Set off for Wells. At Wells – Dined, Mr. Hull, Junr. Mr. Bloom; examined harbour, embankment, cut, down etc. At Holt all night.
June 29	Set off at 6. At Cromer – examined Lighthouse with lamps and reflectors.
July 1	Early, went out of the road to Wickam Mill, on Mr. Dixon's request – viewed it, examined bridge, course of river, banks etc. and cause of law suit – heard explanations and took dimentions of Mill, bridge etc. At London at 4 o'clock.
July 4	At Petersham – taking dimentions – examining drains, cesspools, etc. and afterwards at Isleworth.
July 12	Meeting at March, Isle of Ely. Went to Amwell with Williams at 3 o'clock. Inspected Bridge No. 160 – Bushill ground, Broxbourne Bridge, Sewer, and Mr. Dixon's.
July 13	At work at St. Margaret's – post and rails and sewers.
July 15	On works between Amwell and Coopers House.
July 17	Went to town by 12 o'clock. Met Lord Bute at Mr. Coutts.
July 19	Set off with Mr. Carter for Chelmsford, on Mr. Dixon's Mill and trial at law. At Chelm'd. all night.
July 21	Trial came on – and went off to a Reference proposed by the Judge, who appointed Mr. S. Pater. Arrived in town with Mr. Carter and another.
July 23	Waited on Lord Stair, to Mr. Holland's house; viewed it all over, and said it might be worth £8,000.
July 25	Went to Petersham early and worked there all day – old house – planning new parts etc.
July 27	Went to Amwell at 12 with Mr. Brathwaite & William. Examined sewer at Broxbourne Bridge and ordered works.
Aug. 8	Went to London.
Aug. 12	Expected meeting at Ely. Returned to Amwell.
Aug. 22	Went to town, by Turnpike Road. Finished work of sewer at St. Margaret's. Labourer went away.
Aug. 25	The expenses to the journey to Lynn and round by the coast and returned to London, was this day settled, and Mr. M. received from Capt. Huddart £1 3s. 0d. as the balance on a joint account and equal expense. The majority of the work chargeable to the Eau Brink being £24. 15s. 0d. Returned to Amwell.

Sept. 14	Went to Lymehouse Capt. Huddart with me – went in a boat, from thence to Woolwich. Surveyed wharfs of Kings Yard. Plans thereof, and mud settled in front thereof. Joined by Rennie at 3 o'clock – sulky because he was not waited for. Returned to town by a post chaise with Capt. Huddart.
Sept. 21	Went from Amwell to Luton Park by Welwyn with chaise and boy, 24 miles. Examined propositions relating to Airy, their walls, steps to stairs etc. collecting materials, taking measures to judge from etc. There all night.
Sept. 22	Taking drawings, consulting plans, conversing Mr. Brown, relating to many things. Examining the whole water works of reservoire, the house, the pipe, its defects, course, situation, the water wheel etc. Returned to Amwell.
Sept. 28	Went to Petersham on works there. Then to Isleworth, on works there. A consultation with Mr. Stirling at night, on deepening the other end of Duke's river etc.
Sept. 30	Finished the steps, viewed them, and wrote Lady Mary Duncan.
Oct. 1	Went to Amwell alone, by Green Lanes, Viewed bridges, new sewer, Bushill etc. Expenses by the Company.
Oct. 10	Went to town – Mrs. & Miss Patrick with me by the Turnpike Road.
Oct. 14	Went to Amwell, alone, by the Road.
Oct. 17	Wrote Lord Bute a very long letter, or report on Mr. Brown's estimate, and its objects of Airys, arches thereto, entrances and alterations of great importance at Luton House.
Oct. 20	Waited on Mr. Nicholson, Hertford, relating to land belonging to Mr. Cowper & ditch, at the Lynce Spring & Company's Ditch.
Oct. 26	Mr. Dixon. Attended arbitration before Mr. Serj: Palmer at Serle's coffee house, for 3 hours, Gave evidence on the suit of his Mill, water course etc.
Nov. 17	Waited on L. M. Duncan – received from her to pay Bill of stone steps, by story and my own trouble – £10.
Nov. 18	Mr. Dingwall from Croydon came and dined. A long consultation on the Croydon Canal and the connection with the two rail ways of the Wandle and Mesthane, and on the height of the end of C. Canal at the Common etc. etc.
Nov. 23	Went to Petersham and called at Marsh Gate. Viewed a chimney under a window for Lord Bute. All day at work at Lord Bute's works, and on intended purchases.
Nov. 24	Received a long letter and wrote a long answer to Lord Bute on Petersham and on purchases to be made there.
Dec. 3	Went to Petersham on Lord Bute's works of alterations, and on 2 intended purchases of a Copyhold estate and a leasehold estate. – 1.

Dec. 5   Attended Mr. Coutt's in Stratton Street to examine the effects of fire, etc. in general story. Gave some directions and advice.

Dec. 14   To Petersham & Isleworth – went to both. Long investigation of Lord Bute's purchases of leasehold property.

Dec. 19   Sessions House – all day at work with Mr. Hinley at Sessions House, on 21 designs at Brentford Bridge. Made the County a report on my opinions.

1805 to 1810

Some of the chief items in this period are as follows: 1805: *Work for Lord Bute at Petersham. Tomb for Lord Nelson at St. Paul's.* 1806: *Sir Christopher Wren's monument.* 1807: *Attends committees of East London Waterworks. Surveys British Museum.* 1808: *Work at Stratton Street for Mr. Coutts.* 1809: *Makes design for new market at Smithfield. Almshouses at Ledbury.* 1810: *Bridewell Hospital.*

1805

Jan. 3 At City Solicitor's Office, Guildhall – a long attendance and consultation with Mr. Comptroller, Roach, and Mr. Montague – on claim from Turner's Assizes, relating to an estate at the side of Fleet Ditch, etc. My plan produced.

Jan. 4 Wrote out and sent a joint report on the mud at Woolwich Yard – jointly with Huddart and Renie – long and studied. Settled finally Lord Bute's purchase of the Whitehouse etc. at Petersham for £600. Poundage thereon at 2½ p. cent is 15£.

Jan. 12 Surveyed Mr. Coutts' house, Strand, as to supposed settlement in floor of Dining Room – examined it and the storeys above and below. At work for 3 hours on Bill and Interag. relating to G.J. Canal, with Mr. Stirling.

Jan. 22 Received a visit of Mr. Tate, prop'd. engineer for Prince of Wales Hand – long conversation.

Feb. 11 To Hertford, and poll'd for Mr. Baker. Mr. N. went on to Stevenage and Exon. Went to Amwell – slept there.

Feb. 12 Examined all the late works there etc. and the new Bank, St. Margaret's, Thorpes Bridge, Yard, Shore etc. Returned to town by Bushill – examined sluice and road bridge etc. at Jolly Butchers.

Feb. 14 Stationers Hall – Coutts.

Feb. 18 Lord Bute – Waited on Mr. Danvers about his for Lord Bute and also on Mr. Johnston on his leasehold interest, in ground and houses at Petersham. Wrote Lord Bute. – 2.

Feb. 19 Wrote Mr. Dixon on the subject of altering the Bridge near Wickham Mills.

Feb. 22 Wrote the Duke of North'd. on the Kings River – Mr. Wyatt – attendances, and Lord of Treasury etc.

Mar. 7 Looked at Mr. Greenhill's house – cellar and cesspool. Sent an order – must be repaired. For Mr. Coutts – attended him on a proposed tenant for house in Stratton Street. Called on Mr. Hurrell on do.

Mar. 18	Attended a meeting of land owners at Langbourne B: House, proposing the G.J. Canal new Bill, for further powers, with Mr. Hall & Stirling, and many millers to oppose it.
Mar. 22	Attended a meeting of Crown & An'r. against the Bill for further powers, for G.J. Canal. Bill.
Mar. 23	Went to Petersham – all day at work.
Mar. 25	Attended a meeting on P. of Wales Island – present – Huddart, Rennie & Jessop – considered of the question, gen. outline of the intended work, much wanted. Adjourned to Friday.
Mar. 26	Called on Chairman at India House to procure information of the Plan.
Apr. 3	Went to Isleworth. Set Mr. Barnascorn to work. Went to Petersham – at work all day on house, on dairy, and front yard.
Apr. 6	Made a bargain for leasehold estate at Petersham for Lord Bute for 100 guineas etc.
Apr. 9	Taken very ill.
Apr. 13	Went out and set works out at Coutts House, Piccadilly. Attended a meeting on Prince of Wales Island. Examined Mr. Holingsworth and sent Bordwine.
May 8	Attended Stock Board at Stationers Hall on a window proposed to be allowed to the Porters Lodge House of Amen Corner, etc. Viewing etc. 1.
May 18	Set out on a view of the G.J. Canal with Mr. Stirling etc. To Aldenham Reservoire, Watford, and to Tring.
May 19	To the Wendover Cut, saw it level etc. returned to Tring, then to Watford, and then to Rickmansworth, and Uxbridge.
May 20	At Pounds Loch, early. To London at 12. Attended Com'ee of Commons on G. Canal Bill.
May 25	At Mr. Coutts, Strand – examined floor of Drawing – and wrote letter thereon; and the Pump, Stratton Street. To Cheltenham.
May 29	Went to Isleworth and Petersham on a multitude of business. Took possession of Danver's house.
May 30	Called and gave notice of intended survey; found the erection in the Court and returned and gave notice to pull down.
May 31	Attended Com'ee of Commons on the Eau B. Bill. 3. on the River Lea Bill.
June 1	Att – Took a survey of Mr. Walker's house, late Darley's.
June 8	Went to Isleworth and Petersham. Called on Mr. Gosling, Richmond.
June 14	Brewers Co.
June 15	Went to Petersham all day. Called on Mr. Gosling.
June 18	Chancery.
June 21	Chancery – attended 3 hours on suit again. Engineers – Grand Junction Canal.
June 22	Went to sluice house at Highbury – inspected – set out piece of land for Company at bank.
June 24	Removed family to Amwell, Midsummer.

June 25	Went to Petersham, at the Marquiss's as usual. Called on Mr. Gosling – conversation on addition and Danvers. To Petersham.
July 4	Architects' – Bridewell, Board, Lords, Ash: Leave.
July 6	Went to Isleworth and to Richmond, Petersham, etc. on various works.
July 7	Went to Amwell, by Green Lanes. Surveyed Road Bridge, at Jolly Butchers, Bushill etc.
July 17	Ret'd to town.
July 20	Examined 3 chimneys at Mr. Coutts, Piccadilly, and found them all subject to fire. Examined the proposition, for the pipe of a water closet, near Chambers, in the Adelphi, belonging to Mr. Coutts and Mr. Whitfoors.
July 21	Mr. Macduff received for me 50 guin. at B. House Office.
July 27	To Hampton. Met Navigation Barge, and Com'ee of General Purposes. Floated down to Richmond. Parted with them there etc.
July 28	Breakfasted with Mr. Gosling, and his Plan. Walked to Ferry at Isleworth. Met Mr. Butts. Drove on to Baber Bridge, began survey of Duke's river from thence up to Longford and plans of partition. A tedious walk and minute survey of defects etc.
July 29	Went to Amwell alone, by Green Lanes. Stop't at Bushill – set out plan for weeds on the river.
Aug. 3	Received stones from Mr. Pitt, too large for work and must be cut 9 × 3, to be at his expence.
Aug. 6	Set off at 5 to Luton. In pocket £4 8s. 8½d. There at ½ past 8. Mr. Fairfax's chaise, 12 sh. to Welwyn. All night at Luton.
Aug. 9	Went with Mr. Parkinson to Petersham – surveyed all the works. Examined Coutts' tenants, then witnesses, on the matters of dispute with Danvers.
Aug. 12	Wrote Duke of Northumberland on the Kiosk. Ended dispute with Danvers by his accepting the proposition.
Aug. 15	Dined at Stationers Hall; submitted a new plan for Lobby Room etc. Went to Amwell, with William, on great loss in River etc.
Aug. 20	Wrote the Duke of Northumberland a long letter or report on the state of his own river, and negotiations with Wyat; Lord Glenbervie etc. and transactions of last winter.
Aug. 31	Went to Isleworth and Petersham on business of Duke and Marquiss.
Sept. 2	The note below should have been this day.
Sept. 3	Went to Amwell on great loss of water in river in town. Called on Lord Rockeby's at 8 Mile Stone. Examined hedges, new street, and narrow path etc. Then at Bushill on new arrangement for Wolkesmen etc. Miss Cuming with me.
Sept. 5	D. of North'd. Wrote the Duke on his River and the defects thereof between Baber Mills and Harrond'th. and sent him a copy of the paper of observations made thereon, with particular marks of such works as should be done by His Grace.

Sept. 20	Went to Petersham with Donald'n. Called at Sion, settling several works. Called on Lady M. Duncan's on a little business – then a great deal for Lord Bute.
Sept. 22	Went to Amwell by the Green Lanes, Called at Mr. Radley's, settled all business in Lord Rockeby's garden, Furn, aple ' yew trees. Old Bridge etc.
Sept. 25	Plaisterer came down to-day from Mr. Mott. Young Andrews went away yesterday and this afternoon at 4 o'clock.
Sept. 27	Wrote Mr. Coutts; sent state of Bills for the Sun fire office, and also an abstract and all the Bills for works done for him up to the present time.
Sept. 28	Plumber went on finishing his work. Plaisterer went back to town.
Oct. 4	Attended Mr. Dance on Arbitration of delapidations, Fraser's house in Queen's Square. Henry Cockel came as servant till a better was got.
Oct. 6	Finished the plan of the Grand Junction Canal for answers made in Chancery.
Oct. 10	Went to Amwell by the Green Lanes. Examined the works of the River at Lord Rockeby's and a bridge rebuilt. Miss Godin.
Oct. 11	Mason came from Mr. Perkins. Grigg, and bricklayer at work on stable. Gave him 7/6d. subsc. money.
Oct. 23	Went to town – family and Missis Godin and Cuming. 2 chaises, expenses by self. Go to town for good.
Oct. 26	Went to Isleworth and Petersham – examined plaister at the 1st, and gave many directions on house, offices, and gardens for Lord Bute.
Nov. 7	G. Court Day. Cooper appointed Asst. Surveyor on River.
Nov. 12	Examined in Wapping Estate, of Newman's charity; met Mr. Roper. Done for nothing.
Nov. 20	Beginning of expenses for Lord Nelson's funeral.
Nov. 22	Examined accounts of Mr. Cleghorn's at Edinburgh. Money paid and received, and found a balance in his hands of £59 2s. 1d.
Nov. 23	Set out the works for the sepulchre of Lord Nelson under the Cupola of St. Paul's etc. and all matters relating thereto.
Nov. 24	Wrote the Arch'p. of C'y. relating to the sarcophagus at the B. Museum to the burial of Lord Nelson.
Nov. 25	Waited on A.Bishop. Agreed for scheme. Attended at St. Paul's.
Nov. 26	Henry Cockill, servant, away; paid him at the rate of 1/– a day. Francis Webster came as manservant 18 & 10£.

1806

Jan. 1	Got St. Paul's account signed, and warrant for the last years money. Sir Norborne came to town.
Jan. 9	Lord Nelson's funeral but no interment. Coach-hire to and from – 2 sh.

Jan. 10	Coffin – 7 ft. from floor.
Jan. 23	Attended at Guildhall for renewall of lease at Stationers Hall.
Jan. 26	At work ½ the day on Petitions drawing etc. for Stationers Co. with Mr. Rivings, Clerk.
Feb. 12	Attended on Lord Mayor, on Sir Chris. Wren's monument.
Feb. 14	Set outwork for new iron main to Shoreditch Church.
Mar. 25	Bought at Garroways, sold by Mr. Squib, freehold property in and near Amwell, for £180.
Apr. 12	Went to Bridge at Jolly Butchers, settled lines and works for a new Bridge.
Apr. 21	Went to Isleworth and Petersham on the works of both places, and the bills to be settled.
Apr. 30	Bank.
May 6	Mr. William, went to Fareham. Went to Bushill.
May 8	Took a cursory view of the Sun Publick House.
May 9	Surveyed a house of Stationers Co., the Sun Ale House, on the expiration of lease.
May 19	Attended a Com'ee of G.P. on Licence to Dean & Chapter of Rochester
May 29	No Board – Bridewell, Stationers.
May 31	All servants etc., removed to Amwell. Attended at St. Paul's with Dr. Watson and the Com'ee of Royal Academy on monuments etc. Nothing done. Scaffold in the way.
June 9	Surveyed of the river from end to end. Refreshments at Bushill, and the whole Board. Left off at Theobalds Park, and slept at Waltham Cross.
June 11	Returned to town, by Turnpike Road, with Mr. Tederee and William. Chaises were all paid by the Company. Board.
June 13	Bridge Com'ee at 11 for 12. Went there – surveyed and dined at Canonbury.
June 16	St. Paul's at 11 precisely. No meeting held – adjourned till tomorrow.
July 3	Board – Architects – Claridge – waited on.
July 5	Lord Bovingdon called – a long conference on embankments in Catwater at Plymouth. Looking out, papers, plans, reports etc. 5.
July 6	Went to Isleworth and Petersham. Stop'd at Lady M. Duncan's and exam'd. the works done lately and the bills of the same.
July 7	Attended a com'ee of the Commons on Lord Bovingdon's business, and embankments in Catwater at Plymouth – long investigation. 5.
July 19	Examined party wall, part of Mrs. Vint's house in Ave M. Lane, for Stationers Company. Made a report to Mr. Vallance thereon. (1). Consulted on Walker's trial at Mr. Dalke's chambers.
July 20	Meeting of Witnesses on Walker's suit, at home, & adjourned.
July 21	Trial held at Guildhall – suit against Walker.

July 23	Com'ee went up the River – Committee of Blackfriars Bridge I could not attend. Went to Amwell, by the Green Lanes. Examined Jolly Butchers Bridge; set out works etc.
July 31	Returned to town. Din'd. Day Dinner.
Aug. 3	Returned to Amwell. Mrs. Coxhead called on N. Bridge, Jolly Butchers. Set out works and arch, butements being done.
Aug. 4	Mr. Boodle – at Amwell, with Land Surveyor. Heard evidence; surveyed 2 pieces etc.
Aug. 12	Set out for Norfolk. Left Amwell at 10.
Aug. 13	At Ely.
Aug. 14	(Absent from Board) went to Downham. Inspected the Bridge, wharfs etc.
Aug. 15	Left Down'm. went by water to German's Bridge. At German's Bridge; from thence exam'd. the line. At Lynn all night.
Aug. 16	Set out for Downham. Dined with Mr. Saffery. At Downham all night.
Aug. 17	Visited Down. B. again. Dined with Mr. Semmou. Went to Ely; all night at Mr. Golborne's.
Aug. 18	Wrote out a report on the 4 bridges over the Ouze. Signed and gave it to Mr. Lemmon. Stayed all night at Mr. Golborne's.
Aug. 19	Meeting at Cambridge of Eau Brink. Went to Cambridge; attended meeting of Com'rs. Long discussion on the 4 bridges and the purchase of land for the Cut. Set out for home. All night at Ware.
Aug. 25	Went to Petersham; set things into order. Cleared out all Lawrences things. Received a letter of directions from Lord Bute.
Aug. 30	Went to Amwell with Miss Cuming. Visited and ordered work at Bridge & Mile Stone.
Sept. 2	Bricklayer and labourer marched off at 12 o'clock. Wrote Mr. Ferguson and sent him 3 plans and an elevation for a large addition to his house.
Sept. 9	Arrived in town – attended Com'rs. at 11 o'clock – by Ware coach. Waited on Mr. Coutts about Petersham.
Sept. 13	Went to Petersham alone. Ordered many works and advised others of paternman upholsterers, etc.
Sept. 14	Went to Amwell – Mrs. Cuming with me, by the Green Lanes. Examined new Bridge at Jolly Butchers – ordered works etc.
Sept. 17	Opened monument at Chadwell Spring.
Sept. 23	Went to town, Mrs. Cuming with me. Called at New Bridge – and fault at Highbury Bank, arch etc. By Company £1 4s. 6d.
Sept. 28	Went to Amwell, by Green Lanes, touched on the Bridge at 6 Mile Stone, and Mr. Hill at 40 Hill; Miss Godin with me.
Oct. 15	Lord Bute at London.
Oct. 20	To town by 2 o'clock, by Green Lanes and Bridge. Miss Cuming.
Oct. 21	Attended the Sessions House.

Oct. 22	Went to Petersham alone; all day at work with Lord Bute, who took possession of his house, with family, etc.
Oct. 27	Went to Amwell by Green Lanes. Mr. Troughton with me. Visited Bridge works, sluice at Bushill, Timber at 40 Hill.
Nov. 5	Went to town with family by the Green Lanes etc. Visited Bridge; found it furnished, all but the railings.
Nov. 6	General Court held of N.R. Board. Received a present of a piece of plate, value 50 guineas, from Board for state of River.
Nov. 8	Went to Petersham, alone. Many works attended to – on house, library, dairy Cow-house, gardener's house etc.
Dec. 3	Went to Petersham, alone. Busy all day on various works. Passed a bill of pipes iron for £171 2s. 9d. for Glasgow Co.
Dec. 13	To Petersham – No! Taken very ill – could not go.
Dec. 15	Parliament meeting. Got well again but very weak.
Dec. 19	Engineers, 1st. Could not attend. Sick and recovering.

1807

Jan. 2	Meeting of Engineers – 2nd meeting. Waited on Archbishop.
Jan. 8	Meeting with Mr. Treas'r. and Lewis, on a new Hospital etc.
Jan. 10	Waited on Sr. Rich'd. Glymes of Bedlam Hospital.
Jan. 20	Gave Sir Francis notice of going away.
Jan. 22	Royal Society. Mr. Hodgson's certificate was hurried up.
Jan. 24	Went to Petersham, alone, post chaise, on grates, stoves etc. chiefly.
Jan. 26	Waited on Mr. Tallmarsh and wrote Lord Bute on lands near Petersham house.
Feb. 3	Consulted on bill for E. Lond. W. W. at Mr. Dallas house.
Feb. 5	Attended Com'ee on E. London W. Works. Architects.
Feb. 10	Sale at Ware – Bakers end. College and 15 acres of land – Moistlands green.
Feb. 11	Stationers – Com'ee on the E. London W. Works. Servant to go.
Feb. 23	Attended at H. of Commons on the East London W.W. gave evidence etc. Coach-hire 4s. 6d.
Feb. 24	Settled 2 insurances at Mr. Coutts for Lord Bute, at Petersham, £11,100 on buildings and £3,300 on furniture. Attended com'ee as above – coach hire 5 sh.
Feb. 25	Surveyed the British Museum, 1st time with Mr. Saunders.
Mar. 6	Met Saunders at B. Museum, on the survey etc. Lady Thompson came to town.
Mar. 11	Attended do. c-hire 5s. 6d. Waited on Mr. Talmack.
Mar. 15	Attended Mr. & Mrs. Coutts on new works to be done in Stratton Street.
Mar. 24	Met Mr. Saunders at B. Museum and settled form of report.
Apr. 4	Went to Petersham – at work on the furniture and dry rot – and hot air pipes.
Apr. 18	Opera – Catalani. All day at work, with Mr. Saunders, on estimates etc. – British Museum.

208

Apr. 25	At work with Mr. Saunders on estimates etc. for the Br. Museum.
Apr. 26	Went to Petersham. Met Mr. Coutts there – much dissension about Stratton Street. Tried experiment with Mr. Robinson on the Hot hair.
Apr. 28	At work on Br. Museum with Mr. Saunders, and finished form of report.
Apr. 29	Transferred and assigned over all my Ann's. being 66 in number (their property however) value at this time, of £1,155 which was the produce by accumulation, for many years, by £100 originally.
May 5	Court of Stationers – attended and made a report in writing on a Petition of Mr. Tagg, to have a term of 14 years added to the lease of a house in Wood Street, next to Friars Alley. Viewing and surveying etc. 2.
May 8	Finished the examination of the Report on the British Museum, signed it and sent it to Mr. Saunders.
May 14	Mr. Hodgson – new Planet found.
May 19	Called on Mr. Bloore and gave him a letter of notice to make good his engagement to repair his house to the extent of £200.
May 20	Br. Com'ee.
May 21	Waited on the Archbishop. Gave a drawing of Cr. Wren's monument.
June 11	Surveyed the Bridge, by Com'ee; inscription, stonework.
June 13	Attended at Bridewell Hospital, on cattle fields.
June 20	Got block of marble to St. Paul's. Carriage etc. paid 23s.
July 9	Little Louisa R. Campbell, placed in the Asylum for good.
July 10	Engineers – Col: Beaufoy and self – waited on the Archbishop – got drafts. Waited on Lord Bute a 3rd time. Conference on Lord Bute's desire of 2 pieces of land.

Bill –   £187 13 6

Gratuity £22 6 6

July 20	Went to town with William. Examined Bos. Bridge, The Flash etc. at Cheshurst. Made report thereon.
July 21	Pay Lord Nelson.
July 22	Waited on Lord Dwart – came to an agreement for 2 pieces of land at 10 guineas per annum, for Lord Bute.
July 25	Went to Amwell by G. Lanes. Viewed etc. piece of land, at M: Stone. Examined Bush. Sluice. Izzard etc.
July 29	Went to Mr. Chamberayns in Essex on the exchange of lands, long ago. Not at home.
Aug. 3	Went to town by the Turnpike roads – Miss Coxhead.
Aug. 8	Returned to Amwell, by the Green Lanes, on various business – by the Company. £1 5s. 0d.
Aug. 10	Wrote B. of Lincoln.
Aug. 11	Visited E. J. Comp'ys. new College.
Aug. 17	Came to town by the Turnpike roads.
Aug. 18	Went to Sir F. Burdets – examined house of the hanging bow window. Then to Petersham – examined garden, new ground etc.

Aug. 22	Returned to Amwell by G. L. Road; examined road, Bridge No. Chits Hill – gave directions etc. at Bushill.
Aug. 29	Attended the Com'rs. of Property Tax at Hertford and appeal'd etc. and got the tax on rent of Ballance Engine set to rights at £348.
Aug. 31	Came to town by Green Lanes. Examined Chesham Flash – Made a plan etc. for repair. Gave directions to Treacher etc. about it. Examined bridge at Chits Hill etc.
Sept. 4	Wrote to, and twice waited on, Lord Dyson; settled finally for 12 guineas per annum for the 2 pieces of land. 2.
Sept. 5	Went to Syon and Petersham – examined the Pavilion, as to its state and its being completed. Reported to Lord Bute, the agreement for 2 pieces of land. Set out the work etc.
Oct. 2	Went to Wimbledon. Set out works of bow window etc. Went from thence to Petersham. Set out work of a new chimney in Library, joiner works etc.
Oct. 4	All day at work on letters etc. – St. Paul's.
Oct. 5	At Mr. Coutts all forenoon. Went to Amwell, by Green Lanes. Gave frank directions, several matters on river.
Oct. 12	Went to town at 7 by Turnpike roads. At Mr. Coutts.
Oct. 31	Went to Wimbledon; inspected bow windows and the iron column. All right. Went to Petersham; inspected works, walls, adjusting new chimney etc.
Nov. 5	Architects, New River Day, R. Society.
Nov. 6	Went alone to Amwell by Green Lanes road. Considered new bridge at Chits Hill, the new fences at Cheshurst College etc.
Nov. 11	Went to Wormley Flash. Inspected. Ordered repairs of it and dikes and bridge over the Broc:
Nov. 18	Went to town with family for the Season. Wrote Mr. Golborne on a Bridge at or near Wisbech.
Nov. 21	Visit and conversation with Mr. Brown, and wrote Mr. Golborne on a bridge over Wisbech River.
Nov. 23	Meeting and long consultation with Mr. Stirling on proposals by G.J. Canal to Duke of North'd. and Millers. Calling etc. on Mr. Berry on Chancery proceedings.
Dec. 4	Set out to Thorney Abbey.
Dec. 11	Beds Level Corporation.

1808

Jan. 10	Set out for Thorney Abbey. At Ware at 12. Settled several matters for Comp'y with Cooper. At Arrington all night. In pocket £7 9s. 0d.
Jan. 11	Set off at 9 o'clock; went by Huntingdon, Stilton to Peterbury. Surveyed Bridge, waterway etc. From thence to Mr. Wing's. At Thorney Abbey at 4 o'clock.
Jan. 12	Went to Guyhirn; viewed the stream, examined evidence; the ferry and site of the Bridge proposed. Returned, and all night at Thorney.

55 DURHAM PARK: Second design showing low curved portico.
About 1780

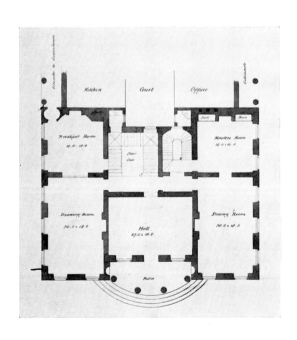

56 DURHAM PARK:
Ground-floor plan;
portico faces east

57 DURHAM PARK: Side elevation

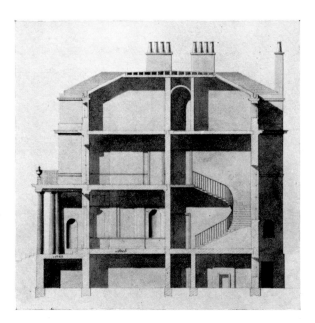

58 DURHAM PARK:
Section

Jan. 13	Went to Guyhirn; surveyed the whole again with other evidence; proceeded down the river, east side, to Wisbech. All night at Wisbech.

Jan. 13   Went to Guyhirn; surveyed the whole again with other evidence; proceeded down the river, east side, to Wisbech. All night at Wisbech.

Jan. 14   Examined the Bridge – sounded river – went by water to the Horse Shoe, and returned. Went to Downham Bridge; examined it etc. Called on Saffery, and then went to Ely. There all night at Mr. Golborne's.

Jan. 16   Made a report on a bridge at Guyhirn, viva voce – long – some opposition. Lord Hardwick in Chan. no conclusion – Instructions for report. In pocket £37 12s. 0d. Arrived in town 6 o'clock.

Feb. 9   Waited on Archbishop and Exchequer Court with St. Paul's account.

Feb. 11   Consulted with Mr. Stirling on Chancery suit of the Colne.

Feb. 25   This morning the Bar'r. was at an 30 In's. 7/10 $\frac{60}{100}$ parts – very little down and slight freezing.

Feb. 27   Went to Woolwich with Mr. Rennie. Examined works of removing the mud, the Engine, the state of the work, the wharf etc. Staid all night with Mr. Whidbey.

Feb. 28   Took soundings at 4 different places cross the River and along the moorings etc. The state of the Dockyard etc. Returned to home.

Mar. 2   Mr. Coutts. At Stationers Hall.

Mar. 6   Met Mr. Rennie & Huddart at Highbury Terrace. Long consultation on Woolwich Dock Wharf and mud annoying it. Stated soundings etc. and agreed on the Heads of a report. Mr. Rennie to state a draft of it.

Mar. 8   Waited on Arch'p. of Canterbury on St. Paul's and his villa.

Mar. 12   Attended Arch'p. and Lord Aylsbury at St. Paul's on inscription of Sir Cr. Wren.

Mar. 19   Signed a long Report with Mr. Rennie & Huddart on Woolwich Dock Wharf, and the River Thames, for the Navy Office.

Apr. 15   6th meeting – Engineers.

Apr. 18   Saw Capt. Huddart on Woolwich Yard.

Apr. 21   Attended Arch'p. of Cant'y. and Bishop of Lincoln on accounts etc. at St. Paul's.

Apr. 23   Went to Petersham; surveyed house, office, gardens, new grounds.

May 1   Went to Twickenham Park with Mr. Gosling. Surveyed the estate, old buildings etc. Considered question of a new villa and division of the grounds. Then went to Petersham; gave the final directions for all works there.

May 2   Went with Col. Huddart, Wool. Yard – examined the River. Took soundings – examined survey of river. Dined, and all night at Mr. Whidbey.

May 4   Waited on the Arch'p. on St. Paul's accounts, and his villa at Addingstone.

May 7   Attended at Chambers of Mr. Com'n. Serjeant's, by desire of Mr. Tyral, Rem'r. of the City to oppose the Bridge at the Savoy etc.

May 8	At work all day on collecting papers and evidence against the Savoy Bridge.
May 9	Attended the Com'ee on the Savoy Bridge Bill. Instructed Counsel, gave evidence etc,
May 12	St. Paul's Board. Attended at H. of Commons and gave long evidence on the Savoy Bridge.
May 15	Went to Croydon, Addington. Surveyed and examined house, stable offices etc. for an alteration and addition to be made to it for the See of Canterbury.
May 16	Attended Com'ee of the Commons on the Savoy or Strand Bridge, proposed by Dodd. The further progress of it was given up, deserted.
June 2	Duncan's arrived from Scotland.
June 3	Coutts – water. Engineers – no attendance by myself.
June 13	View Dorset Street.
June 18	Went to B. of London; Fulham, to Petersham. Settled finally all works to this period, as finished.
June 20	St. Paul's shut up.
June 22	Sent to Mr. Adam a design for Guyhirn Bridge, with a letter to the Duke of Bedford. Set out Mr. B:
July 1	Engineers' – the last this session.
July 9	Went to Amwell, 1st this season. Examined old stone sluice. Old house to be taken down. Stone jambs to be cleaned & opening filled up. Examined works on new bridge at Chitts Hill.
July 13	Sale at Ware.
July 17	Went to town by Green Lanes; examined Bushill sluice, new Bridge and stone sluice.
July 18	Went to Blackwall with Mr. Newman. Examined Dockyard and mud question, to give evidence.
July 19	Attended at trial, West'r. Hall, between the City of London and Messrs. Nigram & Green, on the Mud washed out of Dock into River.
July 21	Board Day, and 1½ yearly Dividend, at £242. Dined free-masons tavern.
July 23	D. of Northumberland:—Went to Longford with Mr. Stirling and Mr. James on a survey of the Duke's river to point of partition, and viewed lands lately enclosed, and encroach-ments on the bank of river. Returned to Longford. Went down the Lines river a mile and then back to Longford on the Duke's river. Dined and staid there all night. Next morning went with Mr. Stirling only to Hounslow Heath. Surveyed broad water at 2 places, and encroachments made on the river and common by late enclosure. Went to Lyon – wrote the Duchess on the Pavilion etc. and then went to town.
July 29	Go to Amwell. Mrs. Godin and Mrs. Thompson with me.
Aug. 11	Went to town, carried Miss Thompson. Examined new bridge in Chitts Hill and the stone sluice at Highbury.
Aug. 14	Meeting at N.R. Head with Capt. Huddart. Canvassed and settled report on Woolwich Dock, Wharf, mud etc. with him and sent it to Mr. Rennie.

214

Aug. 15	Waited on Messrs. Knight & Jones and settled the plan for Portsmouth.
Aug. 17	Capt. Huddart & Rennie met at N.R. Head and finally settled report on Woolwich Wharf and Yard.
Aug. 18	Waited on Lady Guilford.
Aug. 19	Go to Amwell, along Green Lanes. Examined works at old Stone Waste Gate, New Bridge, at Chitts Hill & Bushill etc.
Aug. 25	Came to town, alone, early, by Turnpike Roads. Attended Board. Mr. Coutts, Piccadilly – Nothing done. Attended.
Aug. 26	Trial.
Sept. 1	Set off for Portsmouth with Capt. Huddart. In pocket £17 14s. 6d.
Sept. 2	At Portsmouth.
Sept. 5	Examination to begin by Mr. Gagoly.
Sept. 7	Henry to School.
Sept. 13	Sworn by the Com'rs. to the answers of the interogation. Set out with Mr. Whidby for town. Slept at Godalmin.
Sept. 14	Arrived in town at 1 o'clock.
Sept. 27	Met Mr. Searle, Stratton Street; surveyed etc. both Mr. Coutts houses; completed both plans of the leases etc.
Sept. 29	Mich's. Day – Went to Amwell by Turnpike Roads alone, and to give notice on parcells of land on side of River Lea.
Oct. 1	Threshed the walnut trees. Stopt by bad weather.
Oct. 5	Taken very ill with a cold, side of head.
Oct. 6	Confined to room etc.
Oct. 8	Set out new work at Bank, opposite Thorpe, very unsafe.
Oct. 10	Came to town, alone, by the Green Lanes. Examined bridge at Chitts Hill, and sluice, old, taken down, side of road near Highbury Gate.
Nov. 11	Attended Com'ee of Gen. purposes on the waterway upperside of B. Bridge.
Nov. 15	Returned to Mr. Montague his plan of Blackwall. Wrote to Birmingham on water works.
Nov. 18	Attended at Guildhall on Com'rs. of Sewers and pavements relating to the Comp'y. in Dorset Street. Long evidence.
Dec. 7	Attended on Com'ee of Bridewell, about drains on N.R. Yard.

1809

Jan. 4	Meeting at Ely and a Com'ee appointed on Downham Bridge.
Jan. 16	Wrote the D. of North'd. 3 letters, one on survey taken with Mr. James on the river above Hardmansworth, one Bill to be paid to carpenter; new Br. near Isleworth etc.
Feb. 22	Waited on Mr. Coutts with report on the value of his two houses in Piccadilly. Mr. Brown from Norwich called on a proposed bridge at Norwich.
Mar. 3	Engineers – 3rd meeting. Sewers. Attended meeting of the Com'rs. of Pavement for St. Paul's.
Mar. 5	Consultation with Mr. Pattison & Brown on a bridge and road at Norwich, 3 hours, discarding plans etc.

NB	This should have been entered on the 26th Feb.
Mar. 12	Set off for Downham at 12 in the morning. Called at Amwell – ordered several and various works. At Cambridge all night.
Mar. 13	Met Mr. Golborne at Ely at 10. Went to Downham Bridge – inspected & viewed it etc. All night there.
Mar. 17	Meeting held at Ely; attended and gave a written report on Downham Bridge as to its state, and being rebuilt. Set off for Norwich. At Barton Mills.
Mar. 18	Arrived at Norwich; began the survey; examined the River and proposed site. Dined with Mr. Brown. All night at Irin Market place.
Mar. 19	Examined the River from Blackfriars Bridge to a point below the Towers. Dined with Mr. Brown.
Mar. 20	Set off for Ely. At Ely – Mr. Golborne.
Mar. 23	Left Thorney Abbey at 11 o'clock. At Arrington all night.
Mar. 24	Called in Ware. In pocket £11 17s. 6d. Arrived in town.
Mar. 25	Attended Mr. E. Gorton on a survey etc. to be made in Woucestershire.
Mar. 28	Wrote Mr. Golborne for measures etc. of Downham Bridge.
Apr. 10	Meeting at Thorney Town on 2 bridges over the Old South Eau. Bedford Duke.
Apr. 13	Attended H. of Commons on the Manchester Water Works.
Apr. 14	Attended all day at H. of Commons on the Smithfield – Bill and nothing done. 5 guineas.
Apr. 17	Still at work and finished drawings etc. on Downham Bridge. Sent to Ely by Mr. Golborne 2 drawings of the Old Bridge and for a new bridge proposed for that place, over the Ouze.
Apr. 18	Attended all day at H. of Commons on Bill for a new market – Bill thrown out.
Apr. 19	Delivered to Mr. Harmer design for a new bridge at Norwich and gave him explanations and estimate for it. Long conference and view with Mr. Slade on subject of a New Market for Smithfield. 1.
May 1	Attended Com'ee of Commons on the Bill for a new bridge at Norwich – 5 g's. Gave Messrs. Coutts & Co. an estimate of additions to be made to Lord Bute's – insurances on houses and furniture.
May 4	Attended com'ee of Commons on the Bill for a bridge at Norwich, and also on the Blackfriars Bridge Bill.
May 11	Committee of Com'n. Council; attended the N.R. Board; plans shewn them and explanations given for a proposed change of lands for New Sm. Market.
May 17	Attended Com'ee of House of Lords on the Carrow Bridge Bill at Norwich. Gave evidence. Bill passed and reported.
June 12	Attended House of Lords on B. Bridge Bill. Passed – expenses 6 sh.
June 13	Received from the Bank Property Tax for St. Paul's Cathedral.
June 16	Meeting (10th) Engineers' Society.
June 22	Stationers – attended, on Roof of Great Room.
June 23	Attended S. Com'ee on Toll house, bars etc.

216

June 25	Went to Harmondsworth and examined late enclosures and returned. To Brentford – Dined and returned.
July 1	Set up the Toll House for trial of post chaises etc.
July 2	First day of collecting Tolls by New Act.
July 21	Delivered to Mr. Collison 2 plans of a cottage to be built. Nothing done.
July 31	Set off for Ledbury to inspect the house establishment. At Oxford all night.
Aug. 1	Glocester. Viewed by myself the present and Old bridge and Canal works etc. All night at Glocester.
Aug. 2	Arrived at Ledbury. Inspected the old premises by myself.
Aug. 3	Held a view at Ledbury.
Aug. 5	Arrived home at 8 o'clock.
Aug. 6	All day at work on plans etc. of alms houses at Ledbury.
Aug. 7	11 o'clock set off for Ledbury. All night at Oxford.
Aug. 9	And arrived at Ledbury at one o'clock. Viewed part of the town – waited for the Lawyer. Met Mr. – and Mr. – .
Aug. 10	Surveyed the present Alm houses etc. with an attendance by all parties on either side. Viewed both sites of old and proposed situation for hospital.
Aug. 11	Went to Amwell, the 1st this Season. Wrote to Mr. Joneson on new Dimentions to be taken for Alms houses, Ledbury. Wrote Lord Bute on Petersham.
Aug. 27	Went to Petersham; waited on Lord Bute. Inspected the dry rot etc. Made report on the leases of garden ground; gave him a large plan of all the ground granted by Lord Dysart.
Oct. 7	Went to Fulham on Bishop's accounts of St. Paul's. Coachhire 2s. 2d.
Oct. 12	Mr. Thorpe made trial forcibly to take possession of the parcel of land, late Chamberlains. Not allowed, and at last went off with horse, plough, etc.
Oct. 14	Finished the work on parcel of land and at the bridge. Gave the men, all, entert's. for good state of behaviour.
Oct. 17	Waited on com'ee for arrangement in St. Paul's for Jubilee day – attended to their wishes relating to seats in Church etc.
Oct. 18	Waited on Bishop of London's secretary, Mr. Wright, on St. Paul's accounts. Sent him the accounts to be inspected.
Oct. 21	Wrote Mr. Chamberlayne on Thorpe.
Oct. 25	Kings Coronation – after 50 years – was kept as a Jubilee.
Oct. 27	Delivered letter of proposals on Bridge at Vauxhall etc. to Mr. Nash.
Nov. 4	Wrote Mr. Miphant, Leith.
Nov. 7	Removed totally from Amwell to (?).
Nov. 11	Went to Petersham – surveyed new garden walls. Lord Bute proposes to go to Sicily.
Nov. 30	St. Andrew's day – Bridewell Hospital. N.R. Board – and Royal Society. Dined at Crown & Anchor – Com'ee, Guildhall – B's. Bridge.

Dec. 2	Went to Brentford – Duke of Northumberland. Surveyed mouth of the River, damage done to wall, bank etc. for trial at law.
Dec. 5	Attended Cause at Sessions House on bathing etc. in the New River. Verdict – in favour of River etc. Sentence – to be imprisoned for 2 months – Newgate.
Dec. 6	Duke of North'd. Cause was withdrawn. Time lost to be charged.
Dec. 13	Ballance at Banks £115 13s. 10d. and £20 in pocket.
Dec. 20	Mrs. Coutts and house.

1810

Jan. 1	See last page of former book for receipts of a draft of £78. from Norwich.
Jan. 4	4th Jan'y. – Birthday – but style changed in.
Jan. 6	Met. Mr. Dance – spent the whole day on site and disposition of a New Market Place etc.
Jan. 11	Board – 1st meeting.
Jan. 18	Lady T'n. came to town. At theatre to view it internally.
Jan. 19	Attended com'ee at Guildhall on Bridge business.
Jan. 22	Trial – Scots C.
Jan. 26	Engineers – 1st meeting – Bill left unpaid.
Jan. 30	Paid Mr. Robinson, for Lord Bute, by Messrs. Coutts, £150.
Feb. 7	Delivered all the remaining copies of Mr. Smeaton's work to Messrs. Longman.
Feb. 17	Surveyed Lands-down House, with other persons.
Feb. 21	Conference with Messrs. Farer & Co. and other Surveyors on Lands-down House.
Feb. 22	Trial of Lansdown House.
Feb. 23	Engineers – 3rd meeting, and surrendered up to the Society, Box etc. to Mr. Haden.
Feb. 24	Attended Bridewell Hospital on new building and fields.
Mar. 2	Waited on Mr. Mitford, Clarges Street.
Mar. 6	Surgons 1st lecture – Mr. Home.
Mar. 15	Mr. – Election. Attended at H. of Commons – gave evidence on the wants of Blackfriars Bridge.
Mar. 23	Dined at Civil Engineers Society. Attended at a com'ee of the Commons and heard evidence against the N.R. Com'rs.
Apr. 4	Attended meeting at Guildhall on the sanding place N.W. of Blackfriars Bridge.
Apr. 30	Attended – gave evidence on the Bill for Docks being made and Harbour at Aberdeen – looking out plans etc.
May 3	Board Day – Settled the survey of River. A Lamp on the Bridge, 35 sh. per annum.
May 4	Whitford's Sale – Alas!
May 6	At – Mr. Home & Co.
May 9	Lady Guilford – waited on.
May 18	Went to Amwell at 10. by the Green Lanes – prepare for the survey of the Board at Bushill. At Amwell.

May 19	Getting things ready for Gr. Survey.	
May 21	Getting things ready for horsemen for survey at Amwell.	
May 22	Set out for London at 7 o'clock – Coutts etc.	
May 25	Stationers Co. meet & dine. Waited on Lady Guilford and Mrs. Coutts, 4 hours.	
May 28	Appointed for survey of river. Meet at New River Head. Dine, sleep and breakfast, at Waltham Cross. No!	
May 29	I went to Amwell at once. Com'ee – dined etc. at Amwell.	
June 1	Surveyed the River up to gauge and round the Spring.	
June 3	Go to London.	
June 15	Called on Mr. Groville – examined house for Lady. Went do.	
June 25	Set scaffolding at St. Paul's. Lady T: went to Stanmore.	
July 2	Went to town – at Guildhall also. At St. Paul's – examined the scaffolding.	
July 5	Attended New River Board – settled accounts etc.	
July 6	Set the Great Stone of Sr. Cr. Wren's monument in St. Paul's.	
July 18	Meeting held, Blackfriars Bridge. Viewed it and rode on Surry side. Challenged the encroachment at the Chan(?)	
Aug. 8	Finished monument of Sr. Cr. Wren. Took away the scaffold etc.	
Aug. 9	Attended Sessions House on the sewer, and agreed, and settled it.	
Aug. 10	Surveyed the Church, St. Paul's – found all right, Sir Cr. Wren's monument, and opened for publick.	
Aug. 17	Finished all the works lately in hand at St. Paul's.	
Aug. 20	Received a letter from Bishop of Lincoln and wrote Mr. Tinyard to open the Church.	
Aug. 31	Wrote Mr. Ousby on a chimney piece, D. of North: at Sion Pavilion.	
Sept. 5	Went to Wormley. Met Sir Ab'm. Hume. Settled on a piece of land to be given by him to N.R. Company in exchange for a Walksman's House.	
Sept. 10	Visited and examined the Ballance engine.	
Sept. 19	Attended the meeting at Guildhall – ordered for repairing and paving of bridge.	
Sept. 20	Gave Hammerton's man orders to perform it immediately.	
Sept. 22	Went to Amwell, alone. Viewed by Green roads house at Wormley for Lady Thompson.	
Sept. 24	A 12 months rents to be received in Bridge Street. Viewed house at Ware for Lady T. Could not get it.	
Sept. 25	Went to Brigens – examined a house of Blackmore, said to be Mr. Brown's, the agent to Mr. Blackmore.	
Sept. 29	Wrote Mr. Greenhill, answer to his letter on the Stationers roof.	
Oct. 2	For house etc. Went to town, by T'pike roads, examined works on bridge etc.	
Oct. 22	Visited Lady Thompson's furniture.	
Oct. 25	Meeting at Guildhall.	
Oct. 28	Went to town by G: Lanes.	

Oct. 29	At Guildhall, St. Paul's, Stationers Co. works. Blackfriars Bridge.
Nov. 1	Trial at Sessions House against the Company for taxing to the poor, the lands occupied by the water of the New River.
Nov. 4	Waited on Mr. Disney, relating to a survey etc. of a part of the G. & Bart Canal.
Nov. 12	Examined Lady T's. house at Stansted.
Nov. 13	Meeting of the Thames & Severn. No! At 80 Lombard Street – but at Amwell.
Nov. 15	Royal Society meetg. – 1st time.
Nov. 16	Tinkey's money (he says) was owing, for washing, from George.
Nov. 21	Sumond to attend at Guildhall – could not go – wrote excuse.
Nov. 22	Lec's Sale begins.
Nov. 24	Lady Thomson at Stanstead. Arrow at Stanstead.
Nov. 27	Lady Thompsons' works.
Nov. 29	Court at Bridewell.
Dec. 1	Dined at Stationers Hall.
Dec. 5	Meeting of December Sub-Com'ee.
Dec. 14	Wrote Marq' of Bute.
Dec. 17	Wrote Mr. Lovedon.
Dec. 21	Engineers' Society – begins.
Dec. 25	Mr. Hume and Dr. Wells. Christmas Day.
Dec. 31	Tuesday dinner. Xmas Day.